Course	Annual Editions: Environment, 33/e
Course Number	**Edited by Richard Eathorne**

http://create.mheducation.com

ISBN-10: 1308104464   ISBN-13: 9781308104461

Contents

Unit 4 161

Unit 5 177

Credits

Preface

How we presently consume the earth—transform its raw resources to meet our appetites—as well as the stress we put upon the planet to attend to our waste may be perhaps our most critical environmental issue now and into the future. As the world's population grows, its societies and nations are destined to evolve socioeconomically as well. And with this evolution, global patterns of resource demands and consumption behaviors will change for billions of humans. Herein may lay our greatest future challenge in the history of civilization: How do we change old eating habits and encourage new generations to take on the healthy consumption lifestyles necessary for humanity to create a sustainable relationship with its planet?

Approaching the environmental consumption issue requires a threefold paradigm, a paradigm that implies connections and linkages. Figure 1 illustrates this idea. Whenever we address environmental issues, there is general agreement that we cannot view an issue's environmental aspects independent of the people aspect. However, what is oftentimes overlooked, as well as underappreciated, is that any particular environmental issue must also be "placed" geographically. Only by doing so can we begin to uncover and understand better the variable global patterns of our environmental challenges as well as how those variable patterns (of wealth, access to resources, poverty, political instability, etc.) are connected to finding resolutions or obstructing our quest to succeed in implementing policy. For example, regarding the environmental consumption issue, we understand the role that the earth's natural resources and ecosystem services play in our transforming those resources to meet human needs, and desires (the natural sciences). We also are aware of how peoples, cultures, economies, and politics orchestrate the distribution and access of the materials we create from the earth's resources, and how those environmental-resource-needs and desires are managed and met (the social sciences). But *dealing* with the environmental impacts and challenges all this planetary resource transformation/ecosystem service consumption generates will vary considerably by *place*. For example, impoverished regions/nations will have different challenges to policy implementation compared to wealthy regions/nations. Rural agricultural economies will have different environmental priorities than urban manufacturing economic areas. Dispersed human populations inhabiting desert/dry shrub-land biomes will have far less agency in discourse regarding fresh water management then will the concentrated populations that inhabit the earth's temperate broadleaf/mixed forests.

Annual Editions: Environment is intended to provide a platform for "active learning" regarding environmental

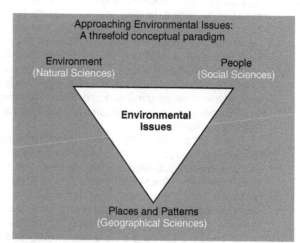

Figure 1 Addressing environmental issues requires a threefold approach that emphasizes the connections and linkages imbedded within any environmental problem. In addition, it is important to remember that the science applied (e.g., available technologies) and the people involved (e.g., cultural/ethnic, gender, religious factors) in a particular environmental problem can vary significantly by "place." Such place variability can significantly influence policy implementations, acceptance, appropriateness, and ultimately, success.

issues and upon which the reader can consider connections with other issues and components of the human–earth relationship. In keeping with the spirit and intent of the entire McGraw-Hill Annual Editions series, the *Unit Overviews,* as well as *Learning Outcomes* and *Critical Thinking Questions,* all converge to encourage the reader to approach this text not for the consumption of more information, but to actively engage in the assessment of the articles' theses and content with regard to their linkages (or lack of) with the classroom, textbook, and reader's real-world experience. This kind of proactive reader approach requires going beyond analytical "consumption reading" (knowledge accumulation/rote response). Critical-thinking environmental science reading seeks to generate questions and insights; help construct predictions and extrapolations; and discover imbedded linkages and components of the environmental consumption issue, which can lead to resolutions. It also encourages exploration of the *connections* between what the reader learns in class and what he/she sees outside of class. And finally, critical thinking of all environmental issues demands assessment of our purpose not only in environmental science, but all scientific disciplines.

Distinguished economist and noted conservationist Barbara Ward (1914–1981) reflected well this need for critical thinking and understanding of connections in environmental science when she noted, "For an increasing number of environmental issues, the difficulty is not to identify remedies. The remedies are well understood. The problem is to make them socially, economically, and politically acceptable. The solutions to environmental problems increasingly involve [seeing the connections between] human social systems as well as natural systems." And the National Science Foundation's Advisory Committee for Environmental Research and Education 2009 report underscores further that to live sustainably on the earth "greater priority must be given to advancing an integrated approach to earth systems, and addressing the complexity of coupled natural and human systems from local to regional to global scales."

The articles in this edition are compiled from a myriad of scientific, professional, and general audience, as well as governmental, publications. They were selected to provide illustrations of the multitude of concerns, views, interpretations, and implications revolving around perhaps the most critical challenge to achieving *sustainability*—changing planetary human consumption behaviors.

Of course, embarking on any new directions of sustainability discourse and addressing the challenges that planetary consumption presents lay not in the exclusive realm of environmental science, but will require insights and inputs from students and scholars of economics, geography, foreign policy, sociology, history, literature and others. Therefore, I would like to express my gratitude to the McGraw-Hill *Annual Editions Series* and its entire editorial staff for providing a forum where scholars, authors, instructors, and students can bring together knowledge, understanding, and insights in an effort to resolve the challenges which lay ahead.

Finally, feedback from readers, instructors, and students is crucial if we hope to maintain the *Annual Editions'* spirit and intent of fostering critical thinking, intellectual inquiry, and insight. Please share your opinions and suggestions regarding not only articles selected, but the *Annual Editions: Environment* thematic organization, pedagogic structure, and construction of critical thinking questions.

Editor

Richard Eathorne
Northern Michigan University

Richard Eathorne is assistant professor in the Department of Earth, Environmental, and Geographical Sciences at Northern Michigan University. His primary academic interest in the field of human geography with particular attention to the human–environment relationship helped create a new major at the university beginning in the 2011 academic year, *Environmental Studies & Sustainability.*

Professor Eathorne lived for a decade in Alaska, where he spent most of his time living within and learning about the human–environment relationships of the Inupiaq Eskimos of the Unalakleet region of western Alaska and the Gwich'in of Arctic Village in the central Brooks Range mountains of northern Alaska. He has also traveled extensively throughout Central America and to the Galapagos Islands, the Ecuadorian rainforest, and highlands of Peru, exploring the man–land relationships of those regions as well. He brings his human geography experiences to the teaching of introductory classes in human geography and environmental science as well as to upper-level classes in economic geography, geography of Latin America, and geography of tourism.

Academic Advisory Board

Members of the Academic Advisory Board are instrumental in the final selection of articles for the *Annual Editions* series. Their review of the articles for content, level, and appropriateness provides critical direction to the editor(s) and staff. We think that you will find their careful consideration reflected in this book.

Correlation Guide

The *Annual Editions* series provides students with convenient, inexpensive access to current, carefully selected articles from the public press. **Annual Editions: Environment, 33/e** is an easy-to-use reader that presents articles on important topics such as *consumption, economics, environmental ethics,* and many more. For more information on *Annual Editions* and other *McGraw-Hill Create*™ titles, visit www.mcgrawhillcreate.com.

This convenient guide matches the articles in **Annual Editions: Environment, 33/e** with **Environmental Science: A Global Concern, 13/e** by Cunningham/Cunningham.

Environmental Science: A Global Concern, 13/e	Annual Editions: Environment, 33/e
Chapter 1: Understanding Our Environment	Climate Change: How a Warming World Is a Threat to Our Food Supplies
	Could Food Shortages Bring Down Civilization?
	Economic Report into Biodiversity Crisis Reveals Price of Consuming the Planet
	Global Water Crisis: Too Little, Too Much, or Lack of a Plan?
	The Issue: Natural Resources, What Are They?
	Michael Pollan on the Links between Biodiversity and Health
	People and the Planet: Executive Summary
	Putting People in the Map: Anthropogenic Biomes of the World
	Theses on Sustainability: A Primer
Chapter 2: Principles of Science and Systems	Climate Change: How a Warming World Is a Threat to Our Food Supplies
	People and the Planet: Executive Summary
	Understanding Water Scarcity: Definitions and Measurements
Chapter 3: Matter, Energy, and Life	Climate Change: How a Warming World Is a Threat to Our Food Supplies
	Global Water Crisis: Too Little, Too Much, or Lack of a Plan?
	Putting People in the Map: Anthropogenic Biomes of the World
Chapter 4: Evolution, Biological Communities, and Species Interactions	Economic Report into Biodiversity Crisis Reveals Price of Consuming the Planet
	The End of a Myth
	Global Urbanization: Can Ecologists Identify a Sustainable Way Forward?
	Michael Pollan on the Links between Biodiversity and Health
	People and the Planet: Executive Summary
Chapter 5: Biomes: Global Patterns of Life	Climate Change: How a Warming World Is a Threat to Our Food Supplies
	Development at the Urban Fringe and Beyond: Impacts on Agriculture and Rural Land
	The End of a Myth
	Global Water Crisis: Too Little, Too Much, or Lack of a Plan?
	Putting People in the Map: Anthropogenic Biomes of the World
	Rich Countries Launch Great Land Grab to Safeguard Food Supply
	What Is a Tree Worth?
Chapter 6: Population Biology	Economic Report into Biodiversity Crisis Reveals Price of Consuming the Planet
	The Human Factor
	Michael Pollan on the Links between Biodiversity and Health
	Putting People in the Map: Anthropogenic Biomes of the World
Chapter 7: Human Populations	2013 World Hunger and Poverty Facts and Statistics
	Consumption and Consumerism
	Do We Consume Too Much?
	How to Feed 8 Billion People
	The Human Factor
	New Consumers: The Influence of Affluence on the Environment
	The New Population Bomb: The Four Megatrends That Will Change the World
	The Psychological Roots of Resource Over-Consumption
	Too Many People, Too Much Consumption
Chapter 8: Environmental Health and Toxicology	Backyard Battlefields: The Bloody Business of Fracking in Arkansas
	Fracking Ourselves to Death in Pennsylvania
	Michael Pollan on the Links between Biodiversity and Health
	Saving the Planet: A Tale of Two Strategies

	Saving the Planet: A Tale of Two Strategies
	Theses on Sustainability: A Primer
	What Is a Tree Worth?
Chapter 24: Environmental Policy, Law, and Planning	Consuming Passions: Everything That Can Be Done to Bring the Age of Heroic Consumption to Its Close Should Be Done
	Development at the Urban Fringe and Beyond: Impacts on Agriculture and Rural Land
	Global Urbanization: Can Ecologists Identify a Sustainable Way Forward?
Chapter 25: What Then Shall We Do?	Collaborative Consumption: Shifting the Consumer Mindset
	Consuming Passions: Everything That Can Be Done to Bring the Age of Heroic Consumption to Its Close Should Be Done
	Consumption and Consumerism
	Do We Consume Too Much?
	The Gospel of Consumption: And the Better Future We Left Behind
	How Much Should a Person Consume?
	Mark Tercek: Valuing Nature
	The Psychological Roots of Resource Over-Consumption
	Saving the Planet: A Tale of Two Strategies
	Theses on Sustainability: A Primer
	Why Do We Over-Consume?

This convenient guide matches the articles in **Annual Editions: Environment, 33/e** with **Principles of Environmental Science: Inquiry & Applications, 7/e** by Cunningham/Cunningham.

Principles of Environmental Science: Inquiry & Applications, 7/e	**Annual Editions: Environment, 33/e**
Chapter 1: Understanding Our Environment	Climate Change: How a Warming World Is a Threat to Our Food Supplies
	Could Food Shortages Bring Down Civilization?
	Economic Report into Biodiversity Crisis Reveals Price of Consuming the Planet
	Global Water Crisis: Too Little, Too Much, or Lack of a Plan?
	The Issue: Natural Resources, What Are They?
	Michael Pollan on the Links between Biodiversity and Health
	People and the Planet: Executive Summary
	Putting People in the Map: Anthropogenic Biomes of the World
	Theses on Sustainability: A Primer
Chapter 2: Environmental Systems: Matter and Energy of Life	Climate Change: How a Warming World Is a Threat to Our Food Supplies
	Global Water Crisis: Too Little, Too Much, or Lack of a Plan?
	People and the Planet: Executive Summary
	Understanding Water Scarcity: Definitions and Measurements
Chapter 3: Evolution, Species Interactions, and Biological Communities	Economic Report into Biodiversity Crisis Reveals Price of Consuming the Planet
	The End of a Myth
	Global Urbanization: Can Ecologists Identify a Sustainable Way Forward?
	Michael Pollan on the Links between Biodiversity and Health
	People and the Planet: Executive Summary
Chapter 4: Human Populations	2013 World Hunger and Poverty Facts and Statistics
	Consumption and Consumerism
	Do We Consume Too Much?
	How to Feed 8 Billion People
	The Human Factor
	New Consumers: The Influence of Affluence on the Environment
	The New Population Bomb: The Four Megatrends That Will Change the World
	The Psychological Roots of Resource Over-Consumption
	Too Many People, Too Much Consumption

This convenient guide matches the articles in **Annual Editions: Environment, 33/e** with **Environmental Science: A Study of Interrelationships, 13/e** by Enger/Smith.

Environmental Science: A Study of Interrelationships, 13/e	Annual Editions: Environment, 33/e
Chapter 1: Environmental Interrelationships	Climate Change: How a Warming World Is a Threat to Our Food Supplies
	Economic Report into Biodiversity Crisis Reveals Price of Consuming the Planet
	Michael Pollan on the Links between Biodiversity and Health
	People and the Planet: Executive Summary
Chapter 2: Environmental Ethics	Mark Tercek: Valuing Nature
	Michael Pollan on the Links between Biodiversity and Health
	Theses on Sustainability: A Primer
	What Is a Tree Worth?
Chapter 3: Environmental Risk: Economics, Assessment, and Management	Economic Report into Biodiversity Crisis Reveals Price of Consuming the Planet
	New Consumers: The Influence of Affluence on the Environment
	Saving the Planet: A Tale of Two Strategies
	What Is a Tree Worth?
Chapter 4: Interrelated Scientific Principles: Matter, Energy, and Environment	Climate Change: How a Warming World Is a Threat to Our Food Supplies
	Global Water Crisis: Too Little, Too Much, or Lack of a Plan?
	Putting People in the Map: Anthropogenic Biomes of the World
Chapter 5: Interactions: Environments and Organisms	Economic Report into Biodiversity Crisis Reveals Price of Consuming the Planet
	The Human Factor
	Michael Pollan on the Links between Biodiversity and Health
Chapter 6: Kinds of Ecosystems and Communities	
Chapter 7: Populations: Characteristics and Issues	2013 World Hunger and Poverty Facts and Statistics
	Consumption and Consumerism
	Do We Consume Too Much?
	How to Feed 8 Billion People
	The Human Factor
	New Consumers: The Influence of Affluence on the Environment
	The New Population Bomb: The Four Megatrends That Will Change the World
	The Psychological Roots of Resource Over-Consumption
	Too Many People, Too Much Consumption
Chapter 8: Energy and Civilization: Patterns of Consumption	Collaborative Consumption: Shifting the Consumer Mindset
	Consuming Passions: Everything That Can Be Done to Bring the Age of Heroic Consumption to Its Close Should Be Done
	Consumption and Consumerism
	Do We Consume Too Much?
	The Efficiency Dilemma
	How Much Should a Person Consume?
	People and the Planet: Executive Summary
	Putting People in the Map: Anthropogenic Biomes of the World
	The Whole Fracking Enchilada
	Why Do We Over-Consume?
Chapter 9: Nonrenewable Energy Sources	Backyard Battlefields: The Bloody Business of Fracking in Arkansas
	Fracking Ourselves to Death in Pennsylvania
	The Whole Fracking Enchilada
Chapter 10: Renewable Energy Sources	
Chapter 11: Biodiversity Issues	Economic Report into Biodiversity Crisis Reveals Price of Consuming the Planet
	Michael Pollan on the Links between Biodiversity and Health

Topic Guide

This topic guide suggests how the selections in this book relate to the subjects covered in your course.
All the articles that relate to each topic are listed below the bold-faced term.

Agriculture

2013 World Hunger and Poverty Facts and Statistics
Climate Change: How a Warming World Is a Threat to Our Food
  Supplies
Could Food Shortages Bring Down Civilization?
Development at the Urban Fringe and Beyond: Impacts on Agriculture
  and Rural Land
How to Feed 8 Billion People
Michael Pollan on the Links between Biodiversity and Health
The New Land Rush
Rich Countries Launch Great Land Grab to Safeguard Food Supply
Too Many People, Too Much Consumption

Behavior

Consuming Passions: Everything That Can Be Done to Bring the Age
  of Heroic Consumption to Its Close Should Be Done
Consumption and Consumerism
Do We Consume Too Much?
The Gospel of Consumption: And the Better Future We Left Behind
How Much Should a Person Consume?
The Human Factor
New Consumers: The Influence of Affluence on the Environment
The Psychological Roots of Resource Over-Consumption
Saving the Planet: A Tale of Two Strategies
Too Many People, Too Much Consumption
Why Do We Over-Consume?

Biodiversity

Climate Change: How a Warming World Is a Threat to Our Food
  Supplies
Could Food Shortages Bring Down Civilization?
Economic Report into Biodiversity Crisis Reveals Price of Consuming
  the Planet
The End of a Myth
The Human Factor
Michael Pollan on the Links between Biodiversity and Health
People and the Planet: Executive Summary

Consumption

Collaborative Consumption: Shifting the Consumer Mindset
Consuming Passions: Everything That Can Be Done to Bring the Age
  of Heroic Consumption to Its Close Should Be Done
Global Water Crisis: Too Little, Too Much, or Lack of a Plan?
The Gospel of Consumption: And the Better Future We Left Behind
How Much Should a Person Consume?
The Issue: Natural Resources, What Are They?
New Consumers: The Influence of Affluence on the Environment
Too Many People, Too Much Consumption

Cultural evolution

Do We Consume Too Much?
How Much Should a Person Consume?
New Consumers: The Influence of Affluence on the Environment
The Psychological Roots of Resource Over-Consumption
Too Many People, Too Much Consumption

Demography/Population

2013 World Hunger and Poverty Facts and Statistics
Consumption and Consumerism
Development at the Urban Fringe and Beyond: Impacts on Agriculture
  and Rural Land
How Much Should a Person Consume?
The Human Factor
New Consumers: The Influence of Affluence on the Environment

The New Population Bomb: The Four Megatrends That Will Change
  the World
People and the Planet: Executive Summary
Putting People in the Map: Anthropogenic Biomes of the World
Too Many People, Too Much Consumption

Economics

Climate Change: How a Warming World Is a Threat to Our Food
  Supplies
Economic Report into Biodiversity Crisis Reveals Price of Consuming
  the Planet
The Efficiency Dilemma
Mark Tercek: Valuing Nature
New Consumers: The Influence of Affluence on the Environment
Saving the Planet: A Tale of Two Strategies
What Is a Tree Worth?

Ecosystem services

Global Water Crisis: Too Little, Too Much, or Lack of a Plan?
Mark Tercek: Valuing Nature
Michael Pollan on the Links between Biodiversity and Health
People and the Planet: Executive Summary
Understanding Water Scarcity: Definitions and Measurements
What Is a Tree Worth?

Energy

Backyard Battlefields: The Bloody Business of Fracking in Arkansas
The Efficiency Dilemma
Fracking Ourselves to Death in Pennsylvania
The Issue: Natural Resources, What Are They?
New Consumers: The Influence of Affluence on the Environment
The Whole Fracking Enchilada

Environmental decision making

Global Urbanization: Can Ecologists Identify a Sustainable Way
  Forward?
Mark Tercek: Valuing Nature
Saving the Planet: A Tale of Two Strategies
What Is a Tree Worth?

Environmental stress

Backyard Battlefields: The Bloody Business of Fracking in Arkansas
Climate Change: How a Warming World Is a Threat to Our Food
  Supplies
Could Food Shortages Bring Down Civilization?
Development at the Urban Fringe and Beyond: Impacts on Agriculture
  and Rural Land
Economic Report into Biodiversity Crisis Reveals Price of Consuming
  the Planet
Global Water Crisis: Too Little, Too Much, or Lack of a Plan?
New Consumers: The Influence of Affluence on the Environment
People and the Planet: Executive Summary
Too Many People, Too Much Consumption
Understanding Water Scarcity: Definitions and Measurements
The Whole Fracking Enchilada
The World's Water Challenge

Environmental values

Consuming Passions: Everything That Can Be Done to Bring the Age
  of Heroic Consumption to Its Close Should Be Done
Consumption and Consumerism
The Gospel of Consumption: And the Better Future We Left Behind
How Much Should a Person Consume?
Mark Tercek: Valuing Nature

Approaching Environmental Issues Paradigm Worksheet

This worksheet can be photocopied and used alongside any of the articles to help you better conceptualize and understand the connections and linkages between an **Environmental Issue** and its three critical components: **Environment** (natural science concepts / principles); **People** (social science concepts / principles); and **Place / Patterns** (geographical science concepts / principles).

Environment
(Natural Science)

List aspects of the "natural sciences" (biology, chemistry, ecology, botany, physics, etc.) linked to the issue:

_____
_____
_____
_____
_____
_____
_____
_____

Environmental Issue / Concern:

_____

People
(Social Science)

List aspects of the "social sciences" (sociology, economics, politics, history, culture, etc.) linked to the issue:

_____
_____
_____
_____
_____
_____
_____

Places and Patterns
(Geographical Science)
Describe *geographic places*, movements, patterns linked to the issue:

_____
_____
_____
_____
_____
_____
_____
_____
_____
_____
_____
_____
_____
_____
_____
_____
_____
_____
_____

World Map

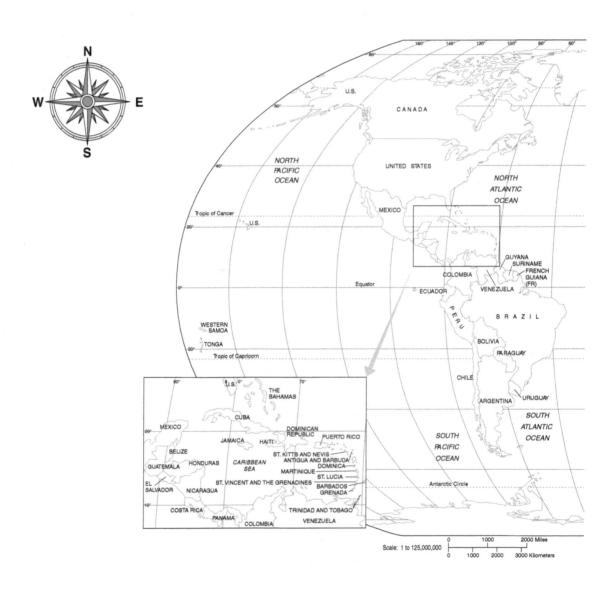

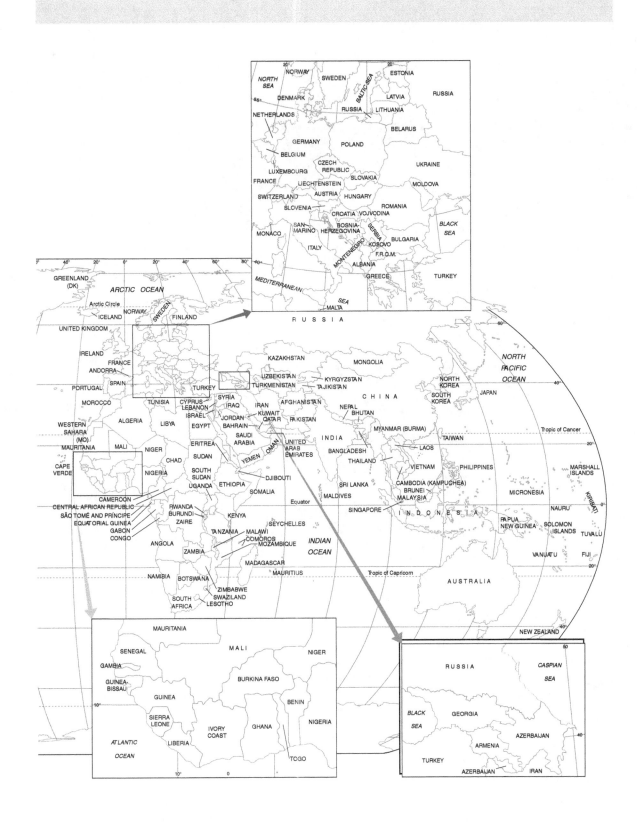

Unit 1

UNIT

Prepared by: Richard Eathorne, *Northern Michigan University*

Ecophagy—A Planet in Distress: The Natural Resources–Human Consumption Nexus

The sun, the moon, and the stars would have disappeared long ago . . . had they happened to be within the reach of predatory human hands.

Havelock Ellis, *The Dance of Life,* 1923

"**O**h, how we consume our planet! How ravenous, how insatiable our appetite seems to be!" Such a sentiment seems to be shared by increasing numbers of Earth's scholars, scientists, philosophers, political and religious leaders, indigenous peoples, and global citizens. Human material consumption behavior, not human population growth, may be our greatest environmental threat. In fact, only a small proportion of the world's population consumes the majority of the world's resources, and as such, is responsible for the majority of its pollution (when we talk about consumption we are talking also about carbon emissions). Who is this "small proportion"? Why are they (we?) eating us out of house and home? More critically, however, is to ask, "Is this minority of the human population serving as a role model for the majority of its population? Or will the larger population of humans, as they evolve into middle class, instinctually become mega-omnivores like their predecessors?"

While the global wealth gap (consumption gap) is reducing and more humans are enjoying better "living conditions," it will become even more important for us to be clear regarding our definition of "better living conditions." Are we referring to *higher standards of living* (increased material production/consumption) or *improved quality of life* (ensuring basic sustenance, self-esteem, and freedom). Consumption (associated with *higher standards of living*), according to the United Nations, is a leading cause of environmental degradation. Nonconsumptive behaviors (reflected in *improvements in quality of life*) such as education, democracy, freedom from tyranny, empowerment of women, ensuring human rights, and the like have yet to demonstrate any associative or causal relationship to environmental degradation.

Unit I introduces the idea of ecophagy, coined by Robert Freitas, a senior research fellow and one of four researchers at the nonprofit foundation Institute for Molecular Manufacturing in Palo Alto, California. According to Freitas, ecophagy essentially refers to the consumption of an ecosystem. In the paper[1] in which Freitas first introduced the word, he wrote,

"Perhaps the earliest-recognized and best known danger of molecular nanotechnology is the risk that self-replicating nanorobots capable of functioning autonomously in the natural environment could quickly convert that natural environment (e.g., biomass) into replicas of themselves (e.g., nanomass) on a global basis, a scenario usually referred to as the "grey goo problem" but perhaps more properly termed global ecophagy."

The term ecophagy, therefore, I think describes well the current nature of our environmental consumption. Not only is humanity gobbling up with impunity everything served at the Whole Earth Café—water, plants, animals, species, land, fossil fuels, and ecosystems—the line out the door keeps getting longer and longer as more and more hungry humans demand a seat at the buffet.

Fortunately, the growing global focus (or fad?) on our finding a sustainable relationship with planet Earth appears to suggest that we may have to begin eating more sensibly. We are now recognizing, reluctantly at times (kicking and screaming at other times as we are hauled out of the Café), that if we continue our consumption misbehavior, the Whole Earth Café may very well be forced to shut its doors. And if the evidence is correct—both scientific and based on our personal daily observations—this recognition of a need to change in our environmental dietary habits is not occurring a moment too soon. Earth has grown to over 7 billion Whole Earth Café patrons. But while our species' birthrates are falling, before this era of population growth levels in 2050, there is a good chance habitat Earth will be home to more than 9 billion humans. Add to this the fact that we are seeing more and more of our offspring living to adulthood, and seeing adults living longer lives, rates of earth-resource consumption are destined to rise, and spread, as well. That's the *biological* aspect of humanity's consumption nature.

On the *sociological* side of those consumption demographics, we see that the percentage of humans who achieve a decent standard of living is higher now than it has ever been. And the gap between the worlds's poorest and richest is now filling with a broad middle-income group that had not existed half a century ago. But is that good news? Could it be possible that within such a "silver lining" may lay hidden an ominous cloud? The articles this unit encourage the reader to seriously, and critically, assess the potential catastrophic impact that this 21st century "middle-income group" of the human species may have on the planet should their Earth consumption behavior be anything like that of their 20th century ancestors.

The question many scholars are beginning to ask is, "Are humans hardwired to be resource over-consumers? Do we have an innate need for status and novelty?" It does appear that we may have had a predisposition to "needing more stuff" that dates as far back as our premodern roots. If so, then providing the material "stuff" necessary to meet such needs requires resource consumption and possible resource depletions and runs contrary to the spirit of sustainability. Furthermore, our original abundance of resources, which allowed such copious consumption, continues to diminish as global competition grows. Also, the association between material production/consumption in industrialized countries and carbon emissions/climate change is clearly documented. Finally, our obsession with work (and overwork) and its associated high levels of productivity is linked directly to our compulsion to amass material wealth. Furthermore, this association is distracting us from making time to nurture the human relationships (nonmaterial production) necessary for sustaining a healthy planet.

But evidence also suggest that the world has the wealth and resources to provide everyone with the opportunity to live a decent life. If this is true, then the question of any conscientious global citizen would then have to be, "How much should a person consume?" Perhaps a place to start to answer this question is to agree that we consume too much when consumption becomes an end in itself and makes us lose affection and reverence for the natural world as well as respect and compassion for all humans.

Then, how much should we consume? Far, far less.

Article

People and the Planet: Executive Summary

ROYAL SOCIETY POLICY CENTER

Summary

The 21st century is a critical period for people and the planet. The global population reached 7 billion during 2011 and the United Nations projections indicate that it will reach between 8 and 11 billion by 2050. Human impact on the Earth raises serious concerns, and in the richest parts of the world per capita material consumption is far above the level that can be sustained for everyone in a population of 7 billion or more. This is in stark contrast to the world's 1.3 billion poorest people, who need to consume more in order to be raised out of extreme poverty.

The highest fertility rates are now seen primarily in the least developed countries while the lowest fertility rates are seen in the more developed countries, and increasingly in Asia and Latin America. Despite a decline in fertility almost everywhere, global population is still growing at about 80 million per year, because of the demographic momentum inherent in a large cohort of young people. The global rate of population growth is already declining, but the poorest countries are neither experiencing, nor benefiting from, this decline.

Population and consumption are both important: the combination of increasing global population and increasing overall material consumption has implications for a finite planet. As both continue to rise, signs of unwanted impacts and feedback (eg climate change reducing crop yields in some areas) and of irreversible changes (eg the increased rate of species extinction) are growing alarmingly. The relationship between population, consumption and the environment is not straightforward, as the natural environment and human socioeconomic systems are complex in their own right. The Earth's capacity to meet human needs is finite, but how the limits are approached depends on lifestyle choices and associated consumption; these depend on what is used, and how, and what is regarded as essential for human wellbeing.

Demographic change is driven by economic development, social and cultural factors as well as environmental change. A transition from high to low birth and death rates has occurred in various cultures, in widely different socio-economic settings, and at different rates. Countries such as Iran and South Korea

have moved through the phases of this transition much more rapidly than Europe or North America. This has brought with it challenges different from those that were experienced by the more developed countries as they reached the late stages of the transition.

Population is not only about the growing numbers of people: changes in age structure, migration, urbanisation and population decline present both opportunities and challenges to human health, wellbeing and the environment. Migrants often provide benefits to their countries of origin, through remittances, and to their host countries by helping to offset a workforce gap in ageing populations. Current and future migration will be affected by environmental change, although lack of resources may mean that the most vulnerable to these changes are the least able to migrate. Policy makers should prepare for international migration and its consequences, for integration of migrants and for protection of their human rights.

Developing countries will be building the equivalent of a city of a million people every five days from now to 2050. The continuing and rapid growth of the urban population is having a marked bearing on lifestyle and behaviour: how and what they consume, how many children they have, the type of employment they undertake. Urban planning is essential to avoid the spread of slums, which are highly deleterious to the welfare of individuals and societies.

The demographic changes and consumption patterns described above lead to three pressing challenges.

First, the world's 1.3 billion poorest people need to be raised out of extreme poverty. This is critical to reducing global inequality, and to ensuring the wellbeing of all people. It will require increased per capita consumption for this group, allowing improved nutrition and healthcare, and reduction in family size in countries with high fertility rates.

Second, in the most developed and the emerging economies unsustainable consumption must be urgently reduced. This will entail scaling back or radical transformation of damaging material consumption and emissions and the adoption of sustainable technologies, and is critical to ensuring a sustainable future for all. At present, consumption is closely linked to economic models based on growth. Improving the wellbeing of individuals so that humanity flourishes rather than survives requires moving from current economic measures to fully valuing natural capital. Decoupling economic activity from material and environmental throughputs is needed urgently for example by reusing equipment and recycling materials, reducing waste, obtaining energy from renewable sources, and by consumers paying for the wider costs of their consumption. Changes to the current socio-economic model and institutions are needed to allow both people and the planet to flourish by collaboration as well as competition during this and subsequent centuries. This requires farsighted political leadership concentrating on long term goals.

Third, global population growth needs to be slowed and stabilised, but this should by no means be coercive. A large unmet need for contraception remains in both developing and developed countries. Voluntary family planning is a key part of continuing the downward trajectory in fertility rates, which brings benefits to the individual wellbeing of men and women around the world. In the long term a stabilised population is an essential prerequisite for individuals to flourish. Education will play an important role: well educated people tend to live longer healthier lives, are more able to choose the number of children they have and are more resilient to, and capable of, change. Education goals have been repeatedly agreed by the international community, but implementation is poor.

Science and technology have a crucial role to play in meeting these three challenges by improving the understanding of causes and effects (such as stratospheric ozone depletion), and in developing ways to limit the most damaging trends (such as enhancing agricultural production with reduced environmental impact). However, attention must be paid to the socio-economic dimensions of technological deployment, as barriers will not be overcome solely by technology but in combination with changes in usage and governance.

Demographic changes and their associated environmental impacts will vary across the globe, meaning that regional and national policy makers will need to adopt their own range of solutions to deal with their specific issues. At an international level, this year's Rio+20 Conference on Sustainable Development, the discussions at the UN General Assembly revisiting the International Conference on Population and Development (ICPD+20) scheduled for 2014/2015 and the review of the Millennium Development Goals in 2015 present opportunities to reframe the relationship between people and the planet. Successfully reframing this relationship will open up a prosperous and flourishing future, for present and future generations.

Recommendations
Recommendation 1
The international community must bring the 1.3 billion people living on less than $1.25 per day out of absolute poverty, and reduce the inequality that persists in the world today. This will require focused efforts in key policy areas including economic development, education, family planning and health.

Recommendation 2
The most developed and the emerging economies must stabilise and then reduce material consumption levels through: dramatic improvements in resource use efficiency, including: reducing waste; investment in sustainable resources, technologies and infrastructures; and systematically decoupling economic activity from environmental impact.

Recommendation 3
Reproductive health and voluntary family planning programmes urgently require political leadership and financial commitment, both nationally and internationally. This is needed to continue the downward trajectory of fertility rates, especially in countries where the unmet need for contraception is high.

Recommendation 4
Population and the environment should not be considered as two separate issues. Demographic changes, and the influences on them, should be factored into economic and environmental debate and planning at international meetings, such as the Rio+20 Conference on Sustainable Development and subsequent meetings.

Recommendation 5
Governments should realise the potential of urbanisation to reduce material consumption and environmental impact through efficiency measures. The well planned provision of water supply, waste disposal, power and other services will avoid slum conditions and increase the welfare of inhabitants.

Recommendation 6
In order to meet previously agreed goals for universal education, policy makers in countries with low school attendance need to work with international funders and organisations, such as UNESCO, UNFPA, UNICEF, IMF, World Bank and Education for All. **Financial and non-financial barriers must be overcome to achieve high-quality primary and secondary education for all the world's young, ensuring equal opportunities for girls and boys.**

Recommendation 7
Natural and social scientists need to increase their **research efforts on the interactions between consumption, demographic change and environmental impact.** They have a unique and vital role in developing a fuller picture of the problems, the uncertainties found in all such analyses, the efficacy of potential solutions, and providing an open, trusted source of information for policy makers and the public.

Recommendation 8

National Governments should accelerate the development of comprehensive wealth measures. This should include reforms to the system of national accounts, and improvement in natural asset accounting.

Recommendation 9

Collaboration between National Governments is needed to **develop socio-economic systems and institutions that are not dependent on continued material consumption growth.** This will inform the development and implementation of policies that allow both people and the planet to flourish.

Critical Thinking

1. Describe what is meant by *demographic change* and explain why it plays an important role in any discussions about planetary consumption.

2. The article states: "Population is not only about the growing numbers of people. . . ." Explain what this means.

3. What are the three pressing challenges confronting us today? Do you think the consuming the Earth/overconsumption issue has contributed to creating these challenges?

4. How do you think the recommendations of the summary report can be implemented (enforced)?

5. Can the recommendations be successful without first addressing the environmental overconsumption issue? Explain.

Article

Putting People in the Map: Anthropogenic Biomes of the World

ERLE C. ELLIS AND NAVIN RAMANKUTTY

Humans have fundamentally altered global patterns of biodiversity and ecosystem processes. Surprisingly, existing systems for representing these global patterns, including biome classifications, either ignore humans altogether or simplify human influence into, at most, four categories. Here, we present the first characterization of terrestrial biomes based on global patterns of sustained, direct human interaction with ecosystems. Eighteen "anthropogenic biomes" were identified through empirical analysis of global population, land use, and land cover. More than 75% of Earth's ice-free land showed evidence of alteration as a result of human residence and land use, with less than a quarter remaining as wildlands, supporting just 11% of terrestrial net primary production. Anthropogenic biomes offer a new way forward by acknowledging human influence on global ecosystems and moving us toward models and investigations of the terrestrial biosphere that integrate human and ecological systems.

Front Ecol Environ 2008; 6(8); 439–447, doi:
10.1890/070062

Humans have long distinguished themselves from other species by shaping ecosystem form and process using tools and technologies, such as fire, that are beyond the capacity of other organisms (Smith 2007). This exceptional ability for ecosystem engineering has helped to sustain unprecedented human population growth over the past half century, to such an extent that humans now consume about one-third of all terrestrial net primary production (NPP; Vitousek *et al.* 1986; Imhoff *et al.* 2004) and move more earth and produce more reactive nitrogen than all other terrestrial processes combined (Galloway 2005; Wilkinson and McElroy 2007). Humans are also causing global extinctions (Novacek and Cleland 2001) and changes in climate that are comparable to any observed in the natural record (Ruddiman 2003; IPCC 2007). Clearly, *Homo sapiens* has emerged as a force of nature rivaling climatic and geologic forces in shaping the terrestrial biosphere and its processes.

In a Nutshell:

- Anthropogenic biomes offer a new view of the terrestrial biosphere in its contemporary, human-altered form
- Most of the terrestrial biosphere has been altered by human residence and agriculture
- Less than a quarter of Earth's ice-free land is wild; only 20% of this is forests and >36% is barren
- More than 80% of all people live in densely populated urban and village biomes
- Agricultural villages are the most extensive of all densely populated biomes and one in four people lives in them

Biomes are the most basic units that ecologists use to describe global patterns of ecosystem form, process, and biodiversity. Historically, biomes have been identified and mapped based on general differences in vegetation type associated with regional variations in climate (Udvardy 1975; Matthews 1983; Prentice *et al.* 1992; Olson *et al.* 2001; Bailey 2004). Now that humans have restructured the terrestrial biosphere for agriculture, forestry, and other uses, global patterns of species composition and abundance, primary productivity, land-surface hydrology, and the biogeochemical cycles of carbon, nitrogen, and phosphorus, have all been substantially altered (Matson *et al.* 1997; Vitousek *et al.* 1997; Foley *et al.* 2005). Indeed, recent studies indicate that human-dominated ecosystems now cover more of Earth's land surface than do "wild" ecosystems (McCloskey and Spalding 1989; Vitousek *et al.* 1997; Sanderson *et al.* 2002, Mittermeier *et al.* 2003; Foley *et al.* 2005).

It is therefore surprising that existing descriptions of biome systems either ignore human influence altogether or describe it using at most four anthropogenic ecosystem classes (urban/built-up, cropland, and one or two cropland/natural vegetation mosaic(s); classification systems include IGBP, Loveland *et al.* 2000; "Olson Biomes", Olson *et al.* 2001; GLC 2000, Bartholome and Belward 2005; and GLOBCOVER, Defourny *et al.* 2006). Here, we present an alternate view of the terrestrial biosphere, based on an empirical analysis of global patterns of sustained direct human interaction with ecosystems, yielding a global map of "anthropogenic biomes". We then examine the potential of anthropogenic biomes to serve as a new global framework for ecology, complete with testable hypotheses, that can advance research, education, and conservation of the terrestrial biosphere as it exists today—the product of intensive reshaping by direct interactions with humans.

Human Interactions with Ecosystems

Human interactions with ecosystems are inherently dynamic and complex (Folke *et al.* 1996; DeFries *et al.* 2004; Rindfuss *et al.* 2004); any categorization of these is a gross oversimplification. Yet there is little hope of understanding and modeling these interactions at a global scale without such simplification. Most global models of primary productivity, species diversity, and even climate depend on stratifying the terrestrial surface into a limited number of functional types, land-cover types, biomes, or vegetation classes (Haxeltine and Prentice 1996; Thomas *et al.* 2004; Feddema *et al.* 2005).

Human interactions with ecosystems range from the relatively light impacts of mobile bands of hunter-gatherers to the complete replacement of pre-existing ecosystems with built structures (Smil 1991). Population density is a useful indicator of the form and intensity of these interactions, as increasing populations have long been considered both a cause and a consequence of ecosystem modification to produce food and other necessities (Boserup 1965, 1981; Smil 1991; Netting 1993). Indeed, most basic historical forms of human-ecosystem interaction are associated with major differences in population density, including foraging (<1 person km^{-2}), shifting (>10 persons km^{-2}), and continuous cultivation (>100 persons km^{-2}); populations denser than 2500 persons km^{-2} are believed to be unsupportable by traditional subsistence agriculture (Smil 1991; Netting 1993).

In recent decades, industrial agriculture and modern transportation have created new forms of human-ecosystem interaction across the full range of population densities, from low-density exurban developments to vast conurbations that combine high-density cities, low-density suburbs, agriculture,

and even forested areas (Smil 1991; Qadeer 2000; Theobald 2004). Nevertheless, population density can still serve as a useful indicator of the form and intensity of human-ecosystem interactions within a specific locale, especially when populations differ by an order of magnitude or more. Such major differences in population density help to distinguish situations in which humans may be considered merely agents of ecosystem transformation (ecosystem engineers), from situations in which human populations have grown dense enough that their local resource consumption and waste production form a substantial component of local biogeo-chemical cycles and other ecosystem processes. To begin our analysis, we therefore categorize human-ecosystem interactions into four classes, based on major differences in population density: high population intensity ("dense", >100 persons km^{-2}), substantial population intensity ("residential", 10 to 100 persons km^{-2}), minor population ("populated", 1 to 10 persons km^{-2}), and inconsequential population ("remote", <1 person km^{-2}). Population class names are defined only in the context of this study.

Identifying Anthropogenic Biomes: An Empirical Approach

We identified and mapped anthropogenic biomes using the multi-stage empirical procedure ... outlined below, based on global data for *population* (urban, non-urban), *land use* (percent area of pasture, crops, irrigation, rice, urban land), and *land cover* (percent area of trees and bare earth); data for NPP, IGBP land cover, and Olson biomes were obtained for later analysis. ... Biome analysis was conducted at 5 arc minute resolution (5' grid cells cover ~86 km^2 at the equator), a spatial resolution selected as the finest allowing direct use of high-quality land-use area estimates. First, "anthropogenic" 5' cells were separated from "wild" cells, based on the presence of human populations, crops, or pastures. Anthropogenic cells were then stratified into the population density classes described above ("dense", "residential", "populated", and "remote"), based on the density of their non-urban population. We then used cluster analysis, a statistical procedure designed to identify an optimal number of distinct natural groupings (clusters) within a dataset (using SPSS 15.01), to identify natural groupings within the cells of each population density class and within the wild class, based on non-urban population density and percent urban area, pasture, crops, irrigated, rice, trees, and bare earth. Finally, the strata derived above were described, labeled, and organized into broad logical groupings, based on their populations, land-use and land-cover characteristics, and their regional distribution, yielding the 18 anthropogenic biome classes and three wild biome classes. ...

A Tour of the Anthropogenic Biomes

When viewed globally, anthropogenic biomes clearly dominate the terrestrial biosphere, covering more than three-quarters of Earth's ice-free land and incorporating nearly 90% of terrestrial

NPP and 80% of global tree cover.... About half of terrestrial NPP and land were present in the forested and rangeland biomes, which have relatively low population densities and potentially low impacts from land use (excluding residential rangelands . . .). However, one-third of Earth's ice-free land and about 45% of terrestrial NPP occurred within cultivated and substantially populated biomes (dense settlemgnts, villages, croplands, and residential rangelands)....

Of Earth's 6.4 billion human inhabitants, 40% live in dense settlements biomes (82% urban population), 40% live in village biomes (38% urban), 15% live in cropland biomes (7% urban), and 5% live in rangeland biomes (5% urban; forested biomes had 0.6% of global population).... Though most people live in dense settlements and villages, these cover just 7% of Earth's ice-free land, and about 60% of this population is urban, living in the cities and towns embedded within these biomes, which also include almost all of the land we have classified as urban (94% of 0.5 million km², although this is probably a substantial underestimate; Salvatore *et al.* 2005)....

Village biomes, representing dense agricultural populations, were by far the most extensive of the densely populated biomes, covering 7.7 million km², compared with 1.5 million km² for the urban and dense settlements biomes. Moreover, village biomes house about one-half of the world's non-urban population (1.6 of ~ 3.2 billion persons). Though about one-third of global urban area is also embedded within these biomes, urban areas accounted for just 2% of their total extent, while agricultural land (crops and pasture) averaged >60% of their area. More than 39% of densely populated biomes were located in Asia, which also incorporated more than 60% of that continent's total global area, even though this region was the fifth largest of seven regions.... Village biomes were most common in Asia, where they covered more than a quarter of all land. Africa was second, with 13% of village biome area, though these covered just 6% of Africa's land. The most intensive land-use practices were also disproportionately located in the village biomes, including about half the world's irrigated land (1.4 of 2.7 million km²) and two-thirds of global rice land (1.1 of 1.7 million km². . . .)

After rangelands, cropland biomes were the second most extensive of the anthropogenic biomes, covering about 20% of Earth's ice-free land. Far from being simple, crop-covered landscapes, cropland biomes were mostly mosaics of cultivated land mixed with trees and pastures.... As a result, cropland biomes constituted only slightly more than half of the world's total crop-covered area (8 of 15 million km²), with village biomes hosting nearly a quarter and rangeland biomes about 16%. The cropland biomes also included 17% of the world's pasture land, along with a quarter of global tree cover and nearly a third of terrestrial NPP. Most abundant in Africa and Asia, residential, rainfed mosaic was by far the most extensive cropland biome and the second most abundant biome overall (16.7 million km²), providing a home to nearly 600 million people, 4 million km² of crops, and about 20% of the world's tree cover and NPP—a greater share than the entire wild forests biome.

Rangeland biomes were the most extensive, covering nearly a third of global ice-free land and incorporating 73% of global pasture (28 million km²), but these were found primarily in arid and other low productivity regions with a high percentage of bare earth cover (around 50% . . .). As a result, rangelands accounted for less than l5% of terrestrial NPP, 6% of global tree cover, and 5% of global population.

Forested biomes covered an area similar to the cropland biomes (25 million km² versus 27 million km² for crop-lands), but incorporated a much greater tree-covered area (45% versus 25% of their global area). It is therefore surprising that the total NPP of the forested biomes was nearly the same as that of the cropland biomes (16.4 versus 16.0 billion tons per year). This may be explained by the lower productivity of boreal forests, which predominate in the forested biomes, while crop-land biomes were located in some of the world's most productive climates and soils.

Wildlands without evidence of human occupation or land use occupied just 22% of Earth's ice-free land in this analysis. In general, these were located in the least productive regions of the world; more than two-thirds of their area occurred in barren and sparsely tree-covered regions. As a result, even though wildlands contained about 20% cover by wild forests (a mix of boreal and tropical forests . . .), wild-lands as a whole contributed only about 11% of total terrestrial NPP.

Anthropogenic Biomes Are Mosaics

It is clear from the biome descriptions above, from the land-use and land-cover patterns . . . , and most of all, by comparing our biome map against high-resolution satellite imagery . . . , that anthropogenic biomes are best characterized as heterogeneous landscape mosaics, combining a variety of different land uses and land covers. Urban areas are embedded within agricultural areas, trees are interspersed with croplands and housing, and managed vegetation is mixed with semi-natural vegetation (eg croplands are embedded within rangelands and forests). Though some of this heterogeneity might be explained by the relatively coarse resolution of our analysis, we suggest a more basic explanation: that direct interactions between humans and ecosystems generally take place within heterogeneous landscape mosaics (Pickett and Cadenasso 1995; Daily 1999). Further, we propose that this heterogeneity has three causes, two of which are anthropogenic and all of which are fractal in nature (Levin 1992), producing similar patterns across spatial scales ranging from the land holdings of individual households to the global patterning of the anthropogenic biomes.

We hypothesize that even in the most densely populated biomes, most landscape heterogeneity is caused by natural variation in terrain, hydrology, soils, disturbance regimes (eg fire), and climate, as described by conventional models of ecosystems and the terrestrial biosphere (eg Levin 1992; Haxeltine and Prentice 1996; Olson *et al.* 2001). Anthropogenic enhancement of natural landscape heterogeneity represents a secondary cause of heterogeneity within anthropogenic biomes, explained in part by the human tendency to seek out and use the most productive lands first and to work and populate these lands most intensively (Huston 1993). At a global scale, this process may explain why wildlands are most common in those parts of the biosphere with the least potential for agriculture (ie polar regions, mountains, low fertility tropical soils . . .) and why, at a given percentage of tree cover, NPP appears higher in anthropogenic biomes with higher population densities (compare NPP with tree cover, especially in wild forests versus forested biomes, . . .). It may also explain why most human populations, both urban and rural, appear to be associated with intensive agriculture (irrigated crops, rice), and not with pasture, forests, or other, less intensive land uses. . . . Finally, this hypothesis explains why most fertile valleys and floodplains in favorable climates are already in use as croplands, while neighboring hillslopes and mountains are often islands of semi-natural vegetation, left virtually undisturbed by local populations (Huston 1993; Daily 1999). The third cause of landscape heterogeneity in anthropogenic biomes is entirely anthropogenic: humans create landscape heterogeneity directly, as exemplified by the construction of settlements and transportation systems in patterns driven as much by cultural as by environmental constraints (Pickett and Cadenasso 1995).

All three of these drivers of heterogeneity undoubtedly interact in patterning the terrestrial biosphere, but their relative roles at global scales have yet to be studied and surely merit further investigation, considering the impacts of landscape fragmentation on biodiversity (Vitousek et al. 1997; Sanderson et al. 2002).

A Conceptual Model for Anthropogenic Biomes

Given that anthropogenic biomes are mosaics—mixtures of settlements, agriculture, forests and other land uses and land covers—how do we proceed to a general ecological understanding of human–ecosystem interactions within and across anthropogenic biomes? Before developing a set of hypotheses and a strategy for testing them, we first summarize our current understanding of how these interactions pattern terrestrial ecosystem processes at a global scale using a simple equation:

Ecosystem processes = f(population density, land use, biota, climate, terrain, geology)

Those familiar with conventional ecosystem-process models will recognize that ours is merely an expansion of these, adding human population density and land use as parameters to explain global patterns of ecosystem processes and their changes. With some modification, conventional land-use and ecosystem-process models should therefore be capable of modeling ecological changes within and across anthropogenic biomes (Turner et al. 1995; DeFries et al. 2004; Foley et al. 2005). We include population density as a separate driver of ecosystem processes, based on the principle that increasing population densities can drive greater intensity of land use (Boserup 1965, 1981) and can also increase the direct contribution of hyumans to local econsystem processes (eg resource consumption, combustion,

excretion; Imhoff et al. 2004). For example, under the same environmental conditions, our model would predict greater fertilizer and water inputs to agricultural land in areas with higher population densities, together with greater emissions from the combustion of biomass and fossil fuel.

Some Hypotheses and Their Tests

Based on our conceptual model of anthropogenic biomes, we propose some basic hypotheses concerning their utility as a model of the terrestrial biosphere. First, we hypothesize that anthropogenic biomes will differ substantially in terms of basic ecosystem processes (eg NPP, carbon emissions, reactive nitrogen . . .) and biodiversity (total, native) when measured across each biome in the field, and that these differences will be at least as great as those between the conventional biomes when observed using equivalent methods at the same spatial scale. Further, we hypothesize that these differences will be driven by differences in population density and land use between the biomes . . ., a trend already evident in the general tendency toward increasing cropped area, irrigation, and rice production with increasing population density. . . . Finally, we hypothesize that the degree to which anthropogenic biomes explain global patterns of ecosystem processes and biodiversity will increase over time, in tandem with anticipated future increases in human influence on ecosystems.

The testing of these and other hypotheses awaits improved data on human-ecosystem interactions obtained by observations made within and across the full range of anthropogenic landscapes. Observations within anthropogenic landscapes capable of resolving individually managed land-use features and built structures are critical, because this is the scale at which humans interact directly with ecosystems and is also the optimal scale for precise measurements of ecosystem parameters and their controls (Ellis et al. 2006). Given the considerable effort involved in making detailed measurements of ecological and human systems across heterogeneous anthropogenic landscapes, this will require development of statistically robust stratified-sampling designs that can support regional and global estimates based on relatively small landscape samples within and across anthropogenic biomes (eg Ellis 2004). This, in turn, will require improved global data, especially for human populations and land-use practices. Fortunately, development of these datasets would also pave the way toward a system of anthropogenic ecore-gions capable of serving the ecological monitoring needs of regional and local stakeholders, a role currently occupied by conventional ecoregion mapping and classification system (Olson et al. 2001).

Are Conventional Biome Systems Obsolete?

We have portrayed the terrestrial biosphere as composed of anthropogenic biomes, which might also be termed "anthromes" or "human biomes" to distinguish them from conventional biome systems. This begs the question: are conventional biome systems obsolete? The answer is certainly "no". Although we have proposed a basic model of ecological processes within and across anthropogenic biomes, our model remains conceptual, while existing models of the terrestrial biomes, based on climate, terrain, and geology, are fully operational and are useful for predicting the future state of the biosphere in response to climate change (Melillo *et al.* 1993; Cox *et al.* 2000; Cramer *et al.* 2001).

On the other hand, anthropogenic biomes are in many ways a more accurate description of broad ecological patterns within the current terrestrial biosphere than are conventional biome systems that describe vegetation patterns based on variations in climate and geology. It is rare to find extensive areas of any of the basic vegetation forms depicted in conventional biome models outside of the areas we have defined as wild biomes. This is because most of the world's "natural" ecosystems are embedded within lands altered by land use and human populations, as is apparent when viewing the distribution of IGBP and Olson biomes within the anthropogenic biomes. . . .

Ecologists Go Home!

Anthropogenic biomes point to a necessary turnaround in ecological science and education, especially for North Americans. Beginning with the first mention of ecology in school, the biosphere has long been depicted as being composed of natural biomes, perpetuating an outdated view of the world as "natural ecosystems with humans disturbing them". Although this model has long been challenged by ecologists (Odum 1969), especially in Europe and Asia (Golley 1993), and by those in other disciplines (Cronon 1983), it remains the mainstream view. Anthropogenic biomes tell a completely different story, one of "human systems, with natural ecosystems embedded within them". This is no minor change in the story we tell our children and each other. Yet it is necessary for sustainable management of the biosphere in the 21st century.

Anthropogenic biomes clearly show the inextricable intermingling of human and natural systems almost everywhere on Earth's terrestrial surface, demonstrating that interactions between these systems can no longer be avoided in any substantial way. Moreover, human interactions with ecosystems mediated through the atmosphere (eg climate change) are even more pervasive and are dis-proportionately altering the areas least impacted by humans directly (polar and arid lands; IPCC 2007 . . .). Sustainable ecosystem management must therefore be directed toward developing and maintaining beneficial interactions between managed and natural systems, because avoiding these interactions is no longer a practical option (DeFries *et al.* 2004; Foley *et al.* 2005). Most importantly, though still at an early stage of development, anthropogenic biomes offer a framework for incorporating humans directly into global ecosystem models, a capability that is both urgently needed and as yet unavailable (Carpenter *et al.* 2006).

Ecologists have long been known as the scientists who travel to uninhabited lands to do their work. As a result, our understanding

of anthropogenic ecosystems remains poor when compared with the rich literature on "natural" ecosystems. Though much recent effort has focused on integrating humans into ecological research (Pickett *et al.* 2001; Rindfuss *et al.* 2004 . . .) and support for this is increasingly available from the US National Science Foundation (www.nsf.gov; eg HERO, CNH, HSD programs), ecologists can and should do more to "come home" and work where most humans live. Building ecological science and education on a foundation of anthropogenic biomes will help scientists and society take ownership of a biosphere that we have already altered irreversibly, and moves us toward understanding how best to manage the anthropogenic biosphere we live in.

Conclusions

Human influence on the terrestrial biosphere is now pervasive. While climate and geology have shaped ecosystems and evolution in the past, our work contributes to the growing body of evidence demonstrating that human forces may now outweigh these across most of Earth's land surface today. Indeed, wildlands now constitute only a small fraction of Earth's land. For the foreseeable future, the fate of terrestrial ecosystems and the species they support will be intertwined with human systems: most of "nature" is now embedded within anthropogenic mosaics of land use and land cover. While not intended to replace existing biome systems based on climate, terrain, and geology, we hope that wide availability of an anthropogenic biome system will encourage a richer view of human-ecosystem interactions across the terrestrial biosphere, and that this will, in turn, guide our investigation, understanding, and management of ecosystem processes and their changes at global and regional scales.

References

Bartholome E and Belward AS. 2005. GLC2000: a new approach to global land cover mapping from Earth observation data. *Int J Remote Sens* **26**: 1959–77.

Boserup E. 1965. The conditions of agricultural growth: the economics of agrarian change under population pressure. London, UK: Allen and Unwin.

Boserup E. 1981. Population and technological change: a study of long term trends. Chicago, IL: University of Chicago Press.

Carpenter SR, DeFries R, Dietz T, *et al.* 2006. Millennium Ecosystem Assessment: research needs. *Science* **314**: 257–58.

Cox PM, Betts RA, Jones CD, *et al.* 2000. Acceleration of global warming due to carbon-cycle feedbacks in a coupled climate model. *Nature* **408**: 184–87.

Cramer W, Bondeau A, Woodward FI, *et al.* 2001. Global response of terrestrial ecosystem structure and function to CO_2 and climate change: results from six dynamic global vegetation models. *Global Change Bioi* **7**: 357–73.

Cronon W. 1983. Changes in the land: Indians, colonists, and the ecology of New England. New York, NY: Hill and Wang.

Daily GC. 1999. Developing a scientific basis for managing Earth's life support systems. *Conserv Ecol* **3**: 14.

DeFries RS, Foley JA, and Asner GP. 2004. Land-use choices: balancing human needs and ecosystem function. *Front Ecol Environ* **2**: 249–57.

Defourny P, Vancutsem C, Bicheron P, *et al.* 2006. GLOBCOVER: a 300 m global land cover product for 2005 using Envisat MERIS time series. In: Proceedings of the ISPRS Commission VII mid-term symposium, *Remote sensing: from pixels to processes;* 2006 May 8–11; Enschede, Netherlands.

Ellis EC. 2004. Long-term ecological changes in the densely populated rural landscapes of China. In: DeFries RS, Asner GP, and Houghton RA (Eds). Ecosystems and land-use change. Washington, DC: American Geophysical Union.

Ellis EC, Wang H, Xiao HS, *et al.* 2006. Measuring long-term ecological changes in densely populated landscapes using current and historical high resolution imagery. *Remote Sens Environ* **100**: 457–73.

Feddema JJ, Oleson KW, Bonan GB, *et al.* 2005. The importance of land-cover change in simulating future climates. *Science* **310**: 1674–78.

Folke C, Holling CS, and Perrings C. 1996. Biological diversity, ecosystems, and the human scale. *Ecol Appl* **6**: 1018–24.

Foley JA, DeFries R, Asner GP, *et al.* 2005. Global consequences of land use. *Science* **309**: 570–74.

Friedl MA, McIver DK, Hodges JCF, *et al.* 2002. Global land cover mapping from MODIS: algorithms and early results. *Remote Sens Environ* **83**: 287–302.

Galloway JN. 2005. The global nitrogen cycle. In: Schlesinger WH (Ed). Treatise on geochemistry. Oxford, UK: Pergamon.

Golley FB. 1993. A history of the ecosystem concept in ecology: more than the sum of the parts. New Haven, CT: Yale University Press.

Haxeltine A and Prentice IC. 1996. BIOME3; an equilibrium terrestrial biosphere model based on ecophysiological constraints, resource availability, and competition among plant functional types. *Global Biogeochem Cy* **10**: 693–710.

Huston M. 1993. Biological diversity, soils, and economics. *Science* **262**: 1676–80.

Imhoff ML, Bounoua L, Ricketts T, *et al.* 2004. Global patterns in human consumption of net primary production. *Nature* **429**: 870.

IPCC (Intergovernmental Panel on Climate Change). 2007. Climate change 2007: the physical science basis. Summary for policy makers. A report of Working Group I of the Intergovernmental Panel on Climate Change. Geneva, Switzerland: IPCC.

Levin SA. 1992. The problem of pattern and scale in ecology. *Ecology* **73**: 1943–67.

Loveland TR, Reed BC, Brown JF, *et al.* 2000. Development of a global land-cover characteristics database and IGBP DISCover from 1 km AVHRR data. *Int J Remote Sens* **21**: 1303–30.

Matson PA, Parton WJ, Power AG, and Swift MJ. 1997. Agricultural intensification and ecosystem properties. *Science* **277**: 504–09.

Matthews E. 1983. Global vegetation and land use: new high-resolution databases for climate studies. *J Clim Appl Meteorol* **22**: 474–87.

McCloskey JM and Spalding H. 1989. A reconnaissance level inventory of the amount of wilderness remaining in the world. *Amino* **18**: 221–27.

Melillo JM, McGuire AD, Kicklighter DW, *et al.* 1993. Global climate change and terrestrial net primary production. *Nature* **363**: 234–40.

Mittermeier RA, Mittermeier CG, Brooks TM, *et al.* 2003. Wilderness and biodiversity conservation. *P Natl Acad Sci USA* **100**: 10309–13.

Netting RM. 1993. Smallholders, householders: farm families and the ecology of intensive sustainable agriculture. Stanford, CA: Stanford University Press.

Novacek MJ and Cleland EE. 2001. The current biodiversity extinction event: scenarios for mitigation and recovery. *P Natl Acad Sci USA* **98**: 5466–70.

Odum EP. 1969. The strategy of ecosystem development. *Science* **164**: 262–70.

Olson DM, Dinerstein E, Wikramanayake ED, *et al.* 2001. Terrestrial ecoregions of the world: a new map of life on Earth. *Bioscience* **51**: 933–38.

Pickett STA and Cadenasso ML. 1995. Landscape ecology: spatial heterogeneity in ecological systems. *Science* **269**: 331–34.

Pickett STA, Cadenasso ML, Grove JM, *et al.* 2001. Urban ecological systems: linking terrestrial ecological, physical, and socioeconomic components of metropolitan areas. *Annu Rev Ecol Syst* **32**: 127–57.

Qadeer MA. 2000. Ruralopolises: the spatial organisation and residential land economy of high-density rural regions in South Asia. *Urban Stud* **37**: 1583–1603.

Rindfuss RR, Walsh SJ, Turner II BL, *et al.* 2004. Developing a science of land change: challenges and methodological issues. *P Natl Acad Sci USA* **101**: 13976–81.

Ruddiman WF. 2003. The anthropogenic greenhouse era began thousands of years ago. *Climatic Change* **61**: 261–93.

Salvatore M, Pozzi F, Ataman E, *et al.* 2005. Mapping global urban and rural population distributions. Rome, Italy: UN Food and Agriculture Organisation. Environment and Natural Resources Working Paper 24.

Sanderson EW, Jaiteh M, Levy MA, *et al.* 2002. The human footprint and the last of the wild. *BioScience* **52**: 891–904.

Smil V. 1991. General energetics: energy in the biosphere and civilization, 1st edn. New York, NY: John Wiley & Sons.

Smith BD. 2007. The ultimate ecosystem engineers. *Science* **315**: 1797–98.

Theobald DM. 2004. Placing exurban land-use change in a human modification framework. *Front Ecol Environ* **2**: 139–44.

Thomas CD, Cameron A, Green RE, *et al.* 2004. Extinction risk from climate change. *Nature* **427**: 145–48.

Turner II BL, Skole D, Sanderson S, *et al.* 1995. Land-use and land cover change: science/research plan. Stockholm, Sweden: International Geosphere-Biosphere Ptrogramme. IGBP Report no 35.

Vitousek PM, Mooney HA, Lubchenco J, and Melillo JM. 1997. Human domination of Earth's ecosystems. *Science* **277**: 494–99.

Wilkinson BH and McElroy BJ. 2007. The impact of humans on continental erosion and sedimentation. *Geol Soc Am Bull* **119**: 140–56.

Critical Thinking

1. How does "putting people on the map" helps us address the consuming the earth issue?

2. What empirical analyses did the authors use to construct their map of anthropogenic biomes of the world?

3. One section of the article is "Ecologist Go Home!" Explain why the authors would say this. Do you agree with their argument? Why or why not?

4. How does this article support the validity and importance of including geography and place (i.e., the Approaching Environmental Issues paradigm) in any discourse regarding our consumption of the planet?

Acknowledgements—ECE thanks S Gliessman of the Department of Environmental Studies at the University of California, Santa Cruz, and C Field of the Department of Global Ecology, Carnegie Institute of Washington at Stanford, for graciously hosting his sabbatical. P Vitousek and his group, G Asner, J Foley, A Wolf, and A de Bremond provided helpful input. T Rabenhorst provided much-needed help with cartography. Many thanks to the Global Land Cover Facility (www.landcover.org) for providing global land-cover data and to C Monfreda for rice data.

Article

The Issue: Natural Resources, What Are They?

WORLD RESOURCE FORUM

Global Resource Use—Worldwide Patterns of Resource Extraction

Economic and thus human development have always been closely linked to the control and production of materials. Due to continued growth of the global economy, the demand for natural resources, such as fossil fuels, metals and minerals, and biomass from agriculture (crops), forestry, fishery, etc, provided by Planet Earth is rapidly increasing, and they are being exploited without metres and bounds. This results in serious environmental damages through the extraction process itself, but also due to the ever longer transport distances between extraction, processing and final consumption.

Global resource extraction grew more or less steadily over the past 25 years, from 40 billion tons in 1980 to 58 billion tons in 2005, representing an aggregated growth rate of 45%.

Figure 1 illustrates the overall material basis and the growing resource extraction of the global economy between 1980 and 2005. However, growth rates were unevenly distributed among the main material categories. Particularly the extraction of metal ores increased (by more than 65%), indicating the continued importance of this resource category for industrial development. Increases in biomass extraction were below average. The share of renewable resources in total resource extraction thus is decreasing on the global level.

Taking into account all the materials that are extracted but not actually used to create value in economic processes (i.e. overburden in mining or "ecological rucksacks"), the resource extraction more than doubled in the last 25 years. Due to simultaneously increasing world population numbers, the average resource extraction per capita remained almost stable, today amounting for nearly nine tons.

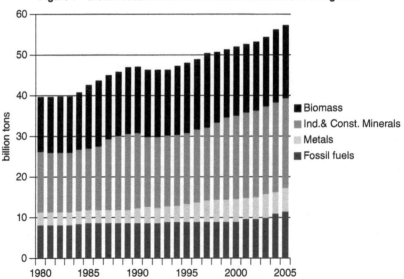

Figure 1   Global used extraction of natural resources in categories.

Regarding material intensity, i.e. economic output per unit of domestic natural resource extraction, Europe is the most 'eco-efficient' region, while Africa produces the smallest economic output per domestic extraction. Nonetheless, Europe's share in worldwide resource extraction is 1.5 times higher than the share of the African continent and Europe is increasingly importing natural resources from other world regions.

Disaggregating the extraction data by world regions, it can be seen that, as a consequence of rapid industrialisation in countries such as China and India, Asia's share in global resource extraction has increased steadily, especially since the early 1990s. From 1980 to 2005 the extraction of fossil fuels in China, for instance, tripled; the total increase in used extraction amounted for 150%.

Europe's resource extraction grew only by 3%, but studies show that these raw materials are increasingly being substituted by imports from other world regions. Latin America, for example, is specialising noticeably in the extraction of resource-intensive export products, such as metal ores or biomass for biofuels. In 2005, Chile extracted fivefold the amount of copper of 1980, Brazil threefold the amount of sugar cane—being the raw material for ethanol fuel.

North America brings in the highest net regional metal imports, receiving 82% of all regional net metal imports. The two territories importing the most metals worldwide (US$ net) are the United States and Mexico. . . . Net imports are imports minus exports. . . . Mineral depletion is the loss of potential future income at current prices due to current quantities of minerals extracted. Included here are gold, lead, zinc, iron, copper, nickel, silver, bauxite, and phosphate. Territories with the highest mineral depletion are Australia, Brazil, Chile and China. Australia is the largest producer of bauxite, Brazil of industrial diamonds, China of tungsten, and South Africa of platinum and gold. Mineral extraction often causes environmental damage, itself a form of depletion. . . .

Global Material Extraction and Resource Efficiency

The above explained exchange of domestic extraction by imported materials does also affect the countries' eco-efficiency, expressed by the material intensity indicator . . ., reflecting economic output per unit of domestic natural resource extraction. One observes that industrialised economies are characterised by the lowest material intensities (or highest eco-efficiency), with Europe being world-leader with around 1.25 tons per 1000 US $ GDP in the 1980s and improving to 0.75 tons at the beginning of this decade. Without a doubt this development is partly the result of the use of new technologies with improved material and energy performance and structural change of economies towards service sectors characterised by less material input per economic output.

Nonetheless, the picture generated by this indicator is distorted, as this leading position is gained, to a certain degree, at the expense of the exporting countries. Figure 2 clearly illustrates that, on a worldwide level, it has been possible to decouple economic growth (GDP) and resource use (extraction); nonetheless, absolute numbers of resource extraction are still increasing, mirroring the fact that efficency gains through structural or technological effects are overcompensated by scale effects brought about by economic growth. The finiteness of important resources as well as constricted regeneration capacities make a reversal of this trend indispensable.

Another effect of an extraction for export is that the added value remaining in the exporting country is very low, which also affects the material intensity. Thus, while steadily increasing raw material prices result in enormous revenue growth for resource rich countries (e.g. through taxes) as well as for the extracting companies, the trickle-down effect to the countries' population is limited, depending on the political strategies of

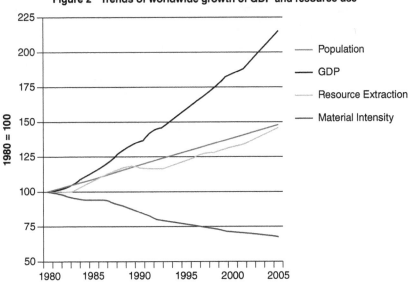

Figure 2   Trends of worldwide growth of GDP and resource use

the local government. Additionally, the dependence on resource exports brings about a high grade of vulnerability, as price changes, or even slumps, have especially severe consequences on the local economy.

Scenarios of Future Resource Extraction

Scenarios on future natural resource extraction, applying integrated economic-environmental models show that in a baseline scenario without additional policies to limit resource use, used domestic extraction within the EU remains roughly constant until 2020, while unused domestic extraction decreases (particularly overburden from mining activities). . . .

The stabilisation of domestic extraction, however, is accompanied by growing imports of material intensive products. This indicates that the material requirements of the European economy will increasingly be met through imports from other world regions, causing shifts of environmental pressures related to material extraction and processing away from Europe towards resource-rich countries.

In order to quantify the use of resources as presented above, the Sustainable Europe Research Institute (SERI) in Vienna built up and maintains the only worldwide comprehensive data base on resource extraction, which comprises data for almost 200 countries, 270 types of resources, and currently a time series of 26 years (1980–2005). The complete aggregated data set is freely accessible on the website www.materialflows.net.

Critical Thinking

1. Make some predictions about how the chart in Figure 1 will look in 2050.

2. According to the data in this article, what nations are consuming the Earth?

3. How will the growing material requirements of the consuming nations cause new shifts of environmental pressures?

Article   Prepared by: Richard Eathorne, *Northern Michigan University*

Too Many People, Too Much Consumption

Four decades after his controversial book, *The Population Bomb,* scientist Paul Ehrlich still believes that overpopulation—now along with overconsumption—is the central environmental crisis facing the world. And, he insists, technological fixes will not save the day.

PAUL R. EHRLICH AND ANNE H. EHRLICH

Learning Outcomes

After reading this article, you will be able to:

- Identify the problems associated with population growth.
- Explain the $I = P \times A \times T$ concept equation.
- Discuss why overconsumption problems and solutions are difficult to address.

Over some 60 million years, *Homo sapiens* has evolved into the dominant animal on the planet, acquiring binocular vision, upright posture, large brains, and—most importantly—language with syntax and that complex store of non-genetic information we call culture. However, in the last several centuries we've increasingly been using our relatively newly acquired power, especially our culturally evolved technologies, to deplete the natural capital of Earth—in particular its deep, rich agricultural soils, its groundwater stored during ice ages, and its biodiversity—as if there were no tomorrow.

The point, all too often ignored, is that this trend is being driven in large part by a combination of population growth and increasing per capita consumption, and it cannot be long continued without risking a collapse of our now-global civilization. Too many people—and especially too many politicians and business executives—are under the delusion that such a disastrous end to the modern human enterprise can be avoided by technological fixes that will allow the population and the economy to grow forever. But if we fail to bring population growth and over-consumption under control—the number of people on Earth is expected to grow from 6.5 billion today to 9 billion by the second half of the 21st century—then we will inhabit a planet where life becomes increasingly untenable because of two looming crises: global heating, and the degradation of the natural systems on which we all depend.

If we fail to bring population growth and overconsumption under control, then we will inhabit a planet where life becomes increasingly untenable.

Our species' negative impact on our own life-support systems can be approximated by the equation $I=PAT$. In that equation, the size of the population (P) is multiplied by the average affluence or consumption per individual (A), and that in turn is multiplied by some measure of the technology (T) that services and drives the consumption. Thus commuting in automobiles powered by subsidized fossil fuels on proliferating freeways creates a much greater T factor than commuting on bikes using simple paths or working at home on a computer network. The product of P, A, and T is Impact (I), a rough estimate of how much humanity is degrading the ecosystem services it depends upon.

The equation is not rocket science. Two billion people, all else being equal, put more greenhouse gases into the atmosphere than one billion people. Two billion rich people disrupt the climate more than two billion poor people. Three hundred million Americans consume more petroleum than 1.3 billion Chinese. And driving an SUV is using a far more environmentally malign transportation technology than riding mass transit.

The technological dimensions of our predicament—such as the need for alternatives to fossil fuel energy—are frequently discussed if too little acted upon. Judging from media reports and the statements of politicians, environmental problems, to the degree they are recognized, can be solved by minor changes in technologies and recycling (T). Switching to ultra-light, fuel-efficient cars will obviously give some short-term advantage, but as population and consumption grow, they will pour still more carbon dioxide (and vaporized rubber) into the atmosphere and require more natural areas to be buried under concrete.

More recycling will help, but many of our society's potentially most dangerous effluents (such as hormone-mimicking chemicals) cannot practically be recycled. There is no technological change we can make that will permit growth in either human numbers or material affluence to continue to expand. In the face of this, the neglect of the intertwined issues of population and consumption is stunning.

Many past human societies have collapsed under the weight of overpopulation and environmental neglect, but today the civilization in peril is global. The population factor in what appears to be a looming catastrophe is even greater than most people suppose. Each person added today to the population on average causes more damage to humanity's critical life-support systems than did the previous addition—everything else being equal. The reason is simple: *Homo sapiens* became the dominant animal by being smart. Farmers didn't settle first on poor soils where water was scarce, but rather in rich river valleys. That's where most cities developed, where rich soils are now being paved over for roads and suburbs, and where water supplies are being polluted or overexploited.

As a result, to support additional people it is necessary to move to ever poorer lands, drill wells deeper, or tap increasingly remote sources to obtain water—and then spend more energy to transport that water ever greater distances to farm fields, homes, and factories. Our distant ancestors could pick up nearly pure copper on Earth's surface when they started to use metals; now people must use vast amounts of energy to mine and smelt gigantic amounts of copper ore of ever poorer quality, some in concentrations of less than one percent. The same can be said for other important metals. And petroleum can no longer be found easily on or near the surface, but must be gleaned from wells drilled a mile or more deep, often in inaccessible localities, such as under continental shelves beneath the sea. All of the paving, drilling, fertilizer manufacturing, pumping, smelting, and transporting needed to provide for the consumption of burgeoning numbers of people produces greenhouse gases and thus tightens the connection between population and climate disruption.

So why is the topic of overpopulation so generally ignored? There are some obvious reasons. Attempts by governments to limit their nation's population growth are anathema to those on the right who believe the only role for governments in the bedroom is to force women to take unwanted babies to term. Those on the left fear, with some legitimacy, that population control could turn racist or discriminatory in other ways—for example, attempting to reduce the numbers of minorities or the poor. Many fear the specter of more of "them" compared to "us," and all of us fear loss of liberty and economic decline (since population growth is often claimed necessary for economic health). And there are religious leaders who still try to promote over-reproduction by their flocks, though in much of the world their efforts are largely futile (Catholic countries in Europe tend to be low-birthrate leaders, for example).

But much of the responsibility must go to ignorance, which leads mainstream media, even newspapers like *The New York Times,* to maintain a pro-natalist stance. For example, the *Times* had an article on June 29 about a "baby bust" in industrialized countries in which the United States (still growing) was noted as a "sparkling exception." Beyond the media, great foundations have turned their "population programs" away from encouraging low fertility rates and toward topics like "changing sexual mores"—avoiding discussion of the contribution demographics is making to a possible collapse of civilization.

Some leading economists are starting to tackle the issue of overconsumption, but the problems and its cures are tough to analyze.

Silence on the overconsumption (Affluence) factor in the I=PAT equation is more readily explained. Consumption is still viewed as an unalloyed good by many economists, along with business leaders and politicians, who tend to see jacking up consumption as a cure-all for economic ills. Too much unemployment? Encourage people to buy an SUV or a new refrigerator. Perpetual growth is the creed of the cancer cell, but third-rate economists can't think of anything else. Some leading economists *are* starting to tackle the issue of overconsumption, but the problem and its cures are tough to analyze. Scientists have yet to develop consumption condoms or morning-after-shopping-spree pills.

And, of course, there are the vexing problems of consumption of people in poor countries. On one hand, a billion or more people have problems of *underconsumption.* Unless their basic needs are met, they are unlikely to be able to make important contributions to attaining sustainability. On the other hand, there is also the issue of the "new consumers" in developing economies such as China and India, where the wealth of a sizable minority is permitting them to acquire the consumption habits (e.g., eating a lot of meat and driving automobiles) of the rich nations. Consumption regulation is a lot more complex than population regulation, and it is much more difficult to find humane and equitable solutions to the problem.

The dominant animal is wasting its brilliance and its wonderful achievements; civilization's fate is being determined by decision makers who determinedly look the other way in favor of immediate comfort and profit. Thousands of scientists recently participated in a Millennium Ecosystem Assessment that outlined our current environmental dilemma, but the report's dire message made very little impact. Absent attention to that message, the fates of Easter Island, the Classic Maya civilization, and Nineveh—all of which collapsed following environmental degradation—await us all.

We believe it is possible to avoid that global denouement. Such mobilization means developing some consensus on goals—perhaps through a global dialogue in which people discuss the human predicament and decide whether they would like to see a maximum number of people living at a minimum standard of living, or perhaps a much lower population size that gives individuals a broad choice of lifestyles. We have suggested a forum for such a dialogue, modeled partly on the

Intergovernmental Panel on Climate Change, but with more "bottom up" participation. It is clear that only widespread changes in norms can give humanity a chance of attaining a sustainable and reasonably conflict-free society.

How to achieve such change—involving everything from demographic policies and transformation of planet-wide energy, industrial, and agricultural systems, to North–South and interfaith relationships and military postures—is a gigantic challenge to everyone. Politicians, industrialists, ecologists, social scientists, everyday citizens, and the media must join this debate. Whether it is possible remains to be seen; societies have managed to make major transitions in the recent past, as the civil rights revolution in the United States and the collapse of communism in the Soviet Union clearly demonstrate.

We'll continue to hope and work for a cultural transformation in how we treat each other and the natural systems we depend upon. We can create a peaceful and sustainable global civilization, but it will require realistic thinking about the problems we face and a new mobilization of political will.

Critical Thinking

1. How can the concept of the IPAT equation help developing countries as well as developed countries in achieving their sustainability goals?

2. Who suffers from "underconsumption" and how might they improve their lives without "overcoming"?

3. On a scale of 1–10, with 10 meaning "absolutely possible," rate the probably of civilization achieving a "sustainable relationship with the earth" by 2050. Discuss your answer.

Create Central

www.mhhe.com/createcentral

Internet References

Alliance for Global Sustainability (AGS)
www.global-sustainability.org

Global Footprint Network
footprints@footprintnetwork.org

People & Planet
www.peopleandplanet.org

Population Action International
www.populationaction.org

Paul and Anne Ehrlich are in the Department of Biology and the Center for Stanford University, where he is Bing Professor of Population Studies and Pro and she is senior research associate. Their latest book, *The Dominant Anima Enuironment* (Island Press), focuses on the issues cited in this article and includes references.

Article   Prepared by: Richard Eathorne, *Northern Michigan University*

New Consumers: The Influence of Affluence on the Environment

Growing consumption can cause major environmental damage. This is becoming specially significant through the emergence of over 1 billion new consumers, people in 17 developing and three transition countries with an aggregate spending capacity, in purchasing power parity terms, to match that of the U.S. Two of their consumption activities have sizeable environmental impacts. First is a diet based strongly on meat, which, because it is increasingly raised in part on grain, puts pressure on limited irrigation water and international grain supplies. Second, these new consumers possess over one-fifth of the world's cars, a proportion that is rising rapidly. Global CO_2 emissions from motor vehicles, of which cars make up 74%, increased during 1990–1997 by 26% and at a rate four times greater than the growth of CO_2 emissions overall. It is in the self-interest of new consumer countries, and of the global community, to restrict the environmental impacts of consumption; this restriction is achievable through a number of policy initiatives.

NORMAN MYERS AND JENNIFER KENT

Learning Outcomes

After reading this article, you will be able to:

- Define who the "new consumers" are.

- Describe the two predominant consumption sectors of the "new consumers."

- Explain how the consumption patterns of India and China can be used to model future patterns of consumption.

Increasing consumption and especially its environmental impacts (1–5) are becoming all the more important now that the 850 million long-established consumers in rich countries have recently been joined by almost 1.1 billion new consumers in 17 developing and three transition countries. Most of these new consumers are far from possessing the spending capacity of the long-established consumers, but they have enough aggregate spending capacity, in terms of purchasing power parity (PPP), to match that of the U.S. Their numbers, consumption activities, and environmental impact are rising fast.

Of course, the new consumers should benefit from their affluence. This is a given, especially in light of the meager lifestyles that many of them have earlier experienced and the far greater consumption of long-affluent countries. But the environmental consequences of this new affluence are so significant that it will be in the self-interest of the 20 countries to restrict the damage with its economic penalties. In addition, and because of the global reach of certain environmental impacts, e.g., the CO_2 emissions from cars that accelerate climate change, the entire world community

has an interest in the emergent phenomenon of the new consumers, on top of its even greater stake in long-established consumers with their far more pronounced environmental impacts. The world community also has an interest in those 1.3 billion people who endure abject poverty and whose basic needs demand far greater consumption forthwith. Their needs, however vital and urgent, lie outside the scope of this paper.

Who Are the New Consumers?

We define new consumers as people within typically four-member households with purchasing power of at least PPP $10,000 per year, i.e., at least PPP $2,500 per person, measured in PPP rather than conventional (international exchange) dollars (PPP dollars are between 1.3 and 5.3 times higher than conventional dollars in the 20 countries). From here on, we speak only of individual consumers, virtually all of whom possess purchasing power far above PPP $2,500. The PPP dollar levels themselves appear to mark a degree of affluence that enables wide-ranging purchases such as household appliances and televisions, air conditioners, personal computers, and other consumer electronics, among other perceived perquisites of an affluent lifestyle. More significantly for environmental purposes, many new consumers enjoy a strongly meat-based diet and buy cars.

The calculations reflect an analytic model by using data on country populations, economic growth, PPP equivalents, income distribution, and consumption patterns (6, 7). The model reveals percentiles of populations at various income levels for the year 2000. The data for this purpose, as for other calculations, have been drawn largely from >600 articles and books in the peer-reviewed literature and from reports and other documents of the World Bank/International Monetary Fund and the United Nations, among other leading agencies (see *Supporting References,* which is published as supporting information on the PNAS web site, www.pnas.org). We believe these are the most reliable information sources available on a singularly wide-ranging issue and recognize that not all data may be as authoritative as one might wish. But the degree of credibility must be balanced against the need to address an emergent phenomenon that has exceptional significance for the world's environmental and economic future alike.

There are sizeable numbers of new consumers in 20 selected countries with records of strong economic growth and populations of at least 20 million people (Tables 1 and 2). They comprise 17 developing and three transition countries. Among them are four countries, South Korea, Mexico, Turkey, and Poland, that are members of the Organisation for Economic Cooperation and Development (OECD), the "rich nations club," even though their per-capita gross national products are far below that of 23 high-income members. They are generally listed in OECD, World Bank, and United Nations documents as "middle income" or "upper middle income" countries as opposed to "high income" countries, hence they are included here as developing or transition countries.

In 14 countries, new consumers make up 12–56% of the population, and in six countries they make up 61–96%. The new consumers' incomes are far greater than national averages because of income skewedness, a factor that applies in all 20 countries. In 16 countries, the top 20% of the population enjoy ≈ 50% or more of national income and in all 20 countries, 40% enjoy 62% or more (Table 2). In addition, the top quintiles generally show an increasing concentration of affluence and hence of consumption (6, 8).

Table 1   New Consumers, 2000

Country	Population, millions, 2000	New consumers, millions, 2000 (and percent of population)	Purchasing power, PPP $ billions (and percent of national total)*
China	1,262	303 (24)	1,267 (52)
India	1,016	132 (13)	609 (39)
South Korea	47	45 (96)	502 (99)
Philippines	76	33 (43)	150 (75)
Indonesia	210	63 (30)	288 (56)
Malaysia	23	12 (53)	79 (84)
Thailand	61	32 (53)	179 (79)
Pakistan	138	17 (12)	62 (31)
Iran	64	27 (42)	136 (71)
Saudi Arabia	21	13 (61)	78 (87)
South Africa	43	17 (40)	202 (83)
Brazil	170	74 (44)	641 (83)
Argentina†	37	31 (84)	314 (97)
Venezuela	24	13 (56)	87 (86)
Colombia	42	19 (45)	136 (83)
Mexico	98	68 (69)	624 (93)
Turkey	65	45 (69)	265 (85)
Poland	39	34 (86)	206 (95)
Ukraine	50	12 (23)	44 (45)
Russia	146	68 (47)	436 (79)
Totals	3,632	1,059 (29)	6,305 (67)‡

*Equates to household consumption.
†Argentina's figures do not reflect the recent economic recession.
‡Comparable to the U.S. (6).

Table 2   Economic Factors

Country	Conversion $/PPP$	Purchasing power, 2000, PPP $billions*	Income, top 40% share	GDP growth, % 1990–1999	Household consumption growth, %, 1990–1999	Household consumption growth, %, 2000
China	4.67	2,434	69	10.7	8.8	6.3
India	5.20	1,554	65	6.1	4.9	4.2
South Korea	1.94	508	62	5.7	5.1	7.9
Philippines	4.06	199	73	3.2	3.7	3.1
Indonesia	4.96	511	66	4.7	6.2	3.6
Malaysia	2.46	94	74	6.3	5.4	12.2
Thailand	3.16	226	70	4.7	4.2	4.5
Pakistan	4.23	201	62	4.0	5.1	0.9
Iran	3.52	191	70†	3.4	2.9	6.9
Saudi Arabia	1.58	90	72†	1.6	n/a	n/a
South Africa	3.03	243	83	1.9	2.6	3.2
Brazil	2.04	760	82	2.9	4.3	9.9
Argentina	1.61	325	72	4.9	3.3	1.3
Venezuela	1.33	101	74	1.7	0.4	3.7
Colombia	3.00	164	79	3.2	3.0	6.5
Mexico	1.73	671	77	2.7	1.9	8.3
Turkey	2.27	312	69	4.1	3.7	6.2

(continued)

Table 2 Economic Factors *(continued)*

Country	Conversion $/PPP$	Purchasing power, 2000, PPP $billions*	Income, top 40% share	GDP growth, % 1990–1999	Household consumption growth, %, 1990–1999	Household consumption growth, %, 2000
Poland	2.15	217	63	4.7	5.2	4.9
Ukraine	5.29	98	63	−10.8	−8.0	5.2
Russia	4.83	553	74	−6.1	1.5	19.2
U.S.	0.00	6,269‡	69	3.4	3.2	5.6
World	1.43	26,914‡	—	2.5	2.6	3.6

n/a, not applicable.
*Equates to household consumption.
†Estimates.
‡Latest data (6).

New consumers have a far-reaching impact on economic activities nationwide, and hence on environmental repercussions. In India, for example, they accounted for less than one-eighth of the year 2000 population but two-fifths of the country's purchasing power (Table 1). With respect to the major sector of transportation, primarily cars, they accounted in the late 1990s for 85% of private spending. Their per-capita energy consumption has been causing CO_2 emissions 15 times greater than those of the rest of India's population (9).

Finally, the new consumers started to emerge in significant numbers only in the early 1980s, and their major increase in numbers occurred largely during the 1990s. True, there were some new consumers before the 1980s in countries such as Saudi Arabia, South Africa, Argentina, Brazil, and Mexico, but collectively they were generally few relative to the 2000 total.

Two Predominant Sectors
Meat

New consumers' diets are shifting toward meat, much of it raised in part on grain (Table 3). Raising 1 kg of beef can use 8 kg of grain, 4 kg of pork, and 2 kg of poultry (10). During

Table 3 Meat

Country	Meat, kg per capita, 2000	Food grain, kg per capita increase, 1990–2000, %	Feed grain, kg per capita increase, 1990–2000	Feed grain as % of total grain, 2000	Grain imports as % of total grain, 2000
China	50	−9	20	23	3
India	5	2	0	1	<0.1
South Korea	46	−7	36	44	75
Philippines	27	−6	14	28	14
Indonesia	8	11	50	4	14
Malaysia	51	19	22	41	76
Thailand	24	11	11	34	9
Pakistan	12	5	33	4	4
Iran	22	3	10	32	44
Saudi Arabia	51	−7	84	65	78
South Africa	39	−1	−4	32	14
Brazil	77	−3	44	54	21
Argentina	98	−1	28	44	1
Venezuela	42	−9	−31	18	68
Colombia	34	15	47	30	53
Mexico	56	1	8	41	36
Turkey	20	−6	3	25	9
Poland	70	6	−23	58	9
Ukraine	31	−12	−40	50	5
Russia	40	−6	−44	48	9
U.S.	122	5	1	66	3
World	38	−2	−11	35	—

See ref. 11.

the period 1990–2000 the amount of grain fed to livestock increased by 31% in China, 52% in Malaysia, and 63% in Indonesia. In nine of the 20 countries, two-fifths or more of grain consumed is now used for livestock (11), and the dietary change often leads to overloading of grainlands with resultant soil erosion and other forms of land degradation (12, 13). In addition, the 20 countries already account for nearly two-fifths of the world's grain imports; eight countries import one-fifth or more of their grain supply. In 2000, Malaysia imported 76% of its supply while feeding 41% to livestock, Saudi Arabia 78% and 65%, South Korea 75% and 44%, and Colombia 53% and 30% (Table 3). These imports serve to put pressure on international grain markets, to the detriment of poor countries that can hardly afford rising prices. Between 1997 and 2020, developing countries as a whole are forecast to increase their demand for meat, the great bulk to serve new consumers, by 92%, for grain by 50%, for food grain by 39%, and for feed grain by 85% (14).

Furthermore, demand for increased grain harvests aggravates water shortages. To produce 1 tonne (1 tonne = 10^3 kg) of grain can take 1,000 tonnes of water (15). Several sectors of China, a country with 29% of new consumers, experience water shortages, accentuated in part by the surging demand for grain. The North China Plain harbors two-fifths of the country's population and produces two-fifths of its grain but contains only one-fifth of its surface water. The region's aquifers have long been declining through overpumping by at least 1 m per year (16). In India, with 13% of new consumers, one-quarter of the grain harvest could be put at risk through groundwater depletion in its main breadbasket areas (17).

Cars

New consumers possess virtually all their countries' cars, and in most of the 20 countries, car totals have been expanding much more rapidly than national incomes. In 1990, these countries had 62 million cars, a total that by 2000 soared to 117 million or 21% of the global fleet (Table 4) (6). This 89% increase was led by China's 445%, South Korea's 319%, India's 259%, and Colombia's 217%. Five other countries registered increases of 100% or more, although the average annual increase for all 20 countries was only 6.4%. In particular, China and India, being the two countries with largest new consumer totals, registered average annual increases of 19% and 14%, respectively. Both these countries plan to push ahead vigorously with the "motorization" of their transport systems.

Allowing for growth in the proportionate numbers of people joining the affluent classes, the present decade could well see an average annual increase in car numbers at least matching the 6.4% rate of the 1990s. That would mean a total of at least 215 million cars in 2010, or one-quarter of the expected global fleet. Were the average annual increase to reach 10% due to disproportionately growing affluence on the part of new consumers both present and prospective, the 2010 total would approach 300 million, around one-third of the global fleet.

In 1997 the world's motor vehicles, of which 525 million, 74%, were passenger cars, emitted 73% of transport-related CO_2, for a 26% increase over 1990 and four times more than the CO_2 emissions increase overall. Cars are expected to make up the fastest-growing sector of energy use as far ahead as 2025 (18, 19).

Cars cause other forms of pollution such as urban smog and acid rain. They generate many other economic and social costs, notably road congestion, traffic accidents, and costly land use. In many cities of new consumer countries, road congestion is already acute and growing rapidly worse (20). In Bangkok, for instance, there are long periods every day when traffic moves at an average speed of just 3 km per hour. The problem has been costing an annual $1.6 billion of fuel wasted in idling car engines and at least $2.3 billion in lost worker productivity (21). Similar findings apply in Manila, Jakarta, and New Delhi, among other cities.

In addition to meat and cars, other new consumer purchases have harmful environmental impacts. A notable instance is electricity (generally derived from fossil fuels), which new consumers use at far above country-wide rates because of household appliances, air conditioners, and the like. The issue is not included in this article, because it is too difficult to pin down the amount used by new consumers, and because household electricity is not so environmentally significant as meat and cars.

Two Country Case Studies

In 2000, China had an estimated 303 million new consumers and India, 132 million, or two-fifths of the 20 countries' total. Let us look at these two countries in detail.

Table 4   Cars, Millions

Country	1990	2000 estimate	Percent change 1990–2000
China	1.1	6.0	445
India	1.7	6.1	259
South Korea	2.1	8.8	319
Philippines	0.4	0.8	100
Indonesia	1.3	2.9	123
Malaysia	1.8	4.1	128
Thailand	0.8	1.9	138
Pakistan	0.5	0.8	60
Iran	1.4	2.1	50
Saudi Arabia	1.6	1.9	19
South Africa	3.4	4.1	21
Brazil	11.8	18.5	57
Argentina	4.4	5.5	25
Venezuela	1.5	1.8	20
Colombia	0.6	1.9	217
Mexico	6.8	10.4	53
Turkey	1.9	4.5	137
Poland	5.3	9.9	87
Ukraine	3.3	5.5	67
Russia	10.1	19.5	93
Totals	62.0	117.0	89
Percent of world	13	21	62
U.S.	152	175*	15
World	478	560	

*Including sport utility vehicles (SUVs) (6).

China

Not only does China possess the most new consumers today, but it offers the greatest scope for generating more new consumers in the future. During 1978–1998, its economic growth doubled per-capita income every 7 yr [compare South Korea at the height of its economic boom (11 yr) and Japan (34 yr)] (22). In 2000, China's gross national income [(GNI), a recent designation of the World Bank to replace gross national product (GNP)] totaled almost PPP $5 trillion, making it the world's second largest economy in PPP terms (seventh largest in conventional dollars) (6).

China's new consumers are enjoying strongly meat-based diets. With one-fifth of the world's population, the country accounts for 28% of the world's meat consumption (compare to the U.S., 15%) (6, 11), virtually all of it attributable to the new consumers. The 1990–2000 114% increase in meat consumption accounted for 25 million tonnes or four-fifths of the country's 7% growth in grain consumption; today 23% of grain is fed to livestock, up from 19% in 1990. Although per-capita meat consumption almost doubled, and per-capita feed grain consumption grew by 20% during 1990–2000, per-capita food grain consumption declined by 9% (11).

As we have seen above, surging demand for grain is aggravating water deficits in the extensive North China Plain. In common with several other new consumer countries, China's grain imports effectively amount in part to water imports. Whatever China's water shortages today, they could become much more acute given that during 1997–2020 the country is forecast to account for 40% of the increased global demand for meat and 27% for grain (14).

China's new consumers are also buying cars in significant numbers. The total has grown from 1.1 million in 1990 to at least 6 million in 2000 (6). If the country maintains its 1990–2000 average annual growth rate of 19%, it will have ≈34 million cars by 2010, an almost 6-fold increase. If the additional new consumers expected to come on stream (300 million, see below) were to markedly increase the 19% rate, conceivably to as high as 25% (19, 23, 24), the 2010 total could be as much as 56 million cars.

How far will the new consumers increase beyond their 303 million in 2000? Let us suppose that during the present decade, the country's annual economic growth averages the forecast 7.0% (less than the 10% of the past two decades), meaning that the economy will more than double to PPP $9.7 trillion (6, 7). Although many of the consumer benefits of the growing prosperity will accrue to the 303 million new consumers of 2000, their total will surely swell by 6% per year (household consumption increases at a rate less than that of economic growth) to ≈543 million in 2010. Because of income skewedness, however, which is likely to become yet more pronounced (25), the increasingly affluent new consumer class seems poised to forge still further ahead of the rest of the population, making for growth of their numbers more like 7% per year. Thus a more probable total in 2010 is ≈600 million, or 44% of the projected population (compare to 24% in 2000). By then, their purchasing power could well climb to PPP $3.5 trillion, or over half that of the U.S. today.

All this means that China's continued economic advance will have a marked impact on environments both national and global, and a good part of these impacts will reflect the rise of the new consumers (26, 27). During the 1990s, environmental damage associated with economic growth (primarily air pollution and water deficits, but also deforestation and desertification) cost at least 8% and possibly 10–15% of gross domestic product, much of the damage being due to new consumers' activities (26, 28, 29). Given China's economic globalization and the spread of Western lifestyles, a potential doubling of the new consumer total within the present decade is a formidable prospect when linked with shortages of grain and water, plus loss of farmland for industry, urbanization, and transport networks (26, 30).

The prospect is further challenging in terms of CO_2 emissions (only a small proportion from cars but rising rapidly), which in 2000 placed China second to the U.S. with 49% as much, even though per capita they were only 2.2 tonnes per year by contrast with the U.S.'s 20.5 tonnes (31). Conversely, China has engaged in broad-scope policy reforms of its energy sector, resulting in a decline in CO_2 emissions estimated at somewhere between 6% and 14% during 1997–2000, although this decline applied far more to industry than to transportation (32–34).

India

India's economic growth rate has averaged >6.0% per year during the 1990s, making its PPP $2.4 trillion economy the fourth largest in the world (12th in conventional dollars) (6–8). The new consumer total in 2000 is estimated at 132 million (Table 1).

India's per-capita meat consumption is still meager, only one-tenth as much as China's (11), although still significant given the large number of new consumers who eat the great bulk of the country's meat. In absolute terms, however, and given that India has the second-highest number of new consumers, the country is the fourth-largest meat eater among all new consumer countries.

In 2000, India's cars totaled ≈6.1 million (Table 4), little more than in Greater Chicago, yet there were enough cars to cause much pollution of several sorts. Motor vehicles of all kinds account for 70% of air pollution, which has increased eight times during the past 20 years, compared with a 4-fold increase for industry. Of the world's 10 cities with the highest air pollution, three are in India. The health costs of air pollution in 36 Indian cities have amounted to at least $500 million per year and possibly four times as much (35). If the economy keeps expanding by at least 5.0% per year, car numbers can be expected to continue increasing by the annual 14% of 1990–2000 on the grounds that, as in the past, the expanding consumer classes will become relatively more affluent than the rest of the population. This prognosis postulates a total of 23 million cars by 2010.

Environmental damage of all kinds has been costing ≈5% of India' gross domestic product, due disproportionately to the activities of new consumers (36).

How many new consumers could there be by the end of this decade? An annual economic growth rate of 5.5% (reflecting the average for 1990–2000, 6.1%, and the expected growth rates for 2001–2003) means that India's economy will almost double to PPP $4.1 trillion. As in the case of China, where household consumption does not increase as fast as economic growth, the new consumer total of 2000 is likely to grow by 1% less than the economy's expansion, namely 4.5% per year (37, 38). This will bring their numbers to ≈205 million (18% of the projected population). In addition, income skewedness is likely to become more pronounced insofar as it is the top quintile that has benefited most from the country's economic advance of the past decade. So the new consumer total could readily soar by 5.5% per year to almost 225 million in 2010 or 19% of the population (compare to 13% in 2000). These new consumers would then have a purchasing power of >PPP $1.2 trillion, putting them on a par with Germany today.

By 2010, then, China and India alone could feature 825 million new consumers with a purchasing power approaching PPP $5.0 trillion (compare to the U.S. in 1999, $6.3 trillion).

Overview of 20 Countries

All new consumers in the 20 countries totaled 1.059 billion in 2000 (Table 1). China and India accounted for 41% of the total. The third-largest total was Brazil with 74 million (7%). Mexico and Russia had 68 million (6%) each and Indonesia had 63 million (6%). The smallest numbers were in Malaysia and Ukraine with 12 million (1%) each, then Saudi Arabia and Venezuela with 13 million (1%) each.

Equally revealing was the new consumers' share of each country's population. South Korea was top with 96%; second was Poland with 86%; and third, Argentina with 84% (the latter's figure will have dropped by today; see below). Lowest was Pakistan with 12%, next India with 13%, and then Ukraine with 23%.

All of the 20 countries' totals in 2000 reflect the latest statistics of the World Bank and International Monetary Fund (6, 7). There have been recent economic downturns in a number of countries, most notably in Argentina. Argentina's new consumer total in 2000 was only 31 million, so a subsequent decline of, say, one-third to 21 million will make <1.0% difference to the 20 countries' aggregate. No other country has registered such a severe and protracted economic decline (there have been transient dips in Saudi Arabia, Mexico, and Turkey), so no other new consumer totals will have dropped. As for the future, virtually all new consumer countries except Argentina are forecast to feature strong economic growth.

The overall purchasing power of the new consumers in 2000 amounted to PPP $6.3 trillion, matching the U.S.'s (where PPP dollars and conventional dollars are the same by definition). In South Korea, overall purchasing power constituted 99% of the country-wide total. Next was Argentina with 97% (although see qualifier above), followed by Poland with 95% and Mexico with 93%. The lowest was Pakistan with 31%, followed by India with 39% and Ukraine with 45% (Table 1).

Thus there is a sizeable "North" in the "South." The 2000 total of new consumers, approaching 1.1 billion, is to be compared with the collective populations of the 23 long-standing and much richer Organisation for Economic Cooperation

and Development (OECD) countries, 850 million (6). True, the collective purchasing power of the new consumers, PPP $6.3 trillion, contrasts with the 23 OECD countries' PPP $15 trillion (6). All the same, the new consumers constitute a major consumer force in the global economy, just as they are becoming a front-rank factor in the global environment. China's environmental impact could eventually match that of the U.S.

An additional 14 countries, not considered here because their populations are <20 million or because their economies are not strong (or their data lacking), probably feature ≈140 million new consumers, meaning their omission does not markedly affect the overall situation.

Policy Responses

How can the new consumers be persuaded to reduce their environmental impacts and move toward sustainable consumption? Of course, the need to make consumption sustainable applies as well, only much more so, to the long-established consumers in the rich world, and the new consumers are unlikely to alter their consumption until the rich-world consumers take solid steps to modify their consumption.

Consider the scope for cleaner cars (39). A few recent models, notably the Toyota Prius and the Honda Insight, have hybrid engines that produce far less CO^2 among other pollutants. Compressed natural gas powers 10% of Argentina's car fleet, and India has introduced the same fuel gas for heavy vehicles in its major cities. The prospective hydrogen fuel-cell car would emit only water vapor. In addition, there are many alternatives to the conventional car culture. Cities in developing country can promote mass transit systems, bicycle networks, and restrictions on cars in congested areas and can make drivers pay the full cost of their activity (40, 41). These diverse routes into the future are already illustrated by Singapore, Bogota, and the Brazilian city of Curitiba, in all of which fewer cars bring benefits all around (42–44).

As for meat, prices are often held down through large subsidies for grain and water (45). Consumers are induced to move up the food chain through dietary fads, taught taste, and social status, all of which can be shifted toward healthier diets through fiscal incentives such as a "food conversion efficiency" tax. The least-efficient converters of grain, notably beef, could be highly taxed, whereas more efficient products, notably poultry, could be moderately taxed (46). Similarly, there are many opportunities to foster more efficient use of water for the growing of grain (47). Use of other natural resources can be improved through full-cost pricing (48, 49), shifts in tax systems (50, 51), substitutes for gross national product as an economic indicator (52, 53), elimination of "perverse" subsidies that foster both environmental and economic inefficiencies (45), and application of the many ecotechnologies available (54–57).

Above all is the need to establish sustainable consumption as a norm, which is not only about quantitative reductions in our use of materials and energy (58–60); it is also about ways in which we can achieve an acceptable quality of life for all in perpetuity and exemplify it throughout our lifestyles (61). How, for instance, can we attain a better balance between work, leisure, and consumption (63, 64)? How can we prevent yester-day's luxuries from becoming today's necessities and tomor-row's relics (65, 66)? How can we make fashion sustainable and sustainability fashionable?

References

1. Daily, G. C. & Ehrlich, P. R. (1996) *Ecol. Appl.* **6,** 991–1001.
2. Holdren, J. P. (2000) *Environment* **42,** 4–6.
3. Holdren, J. P. & Ehrlich P. R. (1974) *Am. Sci.* **62,** 282–292.
4. Princen, T., Maniates, M. & Conca, K., eds. (2002) *Confronting Consumption* (MIT Press, Cambridge, MA).
5. Stern, P. Dietz, T., Ruttan, V., Socolow, R. & Sweeney, J., eds. (1997) *Environmentally Significant Consumption: Research Directions* (Natl. Acad. Press, Washington, DC).
6. The World Bank (2002) *World Development Indicators Online, May 2002* (World Bank, Washington, DC).
7. International Monetary Fund (2002) *World Economic Outlook April 2002* (International Monetary Fund, Washington, DC).
8. The World Bank (1994) *World Development Report 1994* (Oxford Univ. Press, New York).
9. Consumers International (1998) *A Discerning Middle Class? A Preliminary Enquiry of Sustainable Consumption Trends in Selected Countries in the Asia Pacific Region* (Consumers International, Penang, Malaysia).
10. Smil, V. (2000) *Feeding the World: A Challenge for the Twenty-First Century* (MIT Press, Cambridge, MA).
11. Food and Agriculture Organization (2002) *FAOSTAT Food Balance Sheets June 2002* (Food and Agriculture Organization, Rome).
12. World Resources Institute (1999) *Critical Consumption Trends and Implications: Degrading Earth's Ecosystems* (World Resources Institute, Washington, DC).
13. Tilman, D., Fargione, J., Wolff, B., D'Antonio, C., Dobson, A., Howarth, R., Schindler D., Schlesinger, W. H., Simberloff, D., & Swackhamer, D. (2001) *Science* **292,** 281–284.
14. Rosegrant, M. W., Paisner M. S., Meijer, S. & Witcover, J. (2001) *2020 Global Food Outlook: Trends, Alternatives, Choices* (International Food Policy Research Institute, Washington, DC).
15. Gleick, P. (2000) *The World's Water 2000–2001* (Island Press, Washington, DC).
16. Qingcheng, H. (2001) *The North China Plain and Its Aquifers* (Geological Environmental Monitoring Institute, Beijing, P.R. China).
17. Seckler, D., Molden, D. & Barker, R. (1998) *Water Scarcity in the Twenty-First Century* (International Water Management Institute, Colombo, Sri Lanka).
18. International Energy Agency (2000) *International Energy Outlook 2000* (International Energy Agency, Paris).
19. Schipper, L., Marie-Liliu, C. & Lewis-Davis, G. (1999) *Rapid Motorization in the Largest Countries in Asia: Implications for Oil, Carbon Dioxide and Transportation* (International Energy Agency, Paris).
20. Willoughby, C. (2000) *Managing Motorization* (The World Bank, Washington, DC).
21. DuPont, P. & Egan. K. (1997) *World Transport and Policy Practice* **3,** 25–37.
22. The World Bank (1999) *World Development Report, 1999* (Oxford Univ. Press, New York).
23. Schipper, L. (2001) *Designing "Effective" Solutions to the Urban Transport-Environment Dilemma* (Organisation for Economic Cooperation and Development, Paris).
24. Riley, K. (2002) *Popul. Environ.* **23,** 479–494.
25. Atinc, P. M. (1997) *Sharing Rising Incomes: Disparities in China* (The World Bank, Washington, DC).
26. The World Bank (2001) *China Air, Land and Water: Environmental Priorities to a New Milennium* (The World Bank, Washington, DC).
27. Palanivel, T. (2001) *Sustainable Development of China, India and Indonesia: Trends and Responses* (Institute of Advanced Studies, United Nations University, Tokyo).
28. Smil, V. & Yushi, M. (1998) *The Economic Costs of China's Environmental Degradation* (Am. Acad. Arts and Sciences, Cambridge, MA).
29. Takahiro, A. & Nakamura, Y. (2000) *Green GDP Estimates in China, Indonesia and Japan* (Institute for Advanced Studies, United Nations University, Tokyo).
30. Brown, L. R. (2001) *Eco-Economy: Building an Economy for the Earth* (Norton, New York).
31. Energy Information Administration U.S. Department of Energy (2002) *International Energy Database, April 2002* (U.S. Department of Energy, Washington, DC).
32. Natural Resources Defence Council (2001) *Second Analysis Confirms Greenhouse Gas Reductions in China* (Natural Resources Defense Council, Washington, DC).
33. Streets, D. G. Jiang, K., Hu, X., Sinton, J. E., Zhang, X. Q., Xu, D., Jacobson, M. Z. & Hansen, J. E. (2001) *Science* **294,** 1835–1837.
34. Sinton, J. E. & Fridley D. G. (2000) *Environ. Pol.* **28,** 671–687.
35. Agarwal, A. & Narain, S. (1997) *Economic Globalisation: Its Impact on Consumption, Equity and Sustainability* (Center for Science and the Environment, New Delhi, India).
36. Parikh, J. Parikh, K. (2001) *Accounting for Environmental Degradation: A Case Study of India* (Institute for Advanced Studies, United Nations University, Tokyo).
37. Alagh, Y. K. (2001) *India's Sustainable Development Framework: 2020* (Institute for Advanced Studies, United Nations University, Tokyo).
38. Klein, L. R. & Palanivel, T. (2000) *Economic Reforms and Growth Prospects in India* (Institute for Advanced Studies, United Nations University, Tokyo).
39. Motavalli, J. (2002) *Forward Drive: The Race to Build Clean Cars for the Future* (Earthscan, London).
40. Satterthwaite, D., ed. (1999) *Sustainable Cities* (Earthscan, London).
41. Bose, R., Sperling, D., Tiwari, G. & Schipper, L. (2001) *Transportation in Developing Countries* (Pew Center on Global Climate Change, Arlington, VA).
42. Newman, P. (1999) *Automobile Dependence* (Island Press, Washington, DC).
43. Rabinovitch, J. (1996) *Land Use Pol.* **13,** 51–67.
44. Sheehan, M. (2001) *City Limits: Putting the Brakes on Sprawl* (Worldwatch Institute, Washington, DC).
45. Myers, N. & Kent, J. (2001) *Perverse Subsidies: How Tax Dollars Can Undercut the Environment and the Economy* (Island Press, Washington, DC).

46. Pimentel, D., Westra L. & Noss, R. F. (2000) *Ecological Integrity: Integrating Environment, Conservation, and Health* (Island Press, Washington, DC).

47. Postel, S. (1999) *Pillar of Sand: Can the Irrigation Miracle Last?* (Norton, New York).

48. Pearce, D. & Barbier, E. B. (2001) *Blueprint for a Sustainable Economy* (Earthscan, London).

49. Roodman, D. (1998) *The Natural Wealth of Nations* (Norton, New York).

50. Ekins, P. & Speck, S. (2000) *J. Environ. Pol. Plann.* **2,** 93–114.

51. Wallart, N. (1999) *The Political Economy of Environmental Taxes* (Edward Elgar, Cheltenham, U.K.).

52. Cobb, C., Goodman, G. S. & Wackernagel, M. (1999) *Why Bigger Isn't Better: The Genuine Progress Indicator,* 1999 Update (Redefining Progress, San Francisco).

53. Dasgupta, P. & Maler, K.-G. (2000) *Environ. Dev. Econ.* **5,** 69–93.

54. DeSimone, L. D. & Popoff, F. (2000) *Eco-Efficiency: The Business Link to Sustainable Development* (MIT Press, Cambridge, MA).

55. Hawken, P., Lovins, A. B. & Lovins, L. H. (1999) *Natural Capitalism* (Little, Brown, Boston).

56. Russel, T. (2001) *Eco-Efficiency: A Management Guide* (Earthscan, London).

57. McDonough, W. & Braungart, M. (2002) *Cradle to Cradle: Remaking the Way We Make Things* (North Point Press, New York).

58. Arrow, K., Daily, G., Dasgupta, P., Ehrlich, P., Goulder, L., Heal, G., Levin, S., Maler, K.-G., Schneider, S., Starrett, D. & Walker, B. (2003) *J. Econ. Perspect.,* in press.

59. Pauli, G. (1998) *Up Sizing: The Road to Zero Emissions* (Greenleaf Publications, London).

60. Schmidt-Bleek, F. (2000) *Factor 10 Manifesto* (The Factor Ten Institute, Carnoules, France).

61. Frank, R. H. (1999) *Luxury Fever: Why Money Fails to Satisfy in an Era of Excess* (Free Press, New York).

62. Kates, R. W., Clark, W. C., Corell, R., Hall, J. M., Jaeger, C. C., Lowe, I., McCarthy, J. J., Schellnhuber, H. J., Bolin, B. & Dickson, N. M. (2001) *Science* **292,** 641–642.

63. Schor, J. B. (1998) *The Overspent American: Upscaling, Downshifting, and the New Consumer* (Basic Books, New York).

64. Kasser, T. (2002) *The High Price of Materialism* (MIT Press, Cambridge, MA).

65. Daly, H. E. (2000) *Ecological Economics and the Ecology of Economics* (Edward Elgar, Cheltenham, U.K.).

66. Robins, N. & Roberts, S. (1998) *Development (Cambridge, UK)* **41,** 28–36.

Critical Thinking

1. Who are the "new consumers"?
2. Why might these new consumers have far-reaching economic and environmental impacts within their nations?
3. How can the new consumers be persuaded to reduce the potential of their environmental impacts?

Create Central

www.mhhe.com/createcentral

Internet References

The Dismal Scientist
www.dismal.com

IISDnet
www.iisd.org

World Resources Institute (WRI)
www.wri.org

For many helpful comments on an early version of this article, we thank **G. C. DAILY** and **D. M. PIMENTEL**. T. L. Root and S. H. Schneider of Stanford University provided an economic model used to determine income distribution within national populations. We gratefully acknowledge financial support for our original research from the Winslow Foundation (Washington, DC).

Unit 2

UNIT

Prepared by: Richard Eathorne, *Northern Michigan University*

The Psychological Roots beneath Environmental Degradation: The Human Needs/Desires Factor

Man will survive as a species for one reason: He can adapt to the destructive effects of our power-intoxicated technology and of our ungoverned population growth, to the dirt, pollution and noise of a New York or Tokyo. And that is the tragedy. It is not man the ecological crisis threatens to destroy but the quality of human life.

René Dubos, quoted in *Life*, July 28, 1970

There can be no true discourse on the planetary consumption issue without including the primary driving agent of that issue: humans. But it's not simply the nature of our consumption that threatens the planet's ability to sustain our species. It's our population growth *patterns* and the *demographic characteristics* of those patterns that are creating new challenges to the future health of our environment and our own survival as a species. Many scholars have suggested that the earth can support a human population of 9, 10, even 11 billion people. However, the earth's ability to support quantity of life is not the issue. It's quality of life. How do we want our billions to live? To begin to answer this, we first need to recognize, and admit, that humans must consume earth—transform raw resources into a form we can use to ensure our well-being as a species; to ensure our survival. Second, we need to realize that our current human consumption patterns are proving to be unsustainable and damaging to the ecosystems upon which all living things must depend. Third, and most importantly, we need to better understand what possible future human population growth patterns—geographic, demographic, social and economic—may unfold and impact our ability to ensure *quality of life* for all humans and maintain a *sustainable relationship* with our planet.

Science is about being able to make accurate predictions. If we can predict human–environment interaction outcomes better, we can make better decisions and often change the inevitability of unpleasant surprises, and even fatal mistakes. What are the characteristics, patterns, and subsequent challenges to consider regarding the future of human population growth and our need to consume resources? Another question worth considering to ask is, "What will our future relationship with the planet evolve to? Environmental symbiosis or environmental virus?" Environmental scientist E. O. Wilson sees the pattern of population growth of the past 20th century "more bacterial than primate." He believes our greatest threat to survival is not war,

energy, economical or political instability, but rather the destruction of natural habitats which our resource consumption creates and the subsequent loss of genetic and species diversity.

Our consumption patterns are raising other concerns as well. Emerging global demographic changes and consumption patterns are leading to three pressing challenges: reducing poverty and thus global inequality; urgent reduction of consumption in developed and emerging economies; and the slowing and stabilization of global population growth. Population growth pushes the consequences of any level of individual consumption to a higher plateau. If we are to achieve long-term environmental sustainability, action needs to be taken on both population growth and individual consumption.

As global population demographics change, so too do human's relationship to the environment in terms of what is needed to sustain their well-being. Will an aging population place fewer material demands upon the environment? Will such populations require, and demand, *more* clean air and water, *more* sustainable food production? Or will they consume *less* energy than their 20th century predecessors? Some scholars believe that the next "population bomb" and the global megatrends it will set in motion will impact the changing demographics of the industrialized nations' populations. Subsequent political economy consequences will be linked to those changing consumption patterns.

Thus, it will be imperative that we expand our thinking on the issues presented and assess the potential future scenarios in light of both place—local and regional impacts within nations—and the potential environmental impacts (that will vary considerably by place) resulting from these changing human earth-consumption patterns. We must constantly be cognizant of the question: *Who* is currently consuming the earth and at what rate? And *who* will be consuming the earth in the future, and at what rate? Sustainably or unsustainably?

Article

Do We Consume Too Much?

MARK SAGOFF

In 1994, when delegates from around the world gathered in Cairo for the International Conference on Population and Development, representatives from developing countries protested that a baby born in the United States will consume during its lifetime twenty times as much of the world's resources as an African or an Indian baby. The problem for the world's environment, they argued, is overconsumption in the North, not overpopulation in the South.

Discussions of the future of the planet are dominated by those who believe that an expanding world economy will use up natural resources and those who see no reasons, environmental or otherwise, to limit economic growth. Neither side has it right.

Consumption in industrialized nations "has led to overexploitation of the resources of developing countries," a speaker from Kenya declared. A delegate from Antigua reproached the wealthiest 20 percent of the world's population for consuming 80 percent of the goods and services produced from the earth's resources.

Do we consume too much? To some, the answer is self-evident. If there is only so much food, timber, petroleum, and other material to go around, the more we consume, the less must be available for others. The global economy cannot grow indefinitely on a finite planet. As populations increase and economies expand, natural resources must be depleted; prices will rise, and humanity—especially the poor and future generations at all income levels—will suffer as a result.

Other reasons to suppose we consume too much are less often stated though also widely believed. Of these the simplest—a lesson we learn from our parents and from literature since the Old Testament—may be the best: although we must satisfy basic needs, a good life is not one devoted to amassing material possessions; what we own comes to own us, keeping us from fulfilling commitments that give meaning to life, such as those to family, friends, and faith. The appreciation of nature also deepens our lives. As we consume more, however, we are more likely to transform the natural world, so that less of it will remain for us to appreciate.

The reasons for protecting nature are often religious or moral. As the philosopher Ronald Dworkin points out, many Americans believe that we have an obligation to protect species which goes beyond our own well-being; we "think we should admire and protect them because they are important in themselves, and not just if or because we or others want or enjoy them." In a recent survey Americans from various walks of life agreed by large majorities with the statement "Because God created the natural world, it is wrong to abuse it." The anthropologists who conducted this survey concluded that "divine creation is the closest concept American culture provides to express the sacredness of nature."

During the nineteenth century preservationists forthrightly gave ethical and spiritual reasons for protecting the natural world. John Muir condemned the "temple destroyers, devotees of ravaging commercialism" who "instead of lifting their eyes to the God of the mountains, lift them to the Almighty dollar." This was not a call for better cost-benefit analysis: Muir described nature not as a commodity but as a companion. Nature is sacred, Muir held, whether or not resources are scarce.

Philosophers such as Emerson and Thoreau thought of nature as full of divinity. Walt Whitman celebrated a leaf of grass as no less than the journeywork of the stars: "After you have exhausted what there is in business, politics, conviviality, love, and so on," he wrote in *Specimen Days,* and "found that none of these finally satisfy, or permanently wear—what remains? Nature remains." These philosophers thought of nature as a refuge from economic activity, not as a resource for it.

Today those who wish to protect the natural environment rarely offer ethical or spiritual reasons for the policies they favor. Instead they say we are running out of resources or causing the collapse of ecosystems on which we depend. Predictions of resource scarcity appear objective and scientific, whereas pronouncements that nature is sacred or that greed is bad appear judgmental or even embarrassing in a secular society. Prudential and economic arguments, moreover, have succeeded better than moral or spiritual ones in swaying public policy.

These prudential and economic arguments are not likely to succeed much longer. It is simply wrong to believe that nature sets physical limits to economic growth—that is, to prosperity and the production and consumption of goods and services on which it is based. The idea that increasing consumption will inevitably lead to depletion and scarcity, as plausible as it may seem, is mistaken both in principle and in fact. It is based on four misconceptions.

Misconception No. 1: We Are Running Out of Raw Materials

In the 1970s Paul Ehrlich, a biologist at Stanford University, predicted that global shortages would soon send prices for food, fresh water, energy, metals, paper, and other materials sharply higher. "It seems certain," Paul and Anne Ehrlich wrote in *The End of Affluence* (1974), "that energy shortages will be with us for the rest of the century, and that before 1985 mankind will enter a genuine age of scarcity in which many things besides energy will be in short supply." Crucial materials would near depletion during the 1980s, Ehrlich predicted, pushing prices out of reach. "Starvation among people will be accompanied by starvation of industries for the materials they require."

Things have not turned out as Ehrlich expected. In the early 1990s real prices for food overall fell. Raw materials—including energy resources—are generally more abundant and less expensive today than they were twenty years ago. When Ehrlich wrote, economically recoverable world reserves of petroleum stood at 640 billion barrels. Since that time reserves have *increased* by more than 50 percent, reaching more than 1,000 billion barrels in 1989. They have held steady in spite of rising consumption. The pre-tax real price of gasoline was lower during this decade than at any other time since 1947. The World Energy Council announced in 1992 that "fears of imminent [resource] exhaustion that were widely held 20 years ago are now considered to have been unfounded."

The World Resources Institute, in a 1994–1995 report, referred to "the frequently expressed concern that high levels of consumption will lead to resource depletion and to physical shortages that might limit growth or development opportunity." Examining the evidence, however, the institute said that "the world is not yet running out of most nonrenewable resources and is not likely to, at least in the next few decades." A 1988 report from the Office of Technology Assessment concluded, "The nation's future has probably never been less constrained by the cost of natural resources."

It is reasonable to expect that as raw materials become less expensive, they will be more rapidly depleted. This expectation is also mistaken. From 1980 to 1990, for example, while the prices of resource-based commodities declined (the price of rubber by 40 percent, cement by 40 percent, and coal by almost 50 percent), reserves of most raw materials increased. Economists offer three explanations.

First, with regard to subsoil resources, the world becomes ever more adept at discovering new reserves and exploiting old ones. Exploring for oil, for example, used to be a hit-or-miss proposition, resulting in a lot of dry holes. Today oil companies can use seismic waves to help them create precise computer images of the earth. New methods of extraction—for example, using bacteria to leach metals from low-grade ores—greatly increase resource recovery. Reserves of resources "are actually functions of technology," one analyst has written. "The more advanced the technology, the more reserves become known and recoverable."

Second, plentiful resources can be used in place of those that become scarce. Analysts speak of an Age of Substitutability and point, for example, to nanotubes, tiny cylinders of carbon whose molecular structure forms fibers a hundred times as strong as steel, at one sixth the weight. As technologies that use more-abundant resources substitute for those needing less-abundant ones—for example, ceramics in place of tungsten, fiber optics in place of copper wire, aluminum cans in place of tin ones—the demand for and the price of the less-abundant resources decline.

One can easily find earlier instances of substitution. During the early nineteenth century whale oil was the preferred fuel for household illumination. A dwindling supply prompted innovations in the lighting industry, including the invention of gas and kerosene lamps and Edison's carbon-filament electric bulb. Whale oil has substitutes, such as electricity and petroleum-based lubricants. Whales are irreplaceable.

Third, the more we learn about materials, the more efficiently we use them. The progress from candles to carbon-filament to tungsten incandescent lamps, for example, decreased the energy required for and the cost of a unit of household lighting by many times. Compact fluorescent lights are four times as efficient as today's incandescent bulbs and last ten to twenty times as long. Comparable energy savings are available in other appliances: for example, refrigerators sold in 1993 were 23 percent more efficient than those sold in 1990 and 65 percent more efficient than those sold in 1980, saving consumers billions in electric bills.

Amory Lovins, the director of the Rocky Mountain Institute, has described a new generation of ultralight automobiles that could deliver the safety and muscle of today's cars but with far better mileage—four times as much in prototypes and ten times as much in projected models (see "Reinventing the Wheels," January, 1995, *Atlantic*). Since in today's cars only 15 to 20 percent of the fuel's energy reaches the wheels (the rest is lost in the engine and the transmission), and since materials lighter and stronger than steel are available or on the way, no expert questions the feasibility of the high-mileage vehicles Lovins describes.

Computers and cameras are examples of consumer goods getting lighter and smaller as they get better. The game-maker Sega is marketing a hand-held children's game, called Saturn, that has more computing power than the 1976 Cray supercomputer, which the United States tried to keep out of the hands of the Soviets. Improvements that extend the useful life of objects also save resources. Platinum spark plugs in today's cars last for 100,000 miles, as do "fill-for-life" transmission fluids. On average, cars bought in 1993 have a useful life more than 40 percent longer than those bought in 1970.

As lighter materials replace heavier ones, the U.S. economy continues to shed weight. Our per capita consumption of raw materials such as forestry products and metals has, measured by weight, declined steadily over the past twenty years. A recent

World Resources Institute study measured the "materials intensity" of our economy—that is, "the total material input and the hidden or indirect material flows, including deliberate landscape alterations" required for each dollar's worth of economic output. "The result shows a clearly declining pattern of materials intensity, supporting the conclusion that economic activity is growing somewhat more rapidly than natural resource use." Of course, we should do better. The Organization for Economic Cooperation and Development, an association of the world's industrialized nations, has proposed that its members strive as a long-range goal to decrease their materials intensity by a factor of ten.

Communications also illustrates the trend toward lighter, smaller, less materials-intensive technology. Just as telegraph cables replaced frigates in transmitting messages across the Atlantic and carried more information faster, glass fibers and microwaves have replaced cables—each new technology using less materials but providing greater capacity for sending and receiving information. Areas not yet wired for telephones (in the former Soviet Union, for example) are expected to leapfrog directly into cellular communications. Robert Solow, a Nobel laureate in economics, says that if the future is like the past, "there will be prolonged and substantial reductions in natural-resource requirements per unit of real output." He asks, "Why shouldn't the productivity of most natural resources rise more or less steadily through time, like the productivity of labor?"

Misconception No. 2: We Are Running Out of Food and Timber

The United Nations projects that the global population, currently 5.7 billion, will peak at about 10 billion in the next century and then stabilize or even decline. Can the earth feed that many people? Even if food crops increase sufficiently, other renewable resources, including many fisheries and forests, are already under pressure. Should we expect fish stocks to collapse or forests to disappear?

The world already produces enough cereals and oilseeds to feed 10 billion people a vegetarian diet adequate in protein and calories. If, however, the idea is to feed 10 billion people not healthful vegetarian diets but the kind of meat-laden meals that Americans eat, the production of grains and oilseeds may have to triple—primarily to feed livestock. Is anything like this kind of productivity in the cards?

Maybe. From 1961 to 1994 global production of food doubled. Global output of grain rose from about 630 million tons in 1950 to about 1.8 billion tons in 1992, largely as a result of greater yields. Developing countries from 1974 to 1994 increased wheat yields per acre by almost 100 percent, corn yields by 72 percent, and rice yields by 52 percent. "The generation of farmers on the land in 1950 was the first in history to double the production of food," the Worldwatch Institute has reported. "By 1984, they had outstripped population growth enough to raise per capita grain output an unprecedented 40 percent." From a two-year period ending in 1981 to a two-year period ending in 1990 the real prices of basic foods fell 38 percent on world markets, according to a 1992 United Nations report. Prices for food have continually decreased since the end of the eighteenth century, when Thomas Malthus argued that rapid population growth must lead to mass starvation by exceeding the carrying capacity of the earth.

Farmers worldwide could double the acreage in production, but this should not be necessary. Better seeds, more irrigation, multi-cropping, and additional use of fertilizer could greatly increase agricultural yields in the developing world, which are now generally only half those in the industrialized countries. It is biologically possible to raise yields of rice to about seven tons per acre—about four times the current average in the developing world. Super strains of cassava, a potato-like root crop eaten by millions of Africans, promise to increase yields tenfold. American farmers can also do better. In a good year, such as 1994, Iowa corn growers average about 3.5 tons per acre, but farmers more than double that yield in National Corn Growers Association competitions.

In drier parts of the world the scarcity of fresh water presents the greatest challenge to agriculture. But the problem is regional, not global. Fortunately, as Lester Brown, of the Worldwatch Institute, points out, "there are vast opportunities for increasing water efficiency" in arid regions, ranging from installing better water-delivery systems to planting drought-resistant crops. He adds, "Scientists can help push back the physical frontiers of cropping by developing varieties that are more drought resistant, salt tolerant, and early maturing. The payoff on the first two could be particularly high."

As if in response, Novartis Seeds has announced a program to develop water-efficient and salt-tolerant crops, including genetically engineered varieties of wheat. Researchers in Mexico have announced the development of drought-resistant corn that can boost yields by a third. Biotechnologists are converting annual crops into perennial ones, eliminating the need for yearly planting. They also hope to enable cereal crops to fix their own nitrogen, as legumes do, minimizing the need for fertilizer (genetically engineered nitrogen-fixing bacteria have already been test-marketed to farmers). Commercial varieties of crops such as corn, tomatoes, and potatoes which have been genetically engineered to be resistant to pests and diseases have been approved for field testing in the United States; several are now being sold and planted. A new breed of rice, 25 percent more productive than any currently in use, suggests that the Gene Revolution can take over where the Green Revolution left off. Biotechnology, as the historian Paul Kennedy has written, introduces "an entirely new stage in humankind's attempts to produce more crops and plants."

Biotechnology cannot, however, address the major causes of famine: poverty, trade barriers, corruption, mismanagement, ethnic antagonism, anarchy, war, and male-dominated societies that deprive women of food. Local land depletion, itself a consequence of poverty and institutional failure, is also a factor. Those who are too poor to use sound farming practices are compelled to overexploit the resources on which they depend. As the economist Partha Dasgupta has written, "Population growth, poverty and degradation of local resources often fuel one another." The amount of food in world trade is constrained less by the resource base than by the maldistribution of wealth.

Analysts who believe that the world is running out of resources often argue that famines occur not as a result of political or economic conditions but because there are "too many people." Unfortunately, as the economist Amartya Sen has pointed out, public officials who think in Malthusian terms assume that when absolute levels of food supplies are adequate, famine will not occur. This conviction diverts attention from the actual causes of famine, which has occurred in places where food output kept pace with population growth but people were too destitute to buy it.

We would have run out of food long ago had we tried to supply ourselves entirely by hunting and gathering. Likewise, if we depend on nature's gifts, we will exhaust many of the world's important fisheries. Fortunately, we are learning to cultivate fish as we do other crops. Genetic engineers have designed fish for better flavor and color as well as for faster growth, improved disease resistance, and other traits. Two farmed species—silver carp and grass carp—already rank among the ten most-consumed fish worldwide. A specially bred tilapia, known as the "aquatic chicken," takes six months to grow to a harvestable size of about one and a half pounds.

Aquaculture produced more than 16 million tons of fish in 1993; capacity has expanded over the past decade at an annual rate of 10 percent by quantity and 14 percent by value. In 1993 fish farms produced 22 percent of all food fish consumed in the world and 90 percent of all oysters sold. The World Bank reports that aquaculture could provide 40 percent of all fish consumed and more than half the value of fish harvested within the next fifteen years.

Salmon ranching and farming provide examples of the growing efficiency of aquacultural production. Norwegian salmon farms alone produce 400 million pounds a year. A biotech firm in Waltham, Massachusetts, has applied for government approval to commercialize salmon genetically engineered to grow four to six times as fast as their naturally occurring cousins. As a 1994 article in *Sierra* magazine noted, "There is so much salmon currently available that the supply exceeds demand, and prices to fishermen have fallen dramatically."

For those who lament the decline of natural fisheries and the human communities that grew up with them, the successes of aquaculture may offer no consolation. In the Pacific Northwest, for example, overfishing in combination with dams and habitat destruction has reduced the wild salmon population by 80 percent. Wild salmon—but not their bio-engineered aquacultural cousins—contribute to the cultural identity and sense of place of the Northwest. When wild salmon disappear, so will some of the region's history, character, and pride. What is true of wild salmon is also true of whales, dolphins, and other magnificent creatures—as they lose their economic importance, their aesthetic and moral worth becomes all the more evident. Economic considerations pull in one direction, moral considerations in the other. This conflict colors all our battles over the environment.

The transition from hunting and gathering to farming, which is changing the fishing industry, has taken place more slowly in forestry. Still there is no sign of a timber famine. In the United States forests now provide the largest harvests in history, and there is more forested U.S. area today than there was in 1920.

Bill McKibben has observed . . . that the eastern United States, which loggers and farmers in the eighteenth and nineteenth centuries nearly denuded of trees, has become reforested during this century (see "An Explosion of Green," April, 1995, *Atlantic*). One reason is that farms reverted to woods. Another is that machinery replaced animals; each draft animal required two or three cleared acres for pasture.

Natural reforestation is likely to continue as biotechnology makes areas used for logging more productive. According to Roger Sedjo, a respected forestry expert, advances in tree farming, if implemented widely, would permit the world to meet its entire demand for industrial wood using just 200 million acres of plantations—an area equal to only five percent of current forest land. As less land is required for commercial tree production, more natural forests may be protected—as they should be, for aesthetic, ethical, and spiritual reasons.

Often natural resources are so plentiful and therefore inexpensive that they undercut the necessary transition to technological alternatives. If the U.S. government did not protect wild forests from commercial exploitation, the timber industry would have little incentive to invest in tree plantations, where it can multiply yields by a factor of ten and take advantage of the results of genetic research. Only by investing in plantation silviculture can North American forestry fend off price competition from rapidly developing tree plantations in the Southern Hemisphere. Biotechnology-based silviculture can in the near future be expected to underprice "extractive" forestry worldwide. In this decade China will plant about 150 million acres of trees; India now plants four times the area it harvests commercially.

The expansion of fish and tree farming confirms the belief held by Peter Drucker and other management experts that our economy depends far more on the progress of technology than on the exploitation of nature. Although raw materials will always be necessary, knowledge has become the essential factor in the production of goods and services. "Where there is effective management," Drucker has written, "that is, application of knowledge to knowledge, we can always obtain the other resources." If we assume, along with Drucker and others, that resource scarcities do not exist or are easily averted, it is hard to see how economic theory, which after all concerns scarcity, provides the conceptual basis for valuing the environment. The reasons to preserve nature are ethical more often than they are economic.

Misconception No. 3: We Are Running Out of Energy

Probably the most persistent worries about resource scarcity concern energy. "The supply of fuels and other natural resources is becoming the limiting factor constraining the rate of economic growth," a group of experts proclaimed in 1986. They predicted the exhaustion of domestic oil and gas supplies by 2020 and, within a few decades, "major energy shortages as well as food shortages in the world."

Contrary to these expectations, no global shortages of hydrocarbon fuels are in sight. "One sees no immediate danger of 'running out' of energy in a global sense," writes John P.

Holdren, a professor of environmental policy at Harvard University. According to Holdren, reserves of oil and natural gas will last seventy to a hundred years if exploited at 1990 rates. (This does not take into account huge deposits of oil shale, heavy oils, and gas from unconventional sources.) He concludes that "running out of energy resources in any global sense is not what the energy problem is all about."

The global energy problem has less to do with depleting resources than with controlling pollutants. Scientists generally agree that gases, principally carbon dioxide, emitted in the combustion of hydrocarbon fuels can build up in and warm the atmosphere by trapping sunlight. Since carbon dioxide enhances photosynthetic activity, plants to some extent absorb the carbon dioxide we produce. In 1995 researchers reported in *Science* that vegetation in the Northern Hemisphere in 1992 and 1993 converted into trees and other plant tissue 3.5 billion tons of carbon—more than half the carbon produced by the burning of hydrocarbon fuels worldwide.

However successful this and other feedback mechanisms may be in slowing the processes of global warming, a broad scientific consensus, reflected in a 1992 international treaty, has emerged for stabilizing and then decreasing emissions of carbon dioxide and other "greenhouse" gases. This goal is well within the technological reach of the United States and other industrialized countries. Amory Lovins, among others, has described commercially available technologies that can "support present or greatly expanded worldwide economic activity while stabilizing global climate—and saving money." He observes that "even very large expansions in population and industrial activity need not be energy-constrained."

Lovins and other environmentalists contend that pollution-free energy from largely untapped sources is available in amounts exceeding our needs. Geothermal energy—which makes use of heat from the earth's core—is theoretically accessible through drilling technology in the United States in amounts thousands of times as great as the amount of energy contained in domestic coal reserves. Tidal energy is also promising. Analysts who study solar power generally agree with Lester Brown, of the *Worldwatch Institute,* that "technologies are ready to begin building a world energy system largely powered by solar resources." In the future these and other renewable energy sources may be harnessed to the nation's system of storing and delivering electricity.

Last year Joseph Romm and Charles Curtis described . . . advances in photovoltaic cells (which convert sunlight into electricity), fuel cells (which convert the hydrogen in fuels directly to electricity and heat, producing virtually no pollution), and wind power ("Mideast Oil Forever?" April, 1996, *Atlantic*). According to these authors, genetically engineered organisms used to ferment organic matter could, with further research and development, bring down the costs of ethanol and other environmentally friendly "biofuels" to make them competitive with gasoline.

Environmentalists who, like Amory Lovins, believe that our economy can grow and still reduce greenhouse gases emphasize not only that we should be able to move to renewable forms of energy but also that we can use fossil fuels more efficiently.

Some improvements are already evident. In developed countries the energy intensity of production—the amount of fuel burned per dollar of economic output—has been decreasing by about two percent a year.

From 1973 to 1986, for example, energy consumption in the United States remained virtually flat while economic production grew by almost 40 percent. Compared with Germany or Japan, this is a poor showing. The Japanese, who tax fuel more heavily than we do, use only half as much energy as the United States per unit of economic output. (Japanese environmental regulations are also generally stricter than ours; if anything, this has improved the competitiveness of Japanese industry.) The United States still wastes hundreds of billions of dollars annually in energy inefficiency. By becoming as energy-efficient as Japan, the United States could expand its economy and become more competitive internationally.

If so many opportunities exist for saving energy and curtailing pollution, why have we not seized them? One reason is that low fossil-fuel prices remove incentives for fuel efficiency and for converting to other energy sources. Another reason is that government subsidies for fossil fuels and nuclear energy amounted to many billions of dollars a year during the 1980s, whereas support for renewables dwindled to $114 million in 1989, a time when it had been proposed for near elimination. "Lemon socialism," a vast array of subsidies and barriers to trade, protects politically favored technologies, however inefficient, dangerous, filthy, or obsolete. "At heart, the major obstacles standing in the way [of a renewable-energy economy] are not technical in nature," the energy consultant Michael Brower has written, "but concern the laws, regulations, incentives, public attitudes, and other factors that make up the energy market."

In response to problems of climate change, the World Bank and other international organizations have recognized the importance of transferring advanced energy technologies to the developing world. Plainly, this will take a large investment of capital, particularly in education. Yet the "alternative for developing countries," according to José Goldemberg, a former Environment Minister of Brazil, "would be to remain at a dismally low level of development which . . . would aggravate the problems of sustainability."

Technology transfer can hasten sound economic development worldwide. Many environmentalists, however, argue that economies cannot expand without exceeding the physical limits nature sets—for example, with respect to energy. These environmentalists, who regard increasing affluence as a principal cause of environmental degradation, call for economic retrenchment and retraction—a small economy for a small earth. With Paul Ehrlich, they reject "the hope that development can greatly increase the size of the economic pie and pull many more people out of poverty." This hope is "basically a humane idea," Ehrlich has written, "made insane by the constraints nature places on human activity."

In developing countries, however, a no-growth economy "will deprive entire populations of access to better living conditions and lead to even more deforestation and land degradation," as Goldemberg warns. Moreover, citizens of developed countries are likely to resist an energy policy that they associate with poverty, discomfort, sacrifice, and pain. Technological pessimism, then, may not be the best option for environmentalists. It is certainly not the only one.

Misconception No. 4: The North Exploits the South

William Reilly, when he served as administrator of the Environmental Protection Agency in the Bush Administration, encountered a persistent criticism at international meetings on the environment. "The problem for the world's environment is your consumption, not our population," delegates from the developing world told him. Some of these delegates later took Reilly aside. "The North buys too little from the South," they confided. "The real problem is too little demand for our exports."

The delegates who told Reilly that the North consumes too little of what the South produces have a point. "With a few exceptions (notably petroleum)," a report from the World Resources Institute observes, "most of the natural resources consumed in the United States are from domestic sources." Throughout the 1980s the United States and Canada were the world's leading exporters of raw materials. The United States consistently leads the world in farm exports, running huge agricultural trade surpluses. The share of raw materials used in the North that it buys from the South stands at a thirty-year low and continues to decline; industrialized nations trade largely among themselves. The World Resources Institute recently reported that "the United States is largely self-sufficient in natural resources." Again, excepting petroleum, bauxite (from which aluminum is made), "and a few other industrial minerals, its material flows are almost entirely internal."

Sugar provides an instructive example of how the North excludes—rather than exploits—the resources of the South. Since 1796 the United States has protected domestic sugar against imports. American sugar growers, in part as a reward for large contributions to political campaigns, have long enjoyed a system of quotas and prohibitive tariffs against foreign competition. American consumers paid about three times world prices for sugar in the 1980s, enriching a small cartel of U.S. growers. *Forbes* magazine has estimated that a single family, the Fanjuls, of Palm Beach, reaps more than $65 million a year as a result of quotas for sugar.

The sugar industry in Florida, which is larger than that in any other state, makes even less sense environmentally than economically. It depends on a publicly built system of canals, levees, and pumping stations. Fertilizer from the sugarcane fields chokes the Everglades. Sugar growers, under a special exemption from labor laws, import Caribbean laborers to do the grueling and poorly paid work of cutting cane.

As the United States tightened sugar quotas (imports fell from 6.2 to 1.5 million tons annually from 1977 to 1987), the Dominican Republic and other nations with climates ideal for growing cane experienced political turmoil and economic collapse. Many farmers in Latin America, however, did well by switching from sugar to coca, which is processed into cocaine—perhaps the only high-value imported crop for which the United States is not developing a domestic substitute.

Before the Second World War the United States bought 40 percent of its vegetable oils from developing countries. After the war the United States protected its oilseed markets—for example, by establishing price supports for soybeans. Today the United States is one of the world's leading exporters of oil and oilseeds, although it still imports palm and coconut oils to obtain laurate, an ingredient in soap, shampoo, and detergents. Even this form of "exploitation" will soon cease. In 1994 farmers in Georgia planted the first commercial acreage of a high-laurate canola, genetically engineered by Calgene, a biotechnology firm.

About 100,000 Kenyans make a living on small plots of land growing pyrethrum flowers, the source of a comparatively environmentally safe insecticide of which the United States has been the largest importer. The U.S. Department of Commerce, however, awarded $1.2 million to a biotechnology firm to engineer pyrethrum genetically. Industrial countries will soon be able to synthesize all the pyrethrum they need and undersell Kenyan farmers.

An article in *Foreign Policy* in December of 1995 observed that the biotechnological innovations that create "substitutes for everything from vanilla to cocoa and coffee threaten to eliminate the livelihood of millions of Third World agricultural workers." Vanilla cultured in laboratories costs a fifth as much as vanilla extracted from beans, and thus jeopardizes the livelihood of tens of thousands of vanilla farmers in Madagascar. In the past, farms produced agricultural commodities and factories processed them. In the future, factories may "grow" as well as process many of the most valuable commodities—or the two functions will become one. As one plant scientist has said, "We have to stop thinking of these things as plant cells, and start thinking of them as new microorganisms, with all the potential that implies"—meaning, for instance, that the cells could be made to grow in commercially feasible quantities in laboratories, not fields.

The North not only balks at buying sugar and other crops from developing countries; it also dumps its excess agricultural commodities, especially grain, on them. After the Second World War, American farmers, using price supports left over from the New Deal, produced vast wheat surpluses, which the United States exported at concessionary prices to Europe and then the Third World. These enormous transfers of cereals to the South, institutionalized during the 1950s and 1960s by U.S. food aid, continued during the 1970s and 1980s, as the United States and the European Community vied for markets, each outdoing the other in subsidizing agricultural exports.

Grain imports from the United States "created food dependence within two decades in countries which had been mostly self-sufficient in food at the end of World War II," the sociologist Harriet Friedmann has written. Tropical countries soon matched the grain gluts of the North with their own surpluses of cocoa, coffee, tea, bananas, and other export commodities. Accordingly, prices for these commodities collapsed as early as 1970, catching developing nations in a scissors. As Friedmann describes it, "One blade was food import dependency. The other blade was declining revenues for traditional exports of tropical crops."

It might be better for the environment if the North exchanged the crops for which it is ecologically suited—wheat, for example—for crops easily grown in the South, such as coffee, cocoa, palm oil, and tea. Contrary to common belief, these tropical export crops—which grow on trees and bushes, providing canopy and continuous root structures to protect the soil—are less damaging to the soil than are traditional staples such as cereals and root crops. Better markets for tropical crops could help developing nations to employ their rural populations and to protect their natural resources. Allen Hammond, of the World Resources Institute, points out that "if poor nations cannot export anything else, they will export their misery—in the form of drugs, diseases, terrorism, migration, and environmental degradation."

Peasants in less-developed nations often confront intractable poverty, an entrenched land-tenure system, and a lack of infrastructure; they have little access to markets, education, or employment. Many of the rural poor, according to the environmental consultant Norman Myers, "have no option but to over-exploit environmental resource stocks in order to survive"—for example, by "increasingly encroaching onto tropical forests among other low-potential lands." These poorest of the poor "are causing as much natural-resource depletion as the other three billion developing-world people put together."

Myers observes that traditional indigenous farmers in tropical forests moved from place to place without seriously damaging the ecosystem. The principal agents of tropical deforestation are refugees from civil war and rural poverty, who are forced to eke out a living on marginal lands. Activities such as road building, logging, and commercial agriculture have barely increased in tropical forests since the early 1980s, according to Myers; slash-and-burn farming by displaced peasants accounts for far more deforestation—roughly three fifths of the total. Its impact is fast expanding. Most of the wood from trees harvested in tropical forests—that is, those not cleared for farms—is used locally for fuel. The likeliest path to protecting the rain forest is through economic development that enables peasants to farm efficiently, on land better suited to farming than to forest.

Many have argued that economic activity, affluence, and growth automatically lead to resource depletion, environmental deterioration, and ecological collapse. Yet greater productivity and prosperity—which is what economists mean by growth—have become prerequisite for controlling urban pollution and protecting sensitive ecological systems such as rain forests. Otherwise, destitute people who are unable to acquire food and fuel will create pollution and destroy forests. Without economic growth, which also correlates with lower fertility, the environmental and population problems of the South will only get worse. For impoverished countries facing environmental disaster, economic growth may be the one thing that is sustainable.

What Is Wrong with Consumption?

Many of us who attended college in the 1960s and 1970s took pride in how little we owned. We celebrated our freedom when we could fit all our possessions—mostly a stereo—into the back of a Beetle. Decades later, middle-aged and middle-class, many of us have accumulated an appalling amount of stuff. Piled high with gas grills, lawn mowers, excess furniture, bicycles, children's toys, garden implements, lumber, cinder blocks, ladders, lawn and leaf bags stuffed with memorabilia, and boxes yet to be unpacked from the last move, the two-car garages beside our suburban homes are too full to accommodate the family minivan. The quantity of resources, particularly energy, we waste and the quantity of trash we throw away (recycling somewhat eases our conscience) add to our consternation.

Even if predictions of resource depletion and ecological collapse are mistaken, it seems that they *should* be true, to punish us for our sins. We are distressed by the suffering of others, the erosion of the ties of community, family, and friendship, and the loss of the beauty and spontaneity of the natural world. These concerns reflect the most traditional and fundamental of American religious and cultural values.

Simple compassion instructs us to give to relieve the misery of others. There is a lot of misery worldwide to relieve. But as bad as the situation is, it is improving. In 1960 nearly 70 percent of the people in the world lived at or below the subsistence level. Today less than a third do, and the number enjoying fairly satisfactory conditions (as measured by the United Nations Human Development Index) rose from 25 percent in 1960 to 60 percent in 1992. Over the twenty-five years before 1992 average per capita consumption in developing countries increased 75 percent in real terms. The pace of improvements is also increasing. In developing countries in that period, for example, power generation and the number of telephone lines per capita doubled, while the number of households with access to clean water grew by half.

What is worsening is the discrepancy in income between the wealthy and the poor. Although world income measured in real terms has increased by 700 percent since the Second World War, the wealthiest people have absorbed most of the gains. Since 1960 the richest fifth of the world's people have seen their share of the world's income increase from 70 to 85 percent. Thus one fifth of the world's population possesses much more than four fifths of the world's wealth, while the share held by all others has correspondingly fallen; that of the world's poorest 20 percent has declined from 2.3 to 1.4 percent.

Benjamin Barber ("Jihad vs. McWorld," March, 1992, *Atlantic*) described market forces that "mesmerize the world with fast music, fast computers, and fast food—with MTV, Macintosh, and McDonald's, pressing nations into one commercially homogeneous global network: one McWorld tied together by technology, ecology, communications, and commerce." Affluent citizens of South Korea, Thailand, India, Brazil, Mexico, and many other rapidly developing nations have joined with Americans, Europeans, Japanese, and others to form an urban and cosmopolitan international society. Those who participate in this global network are less and less beholden to local customs and traditions. Meanwhile, ethnic, tribal, and other cultural groups that do not dissolve into McWorld often define themselves in opposition to it—fiercely asserting their ethnic, religious, and territorial identities.

The imposition of a market economy on traditional cultures in the name of development—for example, the insistence that everyone produce and consume more—can dissolve the ties to family, land, community, and place on which indigenous peoples traditionally rely for their security. Thus development projects intended to relieve the poverty of indigenous peoples may, by causing the loss of cultural identity, engender the very powerlessness they aim to remedy. Pope Paul VI, in the encyclical *Populorum Progressio* (1967), described the tragic dilemma confronting indigenous peoples: "either to preserve traditional beliefs and structures and reject social progress; or to embrace foreign technology and foreign culture, and reject ancestral traditions with their wealth of humanism."

The idea that everything is for sale and nothing is sacred—that all values are subjective—undercuts our own moral and cultural commitments, not just those of tribal and traditional communities. No one has written a better critique of the assault that commerce makes on the quality of our lives than Thoreau provides in *Walden*. The cost of a thing, according to Thoreau, is not what the market will bear but what the individual must bear because of it: it is "the amount of what I will call life which is required to be exchanged for it, immediately or in the long run."

Many observers point out that as we work harder and consume more, we seem to enjoy our lives less. We are always in a rush—a "Saint Vitus' dance," as Thoreau called it. Idleness is suspect. Americans today spend less time with their families, neighbors, and friends than they did in the 1950s. Juliet B. Schor, an economist at Harvard University, argues that "Americans are literally working themselves to death." A fancy car, video equipment, or a complex computer program can exact a painful cost in the form of maintenance, upgrading, and repair. We are possessed by our possessions; they are often harder to get rid of than to acquire.

That money does not make us happier, once our basic needs are met, is a commonplace overwhelmingly confirmed by sociological evidence. Paul Wachtel, who teaches social psychology at the City University of New York, has concluded that bigger incomes "do not yield an increase in feelings of satisfaction or well-being, at least for populations who are above a poverty or subsistence level." This cannot be explained simply by the fact that people have to work harder to earn more money: even those who hit jackpots in lotteries often report that their lives are not substantially happier as a result. Well-being depends upon health, membership in a community in which one feels secure, friends, faith, family, love, and virtues that money cannot buy. Robert Lane, a political scientist at Yale University, using the concepts of economics, has written, "If 'utility' has anything to do with happiness, above the poverty line the long-term marginal utility of money is almost zero."

Economists in earlier times predicted that wealth would not matter to people once they attained a comfortable standard of living. "In ease of body and peace of mind, all the different ranks of life are nearly upon a level," wrote Adam Smith, the eighteenth-century English advocate of the free market. In the 1930s the British economist John Maynard Keynes argued that after a period of great expansion further accumulation of wealth would no longer improve personal well-being. Subsequent economists, however, found that even after much of

the industrial world had attained the levels of wealth Keynes thought were sufficient, people still wanted more. From this they inferred that wants are insatiable.

Perhaps this is true. But the insatiability of wants and desires poses a difficulty for standard economic theory, which posits that humanity's single goal is to increase or maximize wealth. If wants increase as fast as income grows, what purpose can wealth serve?

Critics often attack standard economic theory on the ground that economic growth is "unsustainable." We are running out of resources, they say; we court ecological disaster. Whether or not growth is sustainable, there is little reason to think that once people attain a decent standard of living, continued growth is desirable. The economist Robert H. Nelson recently wrote in the journal *Ecological Economics* that it is no longer possible for most people to believe that economic progress will "solve all the problems of mankind, spiritual as well as material." As long as the debate over sustainability is framed in terms of the physical limits to growth rather than the moral purpose of it, mainstream economic theory will have the better of the argument. If the debate were framed in moral or social terms, the result might well be otherwise.

Making a Place for Nature

According to Thoreau, "a man's relation to Nature must come very near to a personal one." For environmentalists in the tradition of Thoreau and John Muir, stewardship is a form of fellowship; although we must use nature, we do not value it primarily for the economic purposes it serves. We take our bearings from the natural world—our sense of time from its days and seasons, our sense of place from the character of a landscape and the particular plants and animals native to it. An intimacy with nature ends our isolation in the world. We know where we belong, and we can find the way home.

In defending old-growth forests, wetlands, or species we make our best arguments when we think of nature chiefly in aesthetic and moral terms. Rather than having the courage of our moral and cultural convictions, however, we too often rely on economic arguments for protecting nature, in the process attributing to natural objects more instrumental value than they have. By claiming that a threatened species may harbor lifesaving drugs, for example, we impute to that species an economic value or a price much greater than it fetches in a market. When we make the prices come out right, we rescue economic theory but not necessarily the environment.

There is no credible argument, moreover, that all or even most of the species we are concerned to protect are essential to the functioning of the ecological systems on which we depend. (If whales went extinct, for example, the seas would not fill up with krill.) David Ehrenfeld, a biologist at Rutgers University, makes this point in relation to the vast ecological changes we have already survived. "Even a mighty dominant like the American chestnut," Ehrenfeld has written, "extending over half a continent, all but disappeared without bringing the eastern deciduous forest down with it." Ehrenfeld points out that the species most likely to be endangered are those the biosphere is least likely to miss. "Many of these species were never common or ecologically influential; by no stretch of the imagination can we make them out to be vital cogs in the ecological machine."

Species may be profoundly important for cultural and spiritual reasons, however. Consider again the example of the wild salmon, whose habitat is being destroyed by hydroelectric dams along the Columbia River. Although this loss is unimportant to the economy overall (there is no shortage of salmon), it is of the greatest significance to the Amerindian tribes that have traditionally subsisted on wild salmon, and to the region as a whole. By viewing local flora and fauna as a sacred heritage—by recognizing their intrinsic value—we discover who we are rather than what we want. On moral and cultural grounds society might be justified in making great economic sacrifices—removing hydroelectric dams, for example—to protect remnant populations of the Snake River sockeye, even if, as critics complain, hundreds or thousands of dollars are spent for every fish that is saved.

Even those plants and animals that do not define places possess enormous intrinsic value and are worth preserving for their own sake. What gives these creatures value lies in their histories, wonderful in themselves, rather than in any use to which they can be put. The biologist E. O. Wilson elegantly takes up this theme: "Every kind of organism has reached this moment in time by threading one needle after another, throwing up brilliant artifices to survive and reproduce against nearly impossible odds." Every plant or animal evokes not just sympathy but also reverence and wonder in those who know it.

In *Earth in the Balance* (1992) Al Gore, then a senator, wrote, "We have become so successful at controlling nature that we have lost our connection to it." It is all too easy, Gore wrote, "to regard the earth as a collection of 'resources' having an intrinsic value no larger than their usefulness at the moment." The question before us is not whether we are going to run out of resources. It is whether economics is the appropriate context for thinking about environmental policy.

Even John Stuart Mill, one of the principal authors of utilitarian philosophy, recognized that the natural world has great intrinsic and not just instrumental value. More than a century ago, as England lost its last truly wild places, Mill condemned a world

with nothing left to the spontaneous activity of nature; with every rood of land brought into cultivation, which is capable of growing food for human beings; every flowery waste or natural pasture ploughed up; all quadrupeds or birds which are not domesticated for man's use exterminated as his rivals for food, every hedgerow or superfluous tree rooted out, and scarcely a place left where a wild shrub or flower could grow without being eradicated as a weed in the name of improved agriculture.

The world has the wealth and the resources to provide everyone the opportunity to live a decent life. We consume too much when market relationships displace the bonds of community, compassion, culture, and place. We consume too much when consumption becomes an end in itself and makes us lose affection and reverence for the natural world.

Critical Thinking

1. It has been said that "the global economy cannot grow infinitely on a finite planet." If this is true, then why do many humans behave as though it were not? And if this is not *true,* then why do we have colleges and universities offering classes and degrees in "environmental science"?

2. List the author's "four misconceptions" and consider how the observations made regarding those misconceptions are "place dependent" (e.g., might vary for countries, regions, cultures, geopolitical economies).

3. According to the author, how is the North *not* exploiting the South? Think of some examples of how the industrialized world *is* exploiting developing nations.

4. Aside from wealth, what are some geopolitical-economy factors that make it easy for Americans to amass so many material possessions?

5. The author believes we consume too much when . . .? Do you agree or disagree? Explain.

Article

The Gospel of Consumption

And the Better Future We Left Behind

JEFFREY KAPLAN

Private cars were relatively scarce in 1919 and horse-drawn conveyances were still common. In residential districts, electric streetlights had not yet replaced many of the old gaslights. And within the home, electricity remained largely a luxury item for the wealthy.

Just ten years later things looked very different. Cars dominated the streets and most urban homes had electric lights, electric flat irons, and vacuum cleaners. In upper-middle-class houses, washing machines, refrigerators, toasters, curling irons, percolators, heating pads, and popcorn poppers were becoming commonplace. And although the first commercial radio station didn't begin broadcasting until 1920, the American public, with an adult population of about 122 million people, bought 4,438,000 radios in the year 1929 alone.

But despite the apparent tidal wave of new consumer goods and what appeared to be a healthy appetite for their consumption among the well-to-do, industrialists were worried. They feared that the frugal habits maintained by most American families would be difficult to break. Perhaps even more threatening was the fact that the industrial capacity for turning out goods seemed to be increasing at a pace greater than people's sense that they needed them.

It was this latter concern that led Charles Kettering, director of General Motors Research, to write a 1929 magazine article called "Keep the Consumer Dissatisfied." He wasn't suggesting that manufacturers produce shoddy products. Along with many of his corporate cohorts, he was defining a strategic shift for American industry—from fulfilling basic human needs to creating new ones.

In a 1927 interview with the magazine *Nation's Business,* Secretary of Labor James J. Davis provided some numbers to illustrate a problem that the *New York Times* called "need saturation." Davis noted that "the textile mills of this country can produce all the cloth needed in six months' operation each year" and that 14 percent of the American shoe factories could produce a year's supply of footwear. The magazine went on to suggest, "It may be that the world's needs ultimately will be produced by three days' work a week."

Business leaders were less than enthusiastic about the prospect of a society no longer centered on the production of goods.

For them, the new "labor-saving" machinery presented not a vision of liberation but a threat to their position at the center of power. John E. Edgerton, president of the National Association of Manufacturers, typified their response when he declared: "I am for everything that will make work happier but against everything that will further subordinate its importance. The emphasis should be put on work—more work and better work." "Nothing," he claimed, "breeds radicalism more than unhappiness unless it is leisure."

By the late 1920s, America's business and political elite had found a way to defuse the dual threat of stagnating economic growth and a radicalized working class in what one industrial consultant called "the gospel of consumption"—the notion that people could be convinced that however much they have, it isn't enough. President Herbert Hoover's 1929 Committee on Recent Economic Changes observed in glowing terms the results: "By advertising and other promotional devices . . . a measurable pull on production has been created which releases capital otherwise tied up." They celebrated the conceptual breakthrough: "Economically we have a boundless field before us; that there are new wants which will make way endlessly for newer wants, as fast as they are satisfied."

Today "work and more work" is the accepted way of doing things. If anything, improvements to the labor-saving machinery since the 1920s have intensified the trend. Machines *can* save labor, but only if they go idle when we possess enough of what they can produce. In other words, the machinery offers us an opportunity to work less, an opportunity that as a society we have chosen not to take. Instead, we have allowed the owners of those machines to define their purpose: not reduction of labor, but "higher productivity"—and with it the imperative to consume virtually everything that the machinery can possibly produce.

From the earliest days of the Age of Consumerism there were critics. One of the most influential was Arthur Dahlberg, whose 1932 book *Jobs, Machines, and Capitalism* was well known to policymakers and elected officials in Washington. Dahlberg declared that "failure to shorten the length of the working day . . . is the primary cause of our rationing of opportunity, our excess industrial plant, our enormous wastes of competition, our high pressure advertising, [and] our economic imperialism." Since much of what industry produced was no longer aimed at satisfying human physical needs, a four-hour workday, he claimed, was necessary to prevent society from becoming disastrously materialistic. "By not shortening the working day when all the wood is in," he suggested, the profit motive becomes "both the creator and satisfier of spiritual needs." For when the profit motive can turn nowhere else, "it wraps our soap in pretty boxes and tries to convince us that that is solace to our souls."

There was, for a time, a visionary alternative. In 1930 Kellogg Company, the world's leading producer of ready-to-eat cereal, announced that all of its nearly fifteen hundred workers would move from an eight-hour to a six-hour workday. Company president Lewis Brown and owner W. K. Kellogg noted that if the company ran "four six-hour shifts . . . instead of three eight-hour shifts, this will give work and paychecks to the heads of three hundred more families in Battle Creek."

This was welcome news to workers at a time when the country was rapidly descending into the Great Depression. But as Benjamin Hunnicutt explains in his book *Kellogg's Six-Hour Day,* Brown and Kellogg wanted to do more than save jobs. They hoped to show that the "free exchange of goods, services, and labor in the free market would not have to mean mindless consumerism or eternal exploitation of people and natural resources." Instead "workers would be liberated by increasingly higher wages and shorter hours for the final freedom promised by the Declaration of Independence—the pursuit of happiness."

To be sure, Kellogg did not intend to stop making a profit. But the company leaders argued that men and women would work more efficiently on shorter shifts, and with more people employed, the overall purchasing power of the community would increase, thus allowing for more purchases of goods, including cereals.

A shorter workday did entail a cut in overall pay for workers. But Kellogg raised the hourly rate to partially offset the loss and provided for production bonuses to encourage people to work hard. The company eliminated time off for lunch, assuming that workers would rather work their shorter shift and leave as soon as possible. In a "personal letter" to employees, Brown pointed to the "mental income" of "the enjoyment of the surroundings of your home, the place you work, your neighbors, the other pleasures you have [that are] harder to translate into dollars and cents." Greater leisure, he hoped, would lead to "higher standards in school and civic . . . life" that would benefit the company by allowing it to "draw its workers from a community where good homes predominate."

It was an attractive vision, and it worked. Not only did Kellogg prosper, but journalists from magazines such as *Forbes* and *BusinessWeek* reported that the great majority of company employees embraced the shorter workday. One reporter described "a lot of gardening and community beautification, athletics and hobbies . . . libraries well patronized and the mental background of these fortunate workers . . . becoming richer."

A U.S. Department of Labor survey taken at the time, as well as interviews Hunnicutt conducted with former workers, confirm this picture. The government interviewers noted that "little dissatisfaction with lower earnings resulting from the decrease in hours was expressed, although in the majority of cases very real decreases had resulted." One man spoke of "more time at home with the family." Another remembered: "I could go home and have time to work in my garden." A woman noted that the six-hour shift allowed her husband to "be with 4 boys at ages it was important."

Those extra hours away from work also enabled some people to accomplish things that they might never have been able to do otherwise. Hunnicutt describes how at the end of her interview an eighty-year-old woman began talking about ping-pong. "We'd get together. We had a ping-pong table and all my relatives would come for dinner and things and we'd all play ping-pong by the hour." Eventually she went on to win the state championship.

Many women used the extra time for housework. But even then, they often chose work that drew in the entire family, such as canning. One recalled how canning food at home became "a family project" that "we all enjoyed," including her sons, who "opened up to talk freely." As Hunnicutt puts it, canning became the "medium for something more important than preserving food. Stories, jokes, teasing, quarreling, practical instruction, songs, griefs, and problems were shared. The modern discipline of alienated work was left behind for an older . . . more convivial kind of working together."

This was the stuff of a human ecology in which thousands of small, almost invisible, interactions between family members, friends, and neighbors create an intricate structure that supports social life in much the same way as topsoil supports our biological existence. When we allow either one to become impoverished, whether out of greed or intemperance, we put our long-term survival at risk.

Our modern predicament is a case in point. By 2005 per capita household spending (in inflation-adjusted dollars) was twelve times what it had been in 1929, while per capita spending for durable goods—the big stuff such as cars and appliances—was thirty-two times higher. Meanwhile, by 2000 the average married couple with children was working almost five hundred hours a year more than in 1979. And according to reports by the Federal Reserve Bank in 2004 and 2005, over 40 percent of American families spend more than they earn. The average household carries $18,654 in debt, not including home-mortgage debt, and the ratio of household debt to income is at record levels, having roughly doubled over the last two decades. We are quite literally working ourselves into a frenzy just so we can consume all that our machines can produce.

Yet we could work and spend a lot less and still live quite comfortably. By 1991 the amount of goods and services produced for each hour of labor was double what it had been in 1948. By 2006 that figure had risen another 30 percent. In other words, if as a society we made a collective decision to get by on the amount we produced and consumed seventeen years ago, we could cut back from the standard forty-hour week to 5.3 hours per day—or 2.7 hours if we were willing to return to the 1948 level. We were already the richest country on the planet in 1948 and most of the world has not yet caught up to where we were then.

Rather than realizing the enriched social life that Kellogg's vision offered us, we have impoverished our human communities with a form of materialism that leaves us in relative isolation from family, friends, and neighbors. We simply don't have time for them. Unlike our great-grandparents who passed the time, we spend it. An outside observer might conclude that we are in the grip of some strange curse, like a modern-day King Midas whose touch turns everything into a product built around a microchip.

Of course not everybody has been able to take part in the buying spree on equal terms. Millions of Americans work long hours at poverty wages while many others can find no work at all. However, as advertisers well know, poverty does not render one immune to the gospel of consumption.

Meanwhile, the influence of the gospel has spread far beyond the land of its origin. Most of the clothes, video players, furniture, toys, and other goods Americans buy today are made in distant countries, often by underpaid people working in sweatshop conditions. The raw material for many of those products comes from clearcutting or strip mining or other disastrous means of extraction. Here at home, business activity is centered on designing those products, financing their manufacture, marketing them—and counting the profits.

Kellogg's vision, despite its popularity with his employees, had little support among his fellow business leaders. But Dahlberg's book had a major influence on Senator (and future Supreme Court justice) Hugo Black who, in 1933, introduced legislation requiring a thirty-hour work week. Although Roosevelt at first appeared to support Black's bill, he soon sided with the majority of businessmen who opposed it. Instead, Roosevelt went on to launch a series of policy initiatives that led to the forty-hour standard that we more or less observe today.

By the time the Black bill came before Congress, the prophets of the gospel of consumption had been developing their tactics and techniques for at least a decade. However, as the Great Depression deepened, the public mood was uncertain, at best, about the proper role of the large corporation. Labor unions were gaining in both public support and legal legitimacy, and the Roosevelt administration, under its New Deal program, was implementing government regulation of industry on an unprecedented scale. Many corporate leaders saw the New Deal as a serious threat. James A. Emery, general counsel for the National Association of Manufacturers (NAM), issued a "call to arms" against the "shackles of irrational regulation" and the "back-breaking burdens of taxation," characterizing the New Deal doctrines as "alien invaders of our national thought."

In response, the industrial elite represented by NAM, including General Motors, the big steel companies, General Foods, DuPont, and others, decided to create their own propaganda. An internal NAM memo called for "re-selling all of the individual Joe Doakes on the advantages and benefits he enjoys under a competitive economy." NAM launched a massive public relations campaign it called the "American Way." As the minutes of a NAM meeting described it, the purpose of the campaign was to link "free enterprise in the public consciousness with free speech, free press and free religion as integral parts of democracy."

Consumption was not only the linchpin of the campaign; it was also recast in political terms. A campaign booklet put out by the J. Walter Thompson advertising agency told readers that under "private capitalism, the *Consumer,* the *Citizen* is boss," and "he doesn't have to wait for election day to vote or for the Court to convene before handing down his verdict. The consumer 'votes' each time he buys one article and rejects another."

According to Edward Bernays, one of the founders of the field of public relations and a principal architect of the American Way, the choices available in the polling booth are akin to those at the department store; both should consist of a limited set of offerings that are carefully determined by what Bernays called an "invisible government" of public-relations experts and advertisers working on behalf of business leaders. Bernays claimed that in a "democratic society" we are and should be "governed, our minds . . . molded, our tastes formed, our ideas suggested, largely by men we have never heard of."

NAM formed a national network of groups to ensure that the booklet from J. Walter Thompson and similar material appeared in libraries and school curricula across the country. The campaign also placed favorable articles in newspapers (often citing "independent" scholars who were paid secretly) and created popular magazines and film shorts directed to children and adults with such titles as "Building Better Americans," "The Business of America's People Is Selling," and "America Marching On."

Perhaps the biggest public relations success for the American Way campaign was the 1939 New York World's Fair. The fair's director of public relations called it "the greatest public relations program in industrial history," one that would battle what he called the "New Deal propaganda." The fair's motto was "Building the World of Tomorrow," and it was indeed a forum in which American corporations literally modeled the future they were determined to create. The most famous of the exhibits was General Motors' 35,000-square-foot Futurama, where visitors toured Democracity, a metropolis of multilane highways that took its citizens from their countryside homes to their jobs in the skyscraper-packed central city.

For all of its intensity and spectacle, the campaign for the American Way did not create immediate, widespread, enthusiastic support for American corporations or the corporate vision of the future. But it did lay the ideological groundwork for changes that came after the Second World War, changes that established what is still commonly called our post-war society.

The war had put people back to work in numbers that the New Deal had never approached, and there was considerable fear that unemployment would return when the war ended. Kellogg workers had been working forty-eight-hour weeks during the war and the majority of them were ready to return to a six-hour day and thirty-hour week. Most of them were able to do so, for a while. But W. K. Kellogg and Lewis Brown had turned the company over to new managers in 1937.

The new managers saw only costs and no benefits to the six-hour day, and almost immediately after the end of the war they began a campaign to undermine shorter hours. Management offered workers a tempting set of financial incentives if they would accept an eight-hour day. Yet in a vote taken in 1946, 77 percent of the men and 87 percent of the women wanted to return to a thirty-hour week rather than a forty-hour one. In making that choice, they also chose a fairly dramatic drop in earnings from artificially high wartime levels.

The company responded with a strategy of attrition, offering special deals on a department-by-department basis where eight hours had pockets of support, typically among highly skilled male workers. In the culture of a post-war, post-Depression U.S., that strategy was largely successful. But not everyone went along. Within Kellogg there was a substantial, albeit slowly dwindling group of people Hunnicutt calls the "mavericks," who resisted longer work hours. They clustered in a few departments that had managed to preserve the six-hour day until the company eliminated it once and for all in 1985.

The mavericks rejected the claims made by the company, the union, and many of their co-workers that the extra money they could earn on an eight-hour shift was worth it. Despite the enormous difference in societal wealth between the 1930s and the 1980s, the language the mavericks used to explain their preference for a six-hour workday was almost identical to that used by Kellogg workers fifty years earlier. One woman, worried about the long hours worked by her son, said, "He has no time to live, to visit and spend time with his family, and to do the other things he really loves to do."

Several people commented on the link between longer work hours and consumerism. One man said, "I was getting along real good, so there was no use in me working any more time than I had to." He added, "Everybody thought they were going to get rich when they got that eight-hour deal and it really didn't make a big difference. . . . Some went out and bought automobiles right quick and they didn't gain much on that because the car took the extra money they had."

The mavericks, well aware that longer work hours meant fewer jobs, called those who wanted eight-hour shifts plus overtime "work hogs." "Kellogg's was laying off people," one woman commented, "while some of the men were working really fantastic amounts of overtime—that's just not fair." Another quoted the historian Arnold Toynbee, who said, "We will either share the work, or take care of people who don't have work."

People in the depression-wracked 1930s, with what seems to us today to be a very low level of material goods, readily chose fewer work hours for the same reasons as some of their children and grandchildren did in the 1980s: to have more time for themselves and their families. We could, as a society, make a similar choice today.

But we cannot do it as individuals. The mavericks at Kellogg held out against company and social pressure for years, but in the end the marketplace didn't offer them a choice to work less and consume less. The reason is simple: that choice is at odds with the foundations of the marketplace itself—at least as it is currently constructed. The men and women who masterminded the creation of the consumerist society understood that theirs was a political undertaking, and it will take a powerful political movement to change course today.

Bernays's version of a "democratic society," in which political decisions are marketed to consumers, has many modern proponents. Consider a comment by Andrew Card, George W. Bush's former chief of staff. When asked why the administration waited several months before making its case for war against Iraq, Card replied, "You don't roll out a new product in August." And in 2004, one of the leading legal theorists in the United States, federal judge Richard Posner, declared that "representative democracy . . . involves a division between rulers and ruled," with the former being "a governing class," and the rest of us exercising a form of "consumer sovereignty" in the political sphere with "the power not to buy a particular product, a power to choose though not to create."

Sometimes an even more blatant antidemocratic stance appears in the working papers of elite think tanks. One such example is the prominent Harvard political scientist Samuel Huntington's 1975 contribution to a Trilateral Commission report on "The Crisis of Democracy." Huntington warns against an "excess of democracy," declaring that "a democratic political system usually requires some measure of apathy and non-involvement on the part of some individuals and groups." Huntington notes that "marginal social groups, as in the case of the blacks, are now becoming full participants in the political system" and thus present the "danger of overloading the political system" and undermining its authority.

According to this elite view, the people are too unstable and ignorant for self-rule. "Commoners," who are viewed as factors of production at work and as consumers at home, must adhere to their proper roles in order to maintain social stability. Posner, for example, disparaged a proposal for a national day of deliberation as "a small but not trivial reduction in the amount of productive work." Thus he appears to be an ideological descendant of the business leader who warned that relaxing the imperative for "more work and better work" breeds "radicalism."

As far back as 1835, Boston workingmen striking for shorter hours declared that they needed time away from work to be good citizens: "We have rights, and we have duties to perform as American citizens and members of society." As those workers well understood, any meaningful democracy requires citizens who are empowered to create and re-create their government, rather than a mass of marginalized voters who merely choose from what is offered by an "invisible" government. Citizenship requires a commitment of time and attention, a commitment people cannot make if they are lost to themselves in an ever-accelerating cycle of work and consumption.

We can break that cycle by turning off our machines when they have created enough of what we need. Doing so will give us an opportunity to re-create the kind of healthy communities that were beginning to emerge with Kellogg's six-hour day, communities in which human welfare is the overriding concern rather than subservience to machines and those who own them. We can create a society where people have time to play together as well as work together, time to act politically in their common interests, and time even to argue over what those common interests might be. That fertile mix of human relationships is necessary for healthy human societies, which in turn are necessary for sustaining a healthy planet.

If we want to save the Earth, we must also save ourselves from ourselves. We can start by sharing the work *and* the wealth. We may just find that there is plenty of both to go around.

Critical Thinking

1. Outline briefly how the American work ethic has contributed to the "gospel of consumption."

2. How was Kellogg's "six-hour day" idea intended originally to avoid the mindless consumerism and exploitation of people and resources that he feared our work obsession would create?

3. Why is working too much not good for societies or for the environment?

4. Do you think different cultures (rural, urban, agricultural, etc) have different "work ethics" and different work goals? Explain.

5. Can the industrialized world's obsession with work and production be compatible with the ideals of sustainability? Explain.

Kaplan, Jeffrey. From *Orion*, May/June 2008, pp. 1–8. Copyright © 2008 by Jeffrey Kaplan. Reprinted by permission of the author.

Article

The Psychological Roots of Resource Over-Consumption

Nate Hagens

The Psychological Roots of Resource Over-Consumption

Humans have an innate need for status and for novelty in their lives. Unfortunately, the modern world has adopted very energy—and resource—intensive ways of meeting those needs. Other ways are going to have to be found as part of the move to a more sustainable world.

Most people associate the word "sustainability" with changes to the supply side of our modern way of life such as using energy from solar flows rather than fossil fuels, recycling, green tech and greater efficiency. In this essay, however, I will focus on the demand-side drivers that explain why we continue to seek and consume more stuff.

When addressing 'demand-side drivers', we must begin at the source: the human brain. The various layers and mechanisms of our brain have been built on top of each other via millions and millions of iterations, keeping intact what 'worked' and adding via changes and mutations what helped the pre-human, pre-mammal organism to incrementally advance. Brain structures that functioned poorly in ancient environments are no longer around. Everyone reading this page is descended from the best of the best at both surviving and procreating which, in an environment of privation and danger where most 'iterations' of our evolution happened, meant acquiring necessary resources, achieving status and possessing brains finely tuned to natural dangers and opportunities.

This essay outlines two fundamental ways in which the evolutionarily derived reward pathways of our brains are influencing our modern overconsumption. First, financial wealth accumulation and the accompanying conspicuous consumption are generally regarded as the signals of modern success for our species. This gives the rest of us environmental cues to compete for more and more stuff as a proxy of our status and achievement. A second and more subtle driver is that we are easily hijacked by and habituated to novel stimuli. As we shall see, the prevalence of novelty today eventually demands higher and higher levels of neural stimulation, which often need increased consumption to satisfy. Thus it is this combination of pursuit of social status and the plethora of *novel activities* that underlies our large appetite for resource throughput.

Status

Evolution has honed and culled 'what worked' by combining the substrate of life with eons' worth of iterations. Modern biological research has focused on the concept of 'relative fitness', a term for describing those adaptations that are successful in propelling genes, or suites of genes, into the next generation and that will have out-competed those that were deleterious or did not keep up with environmental change. Though absolute fitness mattered to the individual organisms while they were alive, looking back it was 'relative fitness' that shaped the bodies and brains of the creatures on the planet today.

Status, both in humans and other species, has historically been a signaling mechanism that minimised the costs of competition, whether for reproductive opportunities or for material resources. If you place ten chickens in an enclosure there will ensue a series of fights until a pecking order is established. Each bird quickly learns who it can and cannot beat and a status hierarchy is created, thus making future fights (and wastes of energy) less common. Physical competition is costly behaviour that requires energy and entails risk of injury. Status is one way to determine who one can profitably challenge and who one cannot. In our ancestral environment, those men (and women) that successfully moved up the social hierarchy improved their mating and resource prospects. Those at the bottom of the status rung did not only possess fewer mating opportunities but many did not mate at all. Status among our ancestors was probably linked to those attributes providing consistent benefits to the tribe: hunting prowess, strength, leadership ability, storytelling skills etc. In modern humans, status is defined by what our modern cultures dictate. As we are living through an era of massive energy gain from fossil fuels, pure physical prowess has been replaced by digital wealth, fast cars, political connections, etc.

It follows that the larger a culture's resource subsidy (natural wealth), the more opportunity there is for 'status badges' uncorrelated with basic needs such as strength, intelligence, adaptability, stamina, etc. Though 'what' defines status may be culturally derived, status hierarchies themselves are part of our evolved nature. Ancestral hominids at the bottom of the mating pecking order, ceteris paribus, are not our ancestors. Similarly, many of our ancestors had orders of magnitude more descendants than others. For example, scientists recently discovered an odd geographical preponderance for a particular Y chromosome mutation which turns out to be originally descended from Genghis Khan. Given the 16 million odd male descendants alive today with this Y marker, Mr. Khan is theorised to have had 800,000 times the reproductive success than the average male alive on the planet in 1200 A.D. This does not imply that we are all pillagers and conquerors—only that various phenotypic expressions have had ample opportunity to become hardwired in our evolutionary past.[1]

Mating success is a key driver in the natural world. This is all studied and documented by evolutionary research into the theory of "sexual selection", which Charles Darwin once summarised as the effects of the *struggle between the individuals of one sex, generally the males, for the possession of the other sex.*"[2] Biologists have shown that a primary way to reliably demonstrate one's 'quality' during courtship is to display a high-cost signal—e.g. a heavy and colourful peacock's tail, an energy-expending bird-song concert, or a $100,000 sports car.[3] These costly "handicap" signals are evolutionarily stable indicators of their producer's quality, because cheap signals are too easy for low-quality imitators to fake.[4]

In this sense 'waste' was an evolutionary selection! Think of three major drawbacks to a male peacock of growing such a hugely ornate tail:

1. the energy, vitamins and minerals needed to go into the creation of the tail could have been used for other survival/reproductive needs,
2. the tail makes the bird more likely to be spotted by a predator,
3. If spotted, the cumbersome tail makes escape from a predator less likely.

Overall, though, these negative "fitness hits" must have been outweighed by the drab female peahen's preference for males with larger, more ornate tails. With this filter, we can understand the rationale and prevalence of Veblen goods (named after the 19th-century economist who coined the term 'conspicuous consumption')—a group of commodities that people increasingly prefer to buy as their price gets higher because the greater price confers greater status. This biological precept of signalling theory is alive and well in the human culture.

Novelty

Modern man evolved from earlier hominids under conditions of privation and scarcity at least until about 10,000 years ago. The period since then has been too short a time to make a significant change to millions of years of prior neural sculpture. Nature made the brain's survival systems incredibly efficient. The brain is based on about 40% of all our available genes and consumes over 20% of our calorific intake. Incremental changes in how our brains recognise, process and react to the world around us either contributed to our survival and thus were carried forward, or died out.

Some changes affected *salience*, the ability to notice what is important, different or unusual. Salience recognition is part of what's called the mesolimbic dopamine reward pathway. This

pathway is a system of neurons integral to survival efficiency, helping us to instantly decide what in the environment should command our attention. Historically, immediate feedback on what is 'new' was critical to both avoiding danger and procuring food. Because most of what happens around us each day is predictable, processing every detail of a familiar habitat wastes brain energy. Such activity would also slow down our mental computer so that what are now minor distractions could prove deadly. Thus our ancestors living on the African savanna paid little attention to the stable mountains on the horizon but were quick to detect any movement in the bush, on the plains, or at the riverbank. Those more able to detect and process 'novel cues' were more likely to obtain rewards needed to survive and pass on their suites of genes. Indeed, modern experimental removal of the (dopamine) receptor genes in animals causes them to reduce exploratory behaviour, a key variable related to inclusive fitness in animal biology.[5]

We are instinctually geared for individual survival—being both reward-driven, and curious. It was these two core traits that the father of economics himself, Adam Smith, predicted in *The Wealth of Nations* would be the drivers of world economic growth. According to Smith, uniting the twin economic engines of self-interest (which he termed self-love) and curiosity was ambition—"the competitive human drive for social betterment". About 70 years later, after reading Adam Smith's *Theory of Moral Sentiments,* Charles Darwin recognised the parallel between the pursuit of wealth in human societies and the competition for resources that occurred among animal species. Our market system of allocating resources and 'status' can therefore be seen as the natural social culmination for an intelligent species finding an abundance of resources.

But, as we shall soon see, the revered Scottish philosopher could not have envisioned heli-skiing, Starbucks, slot machines, Facebook, email and many other stimulating and pleasurable objects and activities that people engage in today and to which they so easily become accustomed.

The Mesolimbic Dopaminergic Reward System

Americans find prosperity almost everywhere, but not happiness. For them desire for well-being has become a restless burning passion which increases with satisfaction. To start with emigration was a necessity for them: now it is a sort of gamble, and they enjoy the sensations as much as the profit.

Alexis de Tocqueville, Democracy in America 1831

Traditional drug abuse happens because natural selection has shaped behaviour-regulation mechanisms that function via chemical transmitters in our brains.[6] Addicts can become habituated to the feelings they get from cocaine, heroin or alcohol, and they need to increase their consumption over time to get the same neurotransmitter highs. This same neural reward architecture is present in all of us when considering our ecological footprints: we become habituated via a positive feedback loop to the 'chemical sensations' we receive from shopping, keeping up with the Joneses (conspicuous consumption), pursuing more stock profits, and myriad other stimulating activities that a surplus of cheap energy has provided.

An explosion of neuroscience and brain-imaging research tells us that drugs of abuse activate the brain's dopamine reward system that regulates our ability to feel pleasure and be motivated for "more". When we have a great experience—a glance from a pretty girl, a lovemaking romp in the woods, a plate of fresh sushi, hitting 777 on a one-eyed bandit, catching a lunker pike, watching a sunset, hearing a great guitar riff etc.—our brain experiences a surge in the level of the neurotransmitter dopamine. We feel warm, 'in the zone' and happy. After a while, the extra dopamine gets flushed out of our system and we return to our baseline level. We go about our lives, looking forward to the next pleasurable experience. But the previous experience has been logged into our brain's limbic system, which, in addition to being a centre for pleasure and emotion, holds our memory and motivation circuitry.[7] We now begin to look forward to encores of such heady stimuli and are easily persuaded towards activities that promise such a chemical reprise. These desires have their beginnings outside our conscious awareness. Recent brain-imaging research shows that drug and sexual cues as brief as 33 milliseconds can activate the dopamine circuitry, even if a person is not conscious of the cues. Perhaps there are artistically shaped sexual images hidden in advertisements for whiskey after all. . . .

Historically, this entire system evolved from the biological imperative of survival. Food meant survival, sex meant survival (of genes or suites of genes), and additional stockpiles of both provided success relative to others, both within and between species. There was a discrete payoff to waiting hours for some movement in the brush that signaled 'food', or the sound of a particular bird that circled a tree with a beehive full of honey, etc. Our pattern recognition system on the Pleistocene would have been a grab-bag of various environmental stimuli that 'excited' our brains towards action that correlated with resources (typically food). In sum, the brain's reward pathways record both the actual experience of pleasure as well as ensuring that the behaviours that led to it are remembered and repeated. *Irrespective of whether they are 'good' for the organism in the current context—they 'feel' good, which is the mechanism our brain has left us as a heritage of natural selection.*

The (Very Important) Mechanism of Habituation

Habituation—getting used to something—and subsequent substance abuse and addiction develops because of the way we learn. Learning depends crucially on the discrepancy between the prediction and occurrence of a reward. A reward that is fully predicted does not contribute to learning.[8] The important

implication of this is that learning advances only to the extent to which something is unpredicted and slows progressively as a stimuli becomes more predictable.[9] *As such, unexpected reward is a core driver in how we learn, how we experience life, and how we consume resources.*

Dopamine activation has been linked with addictive, impulsive activity in numerous species. Dopamine is released within the brain not only to rewarding stimuli but also to those events that *predict* rewards. It has long been known that two groups of neurons, in the ventral tegmental and the substantia nigra pars compacta areas, and the dopamine they release, are critical for reinforcing certain kinds of behaviour. Neuroscientist Wolfram Schultz measured the activity of these dopamine neurons while thirsty monkeys waited for a tone which was followed by a squirt of fruit juice into their mouths. After a series of fixed, steady amounts of juice, the volume of juice was suddenly doubled. The rate of neuron firing went from about 3 per second to 80 per second. But after several trials, after the monkeys had become habituated to this new level of reward, their dopamine firing rate returned to the baseline rate of 3 firings per second after the squirt of juice. The monkeys had become habituated to the coming reward! The opposite happened when the reward was reduced without warning. The firing rate dropped dramatically, but eventually returned to the baseline rate of 3 firings per second.[10]

The first time we experience a drug or alcohol high, the amount of chemical we ingest often exceeds the levels of naturally occurring neurotransmitters in our bodies by an order of magnitude.[11] No matter how brief, that experience is stored in our neural homes for motivation and memory—the amygdala and hippocampus. Getting drunk with your friends, getting high on a ski-lift, removing the undergarments of a member of the opposite sex for the first time—all initially flood the brain with dopamine alongside a picture memory of the event chemically linked to the body's pleasurable response to it. As such we look forward to doing it again, not so much because we want to repeat the activity, but because we want to recreate that '*feeling*'.

But in a modern stimuli-laden culture, this process is easily hijacked. After each upward spike, dopamine levels again recede, eventually to below the baseline. The following spike doesn't go quite as high as the one before it. Over time, the rush becomes smaller, and the crash that follows becomes steeper. The brain has been fooled into thinking that achieving that high is equivalent to survival and therefore the 'consume' light remains on all the time. Eventually, the brain is forced to turn on a self-defence mechanism, reducing the production of dopamine altogether—thus weakening the pleasure circuits' intended function. At this point, an 'addicted' person is compelled to use the substance not to get high, but just to feel normal—since one's own body is producing little or no endogenous dopamine response. Such a person has reached a state of "anhedonia", or inability to feel pleasure via normal experiences. Being addicted also raises the risk of having depression; being depressed increases the risk of self-medicating, which then leads to addiction, etc. via positive feedback loops.

In sum, when exposed to novel stimuli, high levels of curiosity (dopamine) are generated, but it is the *unexpected reward* that causes their activation. If I order a fantastic array of sushi and the waiter brings me a toothpick and my check, I am going to have a plunge in dopamine levels which will create an immediate craving for food. It is this interplay between expected reward and reality that underlies much of our behavioural reactions. Ultimately, as it relates to resource consumption, repeated use of any dopamine-generating 'activity' eventually results in tolerance. Withdrawal results in lower levels of dopamine and continuous use is required to keep dopamine at normal levels, and even higher doses to get the 'high' levels of initial use. Consumers in rich nations are arguably reaching higher and higher levels of consumption tolerance. If there was such a thing as 'cultural anhedonia', we might be approaching it.

America and Addiction

It would be pretty hard to be addicted directly to oil; it's toxic, slimy and tastes really bad. But given the above background, we can see how it is possible to become addicted to the energy services that oil provides. Humans are naturally geared for individual survival—curious, reward-driven and self-absorbed—but modern technology has now become a vector for these cravings. Material wealth and the abundant choices available in contemporary US society are unique in human (or animal) experience; never before in the history of our species have so many enjoyed (used?) so much. Within a culture promoting 'more', it is no wonder we have so many addicts. High-density energy and human ingenuity have removed the natural constraints on our behaviour of distance, time, oceans and mountains. For now, these phenomena are largely confined to developed nations—people living in a hut in Botswana or a yurt in Mongolia cannot as easily be exposed to the 'hijacking stimuli' of an average westerner, especially one living in a big city in the West, like London or Los Angeles.

According to *Time Magazine,* July 2007,

- **2 million+** pathological gamblers
- **4 million+** addicted to food
- **15 million+** compulsive shoppers
- **16 million+** addicted to sex or pornography
- **19 million+** addicted to alcohol (7.7%)
- **3.6 million** addicted to illegal drugs
- **71.5 million** addicted to nicotine
- **80–90% of adults** routinely ingest caffeine
- **But USA only has 300 million people!!**

Many activities in an energy-rich society unintentionally target the difference between expected and unexpected reward. Take sportfishing for example. If my brother and I are on a lake fishing and we get a bite, it sends a surge of excitement through our bodies—what kind of fish is it? How big is it? etc. We land an 8-inch perch! Great! A minute later we catch another 8-inch perch—wow, there must be a school! After 45 minutes of catching nothing but 8-inch perch, our brain comes to expect this outcome, and we need something bigger, or a

different species, to generate the same level of excitement, so we will likely move to a different part of the lake in search of 'bigger' and/or 'different' fish. (Though my brother claims he would never tire of catching 8-inch perch I think he's exaggerating). Recreational fishing is benign (if not to the fish), but one can visualise other more resource-intensive pastimes activating similar circuitry. New shoes, new cars, new vacations, new home improvements, new girlfriends are all present on the modern unexpected reward smorgasbord.

The habituation process explains how some initially benign activities can morph into things more destructive. Weekly church bingo escalates to $50 blackjack tables; the *Sports Illustrated* swimsuit edition results, several years down the road, in the monthly delivery (in unmarked brown packaging) of *Jugs* magazine or webcams locked in on a bedroom in Eastern Europe; youthful rides on a rollercoaster evolve into annual heli-skiing trips, etc. The World Wide Web is especially capable of hijacking our neural reward pathways. The 24/7 ubiquity and nearly unlimited options for distraction on the internet almost seem to be perfectly designed to hone in on our brains' g-spot. Shopping, pornography, gambling, social networking, information searches, etc. easily out-compete the non-virtual, more mundane (and necessary) activities of yesteryear. Repetitive internet use can be highly addictive, though psychiatrists in different countries are debating whether it is a true addiction. For better or worse, the first things I do in the morning is a) check what time it is, b) start the coffee machine then c) check my e-mail, to see what 'novelty' might be in my inbox. Bills to pay, and e-mails from people who are not important or interesting, wait until later in the day, or are forgotten altogether.

There are few healthy men on the planet today who do not respond in social settings to the attention of a high-status, attractive 20- to 30-something woman. This is *salient* stimuli, irrespective of the man's marital status. But here is one example of where nature and nurture mesh. Despite the fact that 99%+ of our history was polygynous, modern culture precludes men from running around pell-mell chasing women; we have rules, laws, and institutions such as marriage. However, habituation to various matrimonial aspects combined with exposure to dozens or even hundreds of alternatives annually in the jet age may at least partially explain the 60%+ divorce rate in modern society.

The entire brain and behaviour story is far more complex than just one neurotransmitter but the pursuit of this particular 'substance' is clearly correlated with anxiety, obesity, and the general increasing of conspicuous consumption in our society. That dopamine is directly involved is pretty clear. Parkinson's Disease is a condition where dopamine is lacking in an area of the brain necessary for motor coordination. The drug, Mirapex, increases dopamine levels in that area of the brain, but since pills are not lasers, it also increases dopamine in other areas of the body, including (surprise) the reward pathways. There are numerous lawsuits currently pending by Parkinson's patients who after taking the drug, developed sex, gambling, shopping and overeating compulsions.[12]

Our brain can also be tricked by the food choices prevalent in an abundant-energy society. We evolved in situations where salt and sugar were rare and lacking and signaled nutrition. So now, when we taste Doritos or Ben and Jerry's Chocolate Fudge Brownie ice cream, our reward pathways say 'yes yes—this is good for you!!' Our 'rational' brain attempts to remind us of the science showing obesity comes from eating too much of the wrong type of foods, but often loses out to the desire of the moment. Fully 30% of Americans are now categorised as obese. And, since we are exporting our culture (via the global market system) to developing countries, it is no surprise that China is following in our footsteps. From 1991 to 2004 the percentage of adults who are overweight or obese in China increased from 12.9% to 27.3%.[13] Furthermore, we can become habituated to repeated presentation of the same food type; we quickly get tired of it and crave something different.[14] We like variety—in food and in other things. Finally, when we overstimulate the brain pleasure centres with highly palatable food, these systems adapt by decreasing their own activity. Many of us now require constant stimulation from palatable (fatty) food to avoid entering a persistent state of negative reward. It is this dynamic that has led scientists to recently declare that fatty foods such as cheesecake and bacon are addictive in the same manner as cocaine.[15] And as we shall see, both what we eat and experience not only alters our own health, but also makes it more difficult to act in environmentally benign ways.

Impulsivity, Discount Rates and Preparing for the Future

Overconsumption fueled by increasing neural high water marks is a problem enough in itself, but such widespread neural habituation also diminishes our ability to think and act about the coming societal transition away from fossil fuels. Economists measure how much we prefer the present over the future via something called a 'discount rate'. . . . A discount rate of 100% means we prefer the present completely and put no value on the future. A discount rate of 0% means we treat the future 1000 years from now equally the same as 5 minutes from now.

Certain types of people have steeper discount rates than others; in general, gamblers, drinkers, drug users, men (vs. women), low IQ scorers, risk-takers, those exhibiting cognitive load, etc. all tend to show more preference for small short-term rewards rather than waiting for larger, long-term ones.[16] On average, heroin addicts' discount rates are over double those of control groups. Furthermore, in tests measuring discount rates and preferences among opium addicts, opioid-dependent participants discounted delayed monetary rewards significantly more than did non-drug using controls. Also, the opioid-dependent participants discounted delayed opium significantly more than delayed money, more evidence that brain chemicals are central to an organism's behaviour and that money and other abstractions are secondary.[17] Research has also shown that subjects deprived of addictive substances have an even greater preference for immediate consumption over delayed gratification.[18]

Even if we are not snorting cocaine or binge drinking on a Tuesday night, in a world with so much choice and so many stimulating options vying for our attention, more and more of our time is taken up feeding neural compulsions. In any case,

facing large long-term risks like peak oil and climate change requires dedicated long-term thinking—so having neural wiring that, due to cultural stimuli, focuses more and more on the present instead, is a big problem.

The Fallacy of Reversibility a.k.a. "The Ratchet Effect"

Though our natural tendency is to want more of culturally condoned pursuits, many such desires do have negative feedbacks. For instance, I can only eat about three cheeseburgers before my stomach sends a signal to my brain that I am full—and at 4 or 5 my stomach and esophagus would fill to the level I couldn't physically eat another. However, this is not so with virtual wealth, or many of the "wanting" stimuli promoted in our economic 'more equals better' culture. Professor Juliet Schor of Boston University has demonstrated that irrespective of their baseline salary, Americans always say they'd like to make a little more the following year.[19] Similar research by UCLA economist Richard Easterlin (whose "Easterlin Paradox" points out that average happiness has remained constant over time despite sharp rises in GDP per capita.) followed a cohort of people over a 16-year period. The participants were asked at the onset to list 10 items that they desired (e.g. sports car, snowmobile, house, private jet, etc.) During the 16-year study, all age groups tested did acquire some/many of the things they originally desired. But in each case, their *desires increased more than their acquisitions*.[20] This phenomenon is termed the "Hedonic Treadmill". I believe this behaviour is at the heart of the Limits to Growth problem, and gives me less confidence that we are just going to collectively 'tighten our belts' when the events accompanying resource depletion get a little tougher. That is, unless we somehow change what it is that we want more of.

The Ratchet Effect is a term for a situation in which, once a certain level is reached, there is no going back, at least not all the way. In evolution the effect means once a suite of genes become ubiquitous in a population, there is no easy way to 'unevolve' it. A modern example of this is obesity—as we get fatter the body creates more lipocytes (cells composing adipose tissue). But this system doesn't work in reverse; even though we can lose some of the weight gain, the body can't eliminate these new cells—they are there to stay.

After peak oil/peak credit, the ratchet effect is likely to mean that any rules requiring a more equitable distribution of wealth will not be well received by those who amassed wealth and status when oil was abundant. In biology, we see that animals will expend more energy defending freshly gained territory than they would to gain it if it was unclaimed. In humans, the pain from losing money is greater than the pleasure of gaining it. Economists describe and quantify this phenomenon as the endowment effect and loss aversion. And, as an interesting but disturbing aside, recent research suggests that the dopamine that males receive during acts of aggression rivals that of food or sex.[20,21] All these different dynamics of 'what we have' and 'what we are used to' will come into play in a world with less resources available per head.

Old Brain, New Choices

Humans have always lived in the moment but our gradual habituation to substances and activities that hijack our reward system may be forcing us, in aggregate, to live so much for the present that we are ignoring the necessity for urgent societal change. Unwinding this cultural behaviour may prove difficult. The sensations we seek in the modern world are not only available and cheap, but most are legal, and the vast majority are actually condoned and promoted by our culture. If the rush we get from an accomplishment is tied to something that society rewards we call it ambition, if it is attached to something a little scary, then we label the individual a 'risk taker' and if it is tied to something illegal—only then have we become an 'addict' or substance abuser. So it seems culture has voted on which ways of engaging our evolutionarily derived neurotransmitter cocktails are 'good' to pursue.

Drug addiction is defined as *"the compulsive seeking and taking of a drug despite adverse consequences"*. If we substitute the word 'resource' for 'drug', have we meaningfully violated or changed this definition? That depends on the definition of 'drug'. *"A substance that a person chemically comes to rely upon"* is the standard definition but ultimately it is any activity or substance that generates brain chemicals that we come to require/need. Thus, it is not crude oil's intrinsic qualities we crave but the biochemical sensations to which we have become accustomed arising from the use of its embodied energy.

Take stock trading for example. Neuroscience scans show that stock trading lights up the same brain areas as picking nuts and berries do in other primates.

I think people trade for

1. money/profit (to compete/move up the mating ladder),
2. the feeling of being 'right' (whether they ever spend the money or not) and
3. the excitement/dopamine they get from the unexpected nature of the market puzzle.

While these three are not mutually exclusive, it is not clear to me which objective dominates, especially among people who have already attained infinite wealth. (Technically, infinite wealth is their annual expenses divided by the interest rate on Treasury bills. This gives the sum of money that would provide them with an income to buy all they want forever). When I worked for Lehman Brothers, my billionaire clients seemed less 'happy' on average than the $30k-a-year clerks processing their trades. They had more exciting lives perhaps, but they were not happier; that is, their reward baseline reset to zero each morning irrespective of the financial wealth they had amassed in previous days or years,. They wanted 'more' because they were habituated to getting more—it was how they kept score. Clearly, unless you inherit, you don't get to be a billionaire if you are easily satisfied.

MRI scans show that objects associated with wealth and social dominance activate reward-related brain areas. In one study, people's anterior cingulate (a brain region linked to reward) had more blood and oxygen response to visual cues of sports cars than to limousines or small cars.[22]

If compulsive shopping was a rational process, and our choices were influenced only by need, then brand-name t-shirts would sell no better than less expensive shirts of equal quality. The truth is that many shopping decisions are biased by corporate advertising campaigns or distorted by a desire to satisfy some competitive urge or emotional need. For most of us, the peak 'neurotransmitter cocktail' is the moment we decide to buy that new 'item'. After a brief euphoria and a short respite, the clock starts ticking on the next craving/purchase.

Adaptation Executors

There is a shared mythology in America that we can each enjoy fame and opulence at the top of the social pyramid. 78% of Americans still believe that anybody in America can become rich and live the good life.[23] Although in our economic system, not everyone can be a Warren Buffet or Richard Branson—there are not enough resources—it is the carrot of potential reward that keeps people working 50 hours a week until they retire at 65. All cannot be first. All cannot be wealthy, which makes our current version of capitalism, given the finite resources of the planet, not dissimilar from a Ponzi scheme.

Envy for status is a strong motivator. Increasing evidence in the fields of psychology and economics shows that above a minimum threshold of income/wealth, it's one's relative wealth that matters, not absolute. In an analysis of more than 80,000 observations, the relative rank of an individual's income predicted the individual's general life satisfaction whereas absolute income and reference income had little to no effect.[24] The "aspiration gap" is economic-speak for the relative fitness/status drive towards who/what is at the top of the cultural status hierarchy. For decades (centuries?), China has had a moderate aspiration gap, but since the turbo-capitalist global cues have spread across Asia, hundreds of millions of Chinese have raised their pecuniary wealth targets.

Economist Robert Frank asked people in the US if they would prefer living in a 4,000-square-foot house where all the neighboring houses were 6,000 square feet or a 3,000-square-foot house where the surrounding houses were 2,000 square feet. The majority of people chose the latter—*smaller in absolute terms but bigger in relative size.* A friend of mine says that when he last visited Madagascar, the 5th poorest nation on earth, the villagers huddled around the one TV in the village watching the nation's most popular TV show *Melrose Place,* giving them a window of desire into Hollywood glitz and glamour, and a beacon to dream about and strive for. Recently, a prince in the royal family of U.A.E. paid $14 million for a licence plate with the single numeral "1". "I bought it because I want to be the best in the world", Saeed Abdul Ghafour Khouri explained. What environmental cues do the kids watching TV in the U.A.E. or the U.S. receive?

As a species, we are both cooperative and competitive depending on the circumstances, but it's very important to understand that our neurophysiological scaffolding was assembled during long mundane periods of privation in the ancestral environment. This is still not integrated into the Standard Social Science Model that forms the basis of most liberal arts educations (and economic theory). A new academic study on relative income as a primary driver of life satisfaction had over 50 references, *none of which* linked to the biological literature on status, sexual selection or relative fitness. Furthermore, increasing cognitive neuroscience and evolutionary psychology research illustrates that we are not the self-interested 'utility maximisers' that economists claim, but are highly 'other regarding'—we care about other people's welfare as well as our own. Though high-perceived relative fitness is a powerful behavioural carrot, inequality has pernicious effects on societies; it erodes trust, increases anxiety and illness, and leads to excessive consumption.[25] Health steadily worsens as one descends the social ladder, even within the upper and middle classes.[26]

When a child is born, he has all the genetic material he will ever have. All his ancestors until that moment had their neural wiring shaped for fitness maximisation—but when he is born, his genes will interact with environment cues showing those ways to compete for status, respect, mating prospects, and resources etc. which are socially acceptable. From this point forward, the genes are 'fixed' and the infant goes through life as an '*adaptation executor*' NOT a fitness maximiser. What will a child born in the 21st century 'learn' to compete for? Historically, we have always pursued social status, though status has been measured in dramatically different ways throughout history. Currently, most people pursue money as a short-cut fitness marker, though some compete in other ways—politics, knowledge, etc. Thus, a large looming problem is that the Chinese and other rapidly developing nations don't just aspire to the wealth of average Americans—they want to go the whole hog to be millionaires.

Conclusions

We are a clever, ambitious species that evolved to live almost entirely off of solar flows. Eventually we worked out how to access stored sunlight in the form of fossil fuels which required very little energy/natural resource input to extract. The population and growth trajectory that ensued eventually oversatisfied the "more is better" mantra of evolution and we've now developed a habit of requiring more fossil fuels and more clever ways to use them every year. There also exists a pervasive belief that human ingenuity will create unlimited substitutes for finite natural resources like oil and water. Put simply, it is likely that our abundant natural resources are not only required, but will be taken for granted until they are gone.

This essay has explored some of the underlying drivers of resource depletion and planetary consumption: more humans competing for more stuff that has more novelty. The self-ambition and curiosity that Adam Smith hailed as the twin engines of economic growth have been quite effective over the past 200 years. But Adam Smith did caution in *Moral Sentiments* that human envy and a tendency toward compulsions, if left unchecked, would undermine the empathic social relationships that would be essential to the successful long-term operation of free markets. Amidst so much novel choice and pressure to create wealth, we are discovering some uncomfortable facts, backed up by modern neurobiology, that confirm his concerns.

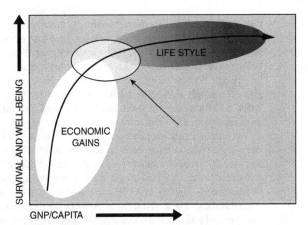

Meeting in the middle? The arrowed circle on this Inglehart Curve represents the highest level of well-being/survival consistent with a low level of resource use. It is therefore a target at which a society should aim.
Source: N. Hagens and R. Inglehart 1997

In an era of material affluence, when wants have not yet been fully constrained by limited resources, the evidence from our ongoing American experiment conclusively shows that humans have trouble setting limits on our instinctual cravings. What's more, our rational brains have quite a hard time acknowledging this uncomfortable but glaring fact.

This essay undoubtedly raises more questions than it answers. If we can be neurally hijacked, what does it suggest about television, advertising, media, etc? The majority of the neuro-economic sources I used in writing this were a *byproduct* of studies funded by neuromarketing research! How does 'rational utility' function in a society where we are being expertly marketed to pull our evolutionary triggers to funnel the money upwards? How does Pareto optimality—the assumption that all parties to an exchange will be made better off—hold up when considering neuro-economic findings? Recent studies show that American young people (between ages of 8–18) use 7.5 hours of electronic media (internet, Ipod, Wii, etc) per day and, thanks to multi-tasking, had a total of 11 hours 'gadget' exposure per day![27] The children with the highest hours of use had markedly poorer grades and more behavioural problems. How will these stimuli-habituated children adapt to a world of fewer resources?

Not all people pursue money, but our cultural system does. An unbridled pursuit of profits has created huge disparities in digitally amassed monetary wealth both within and between nations, thus holding a perpetually unattainable carrot in front of most of the world's population. So it is not just the amount we consume that is unsustainable, but also the message we send to others, internationally, nationally and in our neighbourhoods.

At the same time, traditional land, labour and capital inputs have been subsidised by the ubiquity of cheap energy inputs, and more recently by a large increase in both government and private debt, a spatial and temporal reallocator of resources. These cheap energy/cheap credit drivers will soon be a thing of the past, and this will curtail future global growth aspirations. When this happens, and we face the possibility of currency reform and what it might mean to start afresh with the same resources but a new basket of claims and assumptions, we will need to remember the neural backdrops of competition for relative status, and how people become habituated to high neural stimuli. Perhaps, given the supply-side limits and neural aspirations, some new goals can be attempted at lower absolute levels of consumption by at least partially lowering the amplitude of social rank.

We cannot easily change our penchant to want more. We can only change cultural cues on how we define the 'more' and thereby reduce resource use. In the cross-cultural study referenced in the diagram above, we can see that well-being increases only slightly as GNP increases above some minimum threshold. The arrowed circle would be a logical place for international policymakers concerned about planetary resource and sink capacity to aim to reach via taxes, disincentives to conspicuous consumption and subsidies. However, I fear that nations and governments will do little to slow their consumption and will get increasingly locked into defending the status quo instead.

In a society with significant overall surpluses, people who actively lower their own economic and ecological footprint might get by very well because their relative status—which is typically above average—allows them to make such reductions without reaching limits that compromise their well-being. As these people allocate time and resources away from financial marker capital and towards social, human, built and natural capital, they have an opportunity to redefine what sort of 'wealth' we compete for and thus potentially lead by example. However, personal experience with people in the lifestyle section of the chart leads me to believe that they will probably continue to pursue more resources and status even if it doesn't improve their well-being.

Put aside peak oil and climate change for the moment. Though it is difficult, we have it in us as individuals and as a culture to make small changes to the way our brains get 'hijacked' and, as a result, achieve more benign consequences. For example, we can choose to go for a jog/hike instead of sending ten emails and websurfing, we can choose to have a salad instead of a cheeseburger, we can choose to play a game or read a story with our children instead of making business phone calls. But most of these types of choices require both prior planning and discipline if our brains are not to fall into the neural grooves that modern culture has created. It takes conscious plans to change these behaviours, and for some this will be harder than for others But in choosing to do so, besides slowing and eventually reversing the societal stimulation feedback loop, we are likely to make ourselves healthier and happier. In neuro-speak, many of the answers facing a resource-constrained global society involve the rational neo-cortex suppressing and overriding the primitive and stronger limbic impulses.

So, ultimately, we must start to address new questions. In addition to asking source/sink questions like 'how much do we have' we should begin asking questions like 'how much is enough?' Reducing our addictive behaviours collectively will make it easier to face the situations likely to arise during an energy descent. Changing the environmental cues on what we

compete for, via taxes or new social values, will slow down resource throughput and give future policymakers time to forge a new economic system consistent with our evolutionary heritage and natural resource balance sheet. We will always seek status and have hierarchies in human society but unless we first understand and then integrate our various demand-side constraints into our policies, culture and institutions, sustainability will be another receding horizon. Though there is probably no blanket policy to solve our resource crisis that would both work and gain social approval, an understanding of the main points of this essay might be a springboard to improve one's own happiness and well-being. Which would be a start. . . .

Endnotes

1. news.nationalgeographic.com/news/2003/02/0214_030214_genghis.html.

2. Darwin, C. (1871) *The Descent of Man and Selection in Relation to Sex* John Murray, London.

3. Miller, G. F. (1999). "Sexual selection for cultural displays" in R. Dunbar, C. Knight, & C. Power (Eds.), *The evolution of culture.* Edinburgh U. Press, pp. 71–91.

4. Zahavi, A. and Zahavi, A. (1997). *The handicap principle: a missing piece of Darwin's puzzle.* Oxford University Press.

5. Dulawa et al., "Dopamine D4 Receptor-Knock-Out Mice Exhibit Reduced Exploration of Novel Stimuli", *Journal of NeuroScience,* 19:9550–9556, 1999.

6. Gerald, M. S. and Higley, J. D. (2002) "Evolutionary Underpinnings of Excessive Alcohol Consumption". *Addiction,* 97, 415–425.

7. Whybrow, Peter, "American Mania".

8. Waelti, P., Dickinson, A. and Schultz, W.: "Dopamine responses comply with basic assumptions of formal learning theory". *Nature* 412: 43–48, 2001.

9. Rescorla R.A., Wagner A.R., "A theory of Pavlovian conditioning: Variations in the effectiveness of reinforcement and nonreinforcement" in: *Classical Conditioning II: Current Research and Theory* (Eds Black A.H., Prokasy W.F.) New York: Appleton Century Crofts, pp. 64–99, 1972.

10. Schultz, W., et al., "A Neural Substrate of Prediction and Reward", *Science,* 275:1593–1599.

11. Dudley, R. (2002) "Fermenting Fruit and the Historical Ecology of Ethanol Ingestion: Is Alcoholism in Modern Humans an Evolutionary Hangover?" *Addiction,* 97, 381–388.

12. Dodd et al., "Pathological Gambling Caused by Drugs Used to Treat Parkinson Disease", *Arch Neurol.* 2005;62:1377–1381.

13. Popkin, Barry. "The World Is Fat", *Scientific American,* September, 2007, pp. 94. ISSN 0036-8733.

14. Ernst, M., Epstein, L. "Habituation of Responding for Food in Humans", *Appetite* Volume 38, Issue 3, June 2002, 224–234.

15. Johnson, P., Kenny, P., "Addiction-Like Reward Dysfunction and Compulsive Eating in Obese Rats: Role for Dopamine D2 Receptors", *Nature: Neuroscience* 3/28/2010.

16. Chablis et al., "Intertemporal Choice"—*The New Palgrave Dictionary of Economics,* 2007.

17. Madden et al., "Impulsive and Self-Control Choices in Opioid-Dependent Patients and Non-Drug Using Control Participants:

Drug and Monetary Rewards", *Environmental and Clinical Psychopharmacology* (1997), vol 5 no 3 256–262.

18. Giorodano, L et al., "Mild opioid deprivation increases the degree that opioid-dependent outpatients discount delayed heroin and money", *Psychopharmacology* (2002) 163: 174–182.

19. Schor, Juliet, *The Overspent American: Why We Want What We Don't Need,* Harper Perennial 1999.

20. Easterlin, Richard "Explaining Happiness" September 4, 2003, 10.1073/pnas.1633144100 (Especially Table 3).

21. Couppis, M., Kennedy C., "The rewarding effect of aggression", *Psychopharmacology,* Volume 197, Number 3 / April, 2008.

22. Erk, S, M Spitzer, A Wunderlich, L Galley, H Walter "Cultural objects modulate reward circuitry." *Neuroreport.* 2002 Dec 20;13 (18):2499–503 12499856.

23. Samuelson, Robert, "Ambition and it Enemies" *Newsweek* Aug 23, 1999.

24. Boyce, C., et al., **"Money and Happiness—Rank of Income, Not Income, Affects Life Satisfaction"**, *Psychological Science* Feb 2010.

25. Wilkinson, Richard; Pickett, Kate *"The Spirit Level—Why Greater Equality Makes Societies Stronger"*, Bloomsbury Press 2010.

26. Marmot, Michael, *"The Status Syndrome: How Social Standing Affects Our Health and Longevity"*, Holt Publishing 2005.

27. **Generation M2 – Media in the Lives of 8–18 Year Olds,** Kaiser Family Foundation 2010 According to *Time Magazine,* July 2007, From Ms., Summer 2007, pp. 41–45. Copyright © 2007 by Rebecca Clarren. Reprinted by permission of Ms. Magazine.

Critical Thinking

1. What role does status play in the human species? Is the achievement of status different for different people in different parts of the world?

2. How can the habitation process lead to destructive environmental behaviors?

3. How does an energy-abundant society contribute to over-consumption in their quest for status?

4. Summarize the basic psychological roots of resource over-consumption.

Article

Consumption and Consumerism

ANUP SHAH

Global inequality in consumption, while reducing, is still high.

Using latest figures available, in 2005, the wealthiest 20% of the world accounted for 76.6% of total private consumption. The poorest fifth just 1.5%.

Breaking that down slightly further, the poorest 10% accounted for just 0.5% and the wealthiest 10% accounted for 59% of all the consumption (Figure 1).

In 1995, the inequality in consumption was wider, but the United Nations also provided some eye-opening statistics (which do not appear available, yet, for the later years) worth noting here:

Today's consumption is undermining the environmental resource base. It is exacerbating inequalities. And the dynamics of the consumption-poverty-inequality-environment nexus are accelerating. If the trends continue without change—not redistributing from high-income to low-income consumers, not shifting from polluting to cleaner goods and production technologies, not promoting goods that empower poor producers, not shifting priority from consumption for conspicuous display to meeting basic needs—today's problems of consumption and human development will worsen. . . .

The real issue is not consumption itself but its patterns and effects. . . .

Inequalities in consumption are stark. Globally, the 20% of the world's people in the highest-income countries account for 86% of total private consumption expenditures—the poorest 20% a minuscule 1.3%. More specifically, the richest fifth:

- Consume 45% of all meat and fish, the poorest fifth 5%
- Consume 58% of total energy, the poorest fifth less than 4%
- Have 74% of all telephone lines, the poorest fifth 1.5%
- Consume 84% of all paper, the poorest fifth 1.1%
- Own 87% of the world's vehicle fleet, the poorest fifth less than 1%

Runaway growth in consumption in the past 50 years is putting strains on the environment never before seen.

— *Human Development Report 1998 Overview,*[1]
United Nations Development Programme (UNDP)
— *Emphasis Added. Figures quoted use data from 1995*

If they were available, it would likely be that the breakdowns shown for the 1995 figures will not be as wide in 2005. However, they are likely to still show wide inequalities in consumption. Furthermore, as a few developing countries continue to develop and help make the numbers show a narrowing gap, there are at least two further issues:

- Generalized figures hide extreme poverty and inequality of consumption on the whole (for example, between 1995 and 2005, the inequality in consumption for the poorest fifth of humanity has hardly changed)
- If emerging nations follow the same path as today's rich countries, their consumption patterns will also be damaging to the environment

And consider the following, reflecting world priorities:

Global Priority	$U.S. Billions
Cosmetics in the United States	8
Ice cream in Europe	11
Perfumes in Europe and the United States	12
Pet foods in Europe and the United States	17
Business entertainment in Japan	35
Cigarettes in Europe	50
Alcoholic drinks in Europe	105
Narcotics drugs in the world	400
Military spending in the world	780

And compare that to what was estimated as *additional* costs to achieve universal access to basic social services in all developing countries:

Global Priority	$U.S. Billions
Basic education for all	6
Water and sanitation for all	9
Reproductive health for all women	12

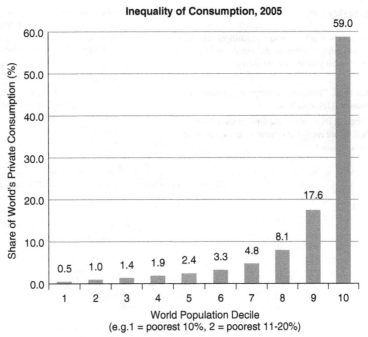

Inequality of Consumption, 2005

Source: World Bank Development Indicators 2008

"Over" population is usually blamed as the major cause of environmental degradation, but the above statistics strongly suggests otherwise. As we will see, consumption patterns today are not to meet everyone's needs. The system that drives these consumption patterns also contributes to inequality of consumption patterns too.

This section of the globalissues.org web site will attempt to provide an introductory look at various aspects of what we consume and how.

- We will see possible "hidden" costs of convenient items to society, the environment and individuals, as well as the relationship with various sociopolitical and economic effects on those who do consume, and those who are unable to consume as much (due to poverty and so on).
- We will look at how some luxuries were turned into necessities in order to increase profits.
- This section goes beyond the "don't buy this product" type of conclusion to the deeper issues and ramifications.
- We will see just a hint at how wasteful all this is on resources, society and capital. The roots of such disparities in consumption are inextricably linked to the roots of poverty. There is such enormous waste in the way we consume that an incredible amount of resources is wasted as well. Furthermore, the processes that lead to such disparities in unequal consumption

are themselves wasteful and is structured deep into the system itself. Economic efficiency is for making profits, not necessarily for social good (which is treated as a side effect). The waste in the economic system is, as a result, deep. Eliminating the causes of this type of waste are related to the elimination of poverty and bringing rights to all. Eliminating the waste also allows for further equitable consumption for all, as well as a decent standard of consumption.

- So these issues go beyond just consumption, and this section only begins to highlight the enormous waste in our economy which is not measured as such.
- A further bold conclusion is also made that elimination of so much wasted capital would actually require a reduction of people's workweek. This is because the elimination of such waste means entire industries are halved in size in some cases. So much labor redundancy cannot be tolerated, and hence the answer is therefore to share the remaining productive jobs, which means reducing the work week!
- We will see therefore, that political causes of poverty are very much related to political issues and roots of consumerism. Hence solutions to things like hunger, environmental degradation, poverty and other problems have many commonalities that would need to be addressed.

Critical Thinking

1. The report states: "The real issue is not consumption itself but its patterns and effects." Refer to the text world map, and sketch on the map what you see are the current "patterns" of consumption.

2. Explain the statement: "Today's consumption is undermining the environmental resource base."

3. What does this report imply about the current use of our fossil fuels? Will future energy alternatives be used as well to maintain consumption?

4. The report argues "There are important issues around consumerism that need to be understood." Select 3 issues and provide a brief answer for each. Try to center your answers around the concept of "environment."

5. Identify in this article three key terms, concepts, or principles that are used in your textbook (environmental science, economics, sociology, history, geography, etc.) or employed in the discipline you are currently studying. (Note: The terms, concepts, or principles may be implicit, explicit, implied, or inferred.)

From *Global Issues*, March 6, 2011. Copyright © 2011 by Anup Shah. Reprinted by permission. www.globalissues.org/issue/235/consumption-and-consumerism

Article

How Much Should a Person Consume?

RAMACHANDRA GUHA

This paper takes as its point of departure an old essay by John Kenneth Galbraith, an essay so ancient and obscure that it might very well have been forgotten even by its prolific author. The essay was written in 1958, the same year that Galbraith published *The Affluent Society,* a book that wryly anatomised the social consequences of the mass-consumption age.

In his book, Galbraith highlighted the "preoccupation with productivity and production" in postwar America and western Europe. The population in these societies had for the most part been adequately housed, clothed and fed; now they expressed a desire for "more elegant cars, more exotic food, more erotic clothing, more elaborate entertainment".[1] When Galbraith termed 1950s America the "affluent society", he meant not only that this was a society most of whose members were hugely prosperous when reckoned against other societies and other times, but also that this was a society so dedicated to affluence that the possession and consumption of material goods became the exclusive standard of individual and collective achievement. He quoted the anthropologist Geoffrey Gorer, who remarked that this was a culture in which "any device or regulation which interferes, or can be conceived as interfering, with [the] supply of more and better things is resisted with unreasoning horror, as the religious resist blasphemy, or the warlike pacifism".[2]

The Unasked Question

The essay I speak of was written months after the book, which made Galbraith's name and reputation. "How Much Should a Country Consume?" is its provocative title, and it can be read as a reflective footnote to *The Affluent Society.* In the book itself, Galbraith had noted the disjunction between "private affluence and public squalor", of how this single-minded pursuit of wealth had diverted attention and resources from the nurturing of true democracy, which he defined as the provision of public infrastructure, the creation of decent schools, parks and hospitals. Now the economist turned his attention, all too fleetingly, to the long-term and global consequences of this collective promotion of consumption, of the "gargantuan and growing appetite" for resources in contemporary America. The American conservation movement, he remarked, had certainly noted the massive exploitation of resources and materials in the postwar period. However, its response was to look for more efficient methods of extraction, or the substitution of one material for another through technological innovation. There was,

wrote Galbraith, a marked "selectivity in the conservationist's approach to materials consumption". For

> if we are concerned about our great appetite for materials, it is plausible to seek to increase the supply, or decrease waste, to make better use of the stocks that are available, and to develop substitutes. But what of the appetite itself? Surely this is the ultimate source of the problem. If it continues its geometric course, will it not one day have to be restrained? Yet in the literature of the resource problem this is the forbidden question. Over it hangs a nearly total silence. It is as though, in the discussion of the chance for avoiding automobile accidents, we agree not to make any mention of speed![3]

A cultural explanation for this silence had been previously provided by the great Berkeley geographer Carl Sauer. Writing in 1938, Sauer remarked that "the doctrine of a passing frontier of nature replaced by a permanent and sufficiently expanding frontier of technology is a contemporary and characteristic expression of occidental culture, itself a historical–geographical product". This frontier attitude, he went on, "has the recklessness of an optimism that has become habitual, but which is residual from the brave days when north European freebooters overran the world and put it under tribute". Warning that the surge of growth at the expense of nature would not last indefinitely, Sauer—speaking for his fellow Americans—noted wistfully that "we have not yet learned the difference between yield and loot. We do not like to be economic realists".[4]

Galbraith himself identified two major reasons for the silence as regards consumption. One was ideological, the worship of the great god Growth. The principle of Growth (always with a capital G) was a cardinal belief of the American people, which necessarily implied a continuous increase in the production of consumer goods. The second reason was political, the widespread scepticism about the state. For the America of the fifties had witnessed the "resurgence of a notably over-simplified view of economic life which [ascribed] a magical automatism to the price system". Now, Galbraith was himself an unreconstructed New Dealer, who would tackle the problem of overconsumption as he would tackle the problem of underemployment, that is, through purposive state intervention. At the time he wrote, however, free-market economics ruled, and "since consumption could not be discussed without raising the question of an increased role for the state, it was not discussed".[5]

Four years later, Rachel Carson published *Silent Spring,* and the modern American environmental movement gathered pace. One might have expected this new voice of civil society to undertake what the market could not. As it happened, consumption continued to be the great unasked question of the conservation movement. The movement principally focused on two things: the threats to human health posed by pollution, and the threats to wild species and wild habitats posed by economic expansion. The latter concern became, in fact, the defining motif of the movement. The dominance of wilderness protection in American environmentalism has promoted an essentially negativist agenda—the protection of the parks and their animals by freeing them of human habitation and productive activities. As the historian Samuel Hays points out, "natural environments, which formerly had been looked upon as 'useless', waiting only to be developed, now came to be thought of as 'useful' for filling human wants and needs. They played no less a significant role in the advanced consumer society than did such material goods as hi-fi sets or indoor gardens".[6] While saving these islands of biodiversity, environmentalists paid scant attention to what was happening outside them. In the American economy as a whole, the consumption of energy and materials continued to rise.

The growing popular interest in the wild and the beautiful thus not merely accepted the parameters of the affluent society but was wont to see nature itself as merely one more good to be consumed. The uncertain commitment of most nature lovers to a more comprehensive environmental ideology is illustrated by the paradox that they were willing to drive thousands of miles—consuming scarce oil and polluting the atmosphere—to visit national parks and sanctuaries, thus using anti-ecological means to marvel at the beauty of forests, swamps or mountains protected as specimens of a "pristine" and "untouched" nature.[7]

The Real Population Problem

The selectivity of the conservationist approach to consumption was underlined in the works of biologists obsessed with the "population problem". Influential American scientists such as Paul Ehrlich and Garret Hardin identified human population growth as the single most important reason for environmental degradation. This is how Ehrlich began the first chapter of his best-selling book, *The Population Bomb:*

> I have understood the population explosion intellectually for a long time. I came to understand it emotionally one stinking hot night in Delhi a couple of years ago. My wife and daughter and I were returning to our hotel in an ancient taxi. The seats were hopping with fleas. The only functional gear was third. As we crawled through the city, we entered a crowded slum area. The temperature was well over 100, and the air was a haze of dust and smoke. The streets seemed alive with people. People eating, people washing, people sleeping. People visiting, people arguing and screaming. People thrusting their hands through the taxi window, begging. People defecating and urinating. People clinging to buses. People herding animals. People, people, people, people.[8]

Here exploding numbers are blamed for increasing pollution, stinking hot air and even technological obsolescence (that ancient taxi!). During the 1970s and 80s, neo-Malthusian interpretations gained wide currency. Countries such as India and Bangladesh were commonly blamed for causing an environmental crisis. Not surprisingly, activists in these countries have been quick to take offence, pointing out that the West, and especially the United States, consumes, per capita as well as in the aggregate, a far greater proportion of the world's resources. Table 1 gives partial evidence of this. For apart from its overuse of nature's stock (which the table documents), the Western world has also placed an unbearable burden on nature's sink (which the table ignores). Thus, the atmosphere and the oceans can absorb about 13 billion metric tons of carbon dioxide annually. This absorptive capacity, if distributed fairly among all the people of the world, would give each human being the right to emit about 2.3 tons of carbon dioxide per year. At present, an American discharges in excess of 20 tons annually, a German 12 tons, a Japanese 9 tons, an Indian less than one ton. If one looks at the process historically the charges mount, for it is the industrialised countries, led by the United States, which have principally been responsible for the build-up of greenhouse gases over the past hundred years.

Table 1 US Share of World Consumption of Key Materials, 1995
(figures in millions of metric tons)

Material	World Production	US Consumption	US Consumption as Percentage of World Production
Minerals	7,641	2,410	31.54
Wood products	724	170	23.48
Metals	1,196	132	11.03
Synthetics	252	131	51.98
All materials	9,813	2,843	28.97

Source: Computed from *State of the World 1999* (New York: Worldwatch Institute and W. W. Norton, 1999).
Note: US population is approximately 4.42 percent of total world population.

These figures explain why Third World scholars and activists like to argue that the real "population problem" is in America, since the birth of a child there has an impact on the global environment equivalent to the birth of (say) seventy Indonesian or Indian children. There was a Bangladeshi diplomat who made this case whenever he could, in the United Nations and elsewhere. But after a visit to an American supermarket he was obliged to modify his argument—to state instead that the birth of an American dog (or cat) was the equivalent, ecologically speaking, of the birth of a dozen Bangladeshi children.[9]

As a long-time admirer of American scholarship, I might add my own words of complaint here. Consider the rich and growing academic field of environmental history, which is most highly developed in the United States. Scholars in other parts of the world have taken much inspiration from the works of American exemplars, from their methodological subtlety and fruitful crisscrossing of disciplinary boundaries. For all this, there is a studied insularity among the historians of North America. There were, at last count, more than three hundred professional environmental historians in the United States, and yet not one has seriously studied the global consequences of the consumer society, the impact on land, soil, forests, climate, etc., of the American Way of Life.

One striking example of this territorial blindness is the Gulf War. In that prescient essay of 1958, John Kenneth Galbraith remarked that "it remains a canon of modern diplomacy that any preoccupation with oil should be concealed by calling on our still ample reserves of sanctimony".[10] To be sure, there were Americans who tore the veil of this sanctimonious hypocrisy, who pointed out that it was the US government that had carefully armed and consolidated the dictator it now wished to overthrow. Yet the essentially material imperatives of the war remained unexamined. It was the left-wing British newspaper, the *Guardian,* which claimed that the Gulf War was carried out to safeguard the American Way of Driving. No American historian, however, has taken to heart the wisdom in that throwaway remark, to reveal in all its starkness the ecological imperialism of the world's sole superpower.

Germany's Greens

I would now like to contrast the American case with the German one. Environmentalists in Germany have been more forthright in their criticisms of the consumer society. "The key to a sustainable development model worldwide," writes Helmut Lippelt, "is the question of whether West European societies really are able to reconstruct their industrial systems in order to permit an ecologically and socially viable way of production and consumption." That Lippelt does not here include the United States or Japan is noteworthy, an expression of his (and his movement's) willingness to take the burden upon themselves. West Europeans should reform themselves, rather than transfer their existing "patterns of high production and high consumption to eastern Europe and the 'Third World' [and thus] destroy the earth".[11]

For the German greens, economic growth in Europe and North America has been made possible only through the economic and ecological exploitation of the Third World. Rudolf

Bahro is characteristically blunt: "The present way of life of the most industrially advanced nations," he remarked in 1984, "stands in a global and antagonistic contradiction to the natural conditions of human existence. We are eating up what other nations and future generations need to live on." From this perspective, indeed,

> The working class here [in the North] is the richest lower class in the world. And if I look at the problem from the point of view of the whole of humanity, not just from that of Europe, then I must say that the metropolitan working class is the worst exploiting class in history.... What made poverty bearable in eighteenth- or nineteenth-century Europe was the prospect of escaping it through exploitation of the periphery. But this is no longer a possibility, and continued industrialism in the Third World will mean poverty for whole generations and hunger for millions.[12]

Bahro was a famous "Fundi", a leader of that section of the German greens which stood in the most uncompromising antagonism to modern society. But even the most hardheaded members of the other, or "Realo", faction acknowledge the unsustainability, on the global plane, of industrial society. The parliamentarian (and now foreign minister) Joschka Fischer, asked by a reporter where he planned to spend his old age, replied: "In the Frankfurt cemetery, although by that time we may pose an environmental hazard with all the poisons, heavy metals and dioxin that we carry around in our bodies." Or as a party document more matter-of-factly put it: "The global spread of industrial economic policies and lifestyles is exhausting the basic ecological health of our planet faster than it can be replenished." This global view, coupled with the stress on accountability, calls for "far-reaching voluntary commitments to restraint by wealthy nations". The industrialised countries, which consume three-quarters of the world's energy and resources, and which contribute the lion's share of "climate-threatening gaseous emissions", must curb their voracious appetite while allowing Southern nations to grow out of poverty. The greens urge the cancellation of all international debt, the banning of trade in products that destroy vulnerable ecosystems, and most radical of all, the freer migration of peoples from poor countries to rich ones.[13]

These elements in the green programme were, of course, forged as an alternative to the policies promoted by the two dominant political parties in Germany, themselves committed to the great god Growth. Since October 1998, the greens find themselves sharing power at the federal level, junior partners, but partners nevertheless, in a coalition dominated by the Social Democrats. Being in power will certainly tame them. They will work only for incremental change, instead of the wholesale restructuring of the consumption and production system some of them previously advocated.

Gandhi

Fifty years before the founding of the German green party, and thirty years before the article by Galbraith alluded to above, an

Indian politician pointed to the unsustainability, at the global level, of the Western model of economic development. "God forbid," he wrote, "that India should ever take to industrialization after the manner of the West. The economic imperialism of a single tiny island kingdom (England) is today keeping the world in chains. If an entire nation of 300 million took to similar economic exploitation, it would strip the world bare like locusts."[14]

The man was Mahatma Gandhi, writing in the weekly journal *Young India* in December 1928. Two years earlier, Gandhi had claimed that to "make India like England and America is to find some other races and places of the earth for exploitation". As it appeared that the Western nations had already "divided all the known races outside Europe for exploitation and there are no new worlds to discover", he pointedly asked: "What can be the fate of India trying to ape the West?"[15]

Gandhi's critique of Western industrialisation has, of course, profound implications for the way we live and relate to the environment today. For him, "the distinguishing characteristic of modern civilisation is an indefinite multiplicity of wants," whereas ancient civilisations were marked by an "imperative restriction upon, and a strict regulating of, these wants".[16] In uncharacteristically intemperate tones, he spoke of his "wholeheartedly detest[ing] this mad desire to destroy distance and time, to increase animal appetites, and [to] go to the ends of the earth in search of their satisfaction. If modern civilization stands for all this, and I have understood it to do so, I call it satanic".[17]

At the level of the individual, Gandhi's code of voluntary simplicity also offered a sustainable alternative to modern lifestyles. One of his best-known aphorisms, that the "world has enough for everybody's need, but not enough for everybody's greed", is in effect an exquisitely phrased one-line environmental ethic. This was an ethic he himself practised, for resource recycling and the minimisation of wants were integral to his life.

Gandhi's arguments have been revived and elaborated by the present generation of Indian environmentalists. Their country is veritably an ecological disaster zone, marked by excessively high rates of deforestation, species loss, land degradation, and air and water pollution. The consequences of this wholesale abuse of nature have chiefly been borne by the poor in the countryside—the peasants, tribespeople, fisherfolk and pastoralists who have seen their resources snatched away or depleted by more powerful economic interests. For in the last few decades, the men who rule India have attempted precisely to "make India like England and America". Without the access to resources and markets enjoyed by those two nations when they began to industrialise, India has had perforce to rely on the exploitation of its own people and environment. The natural resources of the countryside have been increasingly channelled to meet the needs of the urban–industrial sector, the diversion of forests, water, etc., to the elite having accelerated environmental degradation even as it has deprived rural and tribal communities of their traditional rights of access and use. Meanwhile, the modern sector has moved aggressively into the remaining resource frontiers of India—the northeast and the Andaman and Nicobar

islands. This bias towards urban–industrial development has resulted only in a one-sided exploitation of the hinterland, thus proving Gandhi's contention that "the blood of the villages is the cement with which the edifice of the cities is built".[18]

The preceding paragraph brutally summarises arguments and evidence provided in a whole array of Indian environmentalist tracts.[19] Simplifying still further, one might say that the key contribution of the Indian environmental movement has been to point to inequalities of consumption *within* a society (or nation). In this respect they have complemented the work of their German counterparts, who have most effectively documented and criticised the inequalities of consumption *between* societies and nations.

Omnivores and Others

The criticisms of these environmentalists are strongly flavoured by morality, by the sheer injustice of one group or country consuming more than its fair share of the earth's resources, by the political imperative of restoring some sense of equality in global or national consumption. I now present an analytical framework that might more dispassionately explain these asymmetries in patterns of consumption.[20] Derived in the first instance from the Indian experience, this model rests on a fundamental opposition between two groups, *omnivores* and *ecosystem people*. These are distinguished above all by the size of their "resource catchment". Thus, omnivores, who include industrialists, rich farmers, state officials and the growing middle class based in the cities (estimated at in excess of one hundred million people), are able to draw upon the natural resources of the whole of India to maintain their lifestyles. Ecosystem people, on the other hand—who would include roughly two-thirds of the rural population, say about four hundred million people—rely for the most part on the resources of their own vicinity, from a catchment of a few dozen square miles at best. Such are the small and marginal farmers in rain-fed tracts, the landless labourers and also the heavily resource-dependent communities of hunter–gatherers, swidden agriculturists, animal herders and woodworking artisans, all stubborn pre-modern survivals in an increasingly postmodern landscape.

The process of development in independent India has been characterised by a basic asymmetry between omnivores and ecosystem people. A one-sentence definition of development, as it has unfolded over the last fifty years, would be: "Development is the channelling of an ever-increasing volume of natural resources, through the intervention of the state apparatus and at the cost of the state exchequer, to serve the interests of the rural and urban omnivores." Some central features of this process have been:

1. The concentration of political power/decision-making in the hands of omnivores.[21]
2. Hence the use of the state machinery to divert natural resources to islands of omnivore prosperity, especially through subsidies. Wood for paper mills, fertilisers for rich farmers, water and power for urban dwellers are all supplied by the state to omnivores at well below market prices.

3. The culture of subsidies has fostered an indifference among omnivores to the environmental degradation they cause, aided by their ability to pass on its costs to ecosystem people or to society at large.

4. Projects based on the capture of wood, water or minerals—such as eucalyptus plantations, large dams or opencast mining—have tended to dispossess the ecosystem people who previously enjoyed ready access to those resources. This has led to a rising tide of protests by the victims of development—Chipko, Narmada and dozens of other protests that we know collectively as the "Indian environmental movement".

5. But development has also *permanently* displaced large numbers of ecosytem people from their homes. Some twenty million Indians have been uprooted by steel mills, dams and the like; countless others have been forced to move to the cities in search of a legitimate livelihood denied to them in the countryside (sometimes as a direct consequence of environmental degradation).[22] Thus has been created a third class, of *ecological refugees,* living in slums and temporary shelters in the towns and cities of India.

This framework, which divides the Indian population into the three socio-ecological classes of omnivores, ecosystem people and ecological refugees, can help us understand why economic development since 1947 has destroyed nature while failing to remove poverty. The framework synthesises the insights of ecology with sociology, in that it distinguishes social classes by their respective resource catchments, by their cultures and styles of consumption, and also by their widely varying powers to influence state policy.

The framework is analytical as well as value-laden, descriptive and prescriptive. It helps us understand and interpret nature-based conflicts at various spatial levels: from the village community upwards through the district and region and on to the nation. Stemming from the study of the history of modern India, it might also throw light on the dynamics of socio-ecological change in other large developing "Third World" countries such as Brazil and Malaysia, where conflicts between omnivores and ecosystem people have also erupted and whose cities are likewise marked by a growing population of "ecological refugees". At a pinch, it might explain asymmetries and inequalities at the global level, too. More than a hundred years ago a famous German radical proclaimed, "Workers of the World, Unite!" But as another German radical[23] recently reminded this writer, the reality of our times is very nearly the reverse: the process of globalisation, whose motto might well be, "Omnivores of the World, Unite!"

Conflicting Fallacies

What, then, is the prospect for the future? Consider two well-known alternatives already prominent in the market place of ideas:

1. *The Fallacy of the Romantic Economist,* which states that everyone can become an omnivore if only we allow the market full play. That is the hope, and the illusion, of globalisation, which promises a universalisation of American styles of consumption. But this is nonsense, for although businessmen and economists resolutely refuse to recognise it, there are clear ecological limits to a global consumer society, to all Indians or Mexicans attaining the lifestyle of an average middle-class North American. Can there be a world with one billion cars, an India with two hundred million cars?

2. *The Fallacy of the Romantic Environmentalist,* which claims that ecosystem people want to remain ecosystem people. This is the anti-modern, anti-Western, anti-science position of some of India's best-known, neo-Gandhian environmentalists.[24] This position is also gaining currency among some sections of Western academia. Anthropologists in particular are almost falling over themselves in writing epitaphs for development, in works that seemingly dismiss the very prospect of directed social change in much of the Third World. It is implied that development is a nasty imposition on the innocent peasant and tribesperson who, left to themselves, would not willingly partake of Enlightenment rationality, modern technology or modern consumer goods.[25] This literature has become so abundant and so influential that it has even been anthologised, in a volume called (what else?) *The Post-Development Reader.*[26]

The editor of this volume is a retired Iranian diplomat now living in the south of France. The authors of those other demolitions of the development project mentioned in footnote 25 are, without exception, tenured professors at well-established American universities. I rather suspect that the objects of their sympathy would cheerfully exchange their own social position for that of their chroniclers. For it is equally a fallacy that ecosystem people want to remain as they are, that they do not want to enhance their own resource consumption, to get some of the benefits of science, development and modernity.

This point can be made more effectively by way of anecdote. Some years ago, a group of Indian scholars and activists gathered in the southern town of Manipal for a national meeting in commemoration of the 125th anniversary of the birth of Mahatma Gandhi. They spoke against the backdrop of a life-size portrait of Gandhi, depicting him clad in the loincloth he wore for the last thirty-three years of his life. Speaker after speaker invoked his mode of dress as symbolising the Mahatma's message. Why did we all not follow his example and give up everything, thus to mingle more definitively with the masses?

Then, on the last evening of the conference, the Dalit (low-caste) poet Devanur Mahadeva got up to speak. He read out a short poem in the Kannada language of southwest India, written not by him but by a Dalit woman of his acquaintance. The poem spoke reverentially of the great Untouchable leader B. R. Ambedkar (1889–1956) and especially of the dark blue suit that Ambedkar invariably wore in the last three decades of *his* life. Why did the Dalit lady focus on Ambedkar's suit, asked Mahadeva? Why, indeed, did the countless statues of Ambedkar put up in Dalit hamlets always have him clad in suit and tie? His answer was deceptively and eloquently simple: if Gandhi wears a loincloth, we all marvel at his *tyaga,* his sacrifice. The scantiness of dress is in this case a marker of what the man has given up. A high-caste, well-born, English-educated lawyer had voluntarily chosen to renounce power and position and live the life of an Indian peasant. That is why we memorialise that loincloth.

However, if Ambedkar had worn a loincloth, that would not occasion wonder or surprise. He is a Dalit, we would say—what else should he wear? Millions of his caste fellows wear nothing else. It is the fact that he has escaped this fate, that his extraordinary personal achievements (a law degree from Lincoln's Inn, a PhD from Columbia University, the drafting of the Constitution of India) have allowed him to escape the fate that society and history had allotted him, that is so effectively symbolised in that blue suit. Modernity, not tradition, development, not stagnation, are responsible for this inversion, for this successful and all-too infrequent storming of the upper-caste citadel.

A Blueprint for India

Let me now attempt to represent the story of Dr B. R. Ambedkar's suit in more material terms. Consider the simple hierarchies of fuel, housing and transportation set out in Table 2.

To move down any level of this table is to move towards a more reliable, more efficient, longer-lasting and generally safer mode of consumption. Why, then, would one abjure cheap and safe cooking fuel, for example, or quick and reliable transport, or stable houses that can outlive one monsoon? To prefer gas to dung for your stove, a car to a bullock-cart for your mobility, a wooden home to a straw hut for your family's shelter, is to choose greater comfort, wellbeing and freedom. These are choices that, despite specious talk of cultural difference, must be made available to all humans.

At the same time, to move down these levels is generally to move towards a more intensive and possibly unsustainable use of resources. Unsustainable at the global level, that is, for while a car admittedly expands freedom, there is no possibility whatsoever of every human on Earth being able to possess a car. As things stand, some people consume too much, while others consume far too little. It is these asymmetries that a responsible politics would seek to address. Confining ourselves to India, for instance, one would work to enhance the social power of ecological refugees and ecosystem people, their ability to govern their lives and to gain from the transformation of nature into artefact. This policy would simultaneously force omnivores to

internalise the costs of their profligate behaviour. A new, "left–green" development strategy would feature the following five central elements:

1. A move towards a genuinely participatory democracy, with a strengthening of the institutions of local governance (at village, town or district levels) mandated by the Constitution of India but aborted by successive central governments in New Delhi. The experience of the odd state, such as West Bengal and Karnataka, which has experimented successfully with the *panchayat* or self-government system suggests that local control is conducive to the successful management of forests, water, etc.

2. Creation of a process of natural resource use which is open, accessible and accountable. This would include a Freedom of Information Act, so that citizens are fully informed about the intentions of the state and better able to challenge or welcome them, thus making officials more responsive to their public.

3. The use of decentralisation to stop the widespread undervaluing of natural resources. The removal of subsidies and the putting of proper price tags will make resource use more efficient and less destructive of the environment.

4. The encouragement of a shift to private enterprise for producing goods and services, while ensuring that there are no hidden subsidies and that firms properly internalise externalities. There is at present an unfortunate distaste for the market among Indian radicals, whether Gandhian or Marxist. But one cannot turn one's back on the market; the task rather is to tame it. The people and environment of India have already paid an enormous price for allowing state monopolies in sectors such as steel, energy, transport and communications.

5. This kind of development can, however, succeed only if India is a far more equitable society than is the case at present. Three key ways of enhancing the social power of ecological refugees and ecosystem people (in all of which India has conspicuously failed) are land reform, literacy (especially female literacy) and proper health care. These measures would also help bring population growth under control. In the provision of health and education the state might be aided by the voluntary sector, paid for by communities out of public funds.

Remedying Global Inequalities

The charter of sustainable development outlined here[27] applies, of course, only to one country, albeit a large and representative one. Its *raison d'etre* is the persistent and grave inequalities of consumption within the nation. What, then, of inequalities of consumption between nations? This question has been authoritatively addressed in a recent study of the prospects for a "sustainable Germany" sponsored by the Wüppertal Institute for Climate and Ecology.[28] Its fundamental premise is that the

Table 2   Hierarchies of Resource Consumption

Fuel Used	Mode of Housing	Mode of Transport
Grass	Cave	Feet
Wood	Thatched hut	Bullock cart
Coal	Wooden house	Bicycle
Gas	Stone house	Motor scooter
Electricity	Cement house	Car

North lays excessive claim to the "environmental space" of the South. The way the global economy is currently structured,

> The North gains access to cheap raw materials and hinders access to markets for processed products from those countries; it imposes a system (World Trade Organisation) that favours the strong; it makes use of large areas of land in the South, tolerating soil degradation, damage to regional eco-systems, and disruption of local self-reliance; it exports toxic waste; it claims patent rights to utilisation of biodiversity in tropical regions, etc.[29]

Seen "against the backdrop of a divided world," says the report, "the excessive use of nature and its resources in the North is a principal block to greater justice in the world. . . . A retreat of the rich from overconsumption is thus a necessary first step towards allowing space for improvement of the lives of an increasing number of people." The problem thus identified, the report goes on to itemise, in meticulous detail, how Germany can take the lead in reorienting its economy and society towards a more sustainable path. It begins with an extended treatment of overconsumption, of the excessive use of the global commons by the West over the past two hundred years, of the terrestrial consequences of profligate lifestyles—soil erosion, forest depletion, biodiversity loss, air and water pollution. It then outlines a long-term plan for reducing the "throughput" of nature in the economy and cutting down on emissions. The report sets targets for substantial cuts by the year 2010 in the consumption of energy (at least 30 percent) and non-renewable raw materials (25 percent), and in the release of substances such as carbon dioxide (35 percent), sulphur dioxide (80–90 percent), synthetic nitrogen fertilisers (100 percent) and agricultural biocides (100 percent).

The policy and technical changes necessary to achieve these targets are identified as including the elimination of subsidies for chemical farming, the levying of ecological taxes (on gasoline, for example), the adoption of slower and fuel-efficient cars and the movement of goods by rail instead of road. Some examples of resource conservation in practice are given, such as the replacement of concrete girders by those made with steel, water conservation and recycling within the city, and a novel contract between the Munich municipal authorities and organic farmers in the countryside. By adopting such measures, Germany would transform itself from a nature-abusing to a nature-saving country.

The Wüppertal Institute study is notable for its mix of moral ends with material means, as well as its judicious blending of economic and technical options. More striking still has been its reception. The original German book sold forty thousand copies, an abbreviated version selling an additional hundred thousand copies. It was made into an award-winning television film and discussed by trade unions, political parties, consumer groups, scholars, church congregations and countless lay citizens. In several German towns and regions attempts have begun to put some of its proposals into practice.

Inequalities of consumption thus need to be addressed at both national and international levels. Indeed, the two are interconnected. The Spanish economist Juan Martinez-Alier provides one telling example. In the poorer countries of Asia and Africa, firewood and animal dung are often the only sources of cooking fuel. These are inefficient and polluting, and their collection involves mwuch drudgery. The provision of oil or liquefied petroleum gas for the cooking stoves of Somali or Nepalese peasant women would greatly improve the quality of their lives. This could easily be done, says Martinez-Alier, if the rich were very moderately taxed. He calculates that to replace the fuel used by the world's three thousand million poor people would require about two hundred million tons of oil a year. Now, this is only a quarter of the United States' annual consumption. But the bitter irony is that "oil at $15 a barrel is so cheap that it can be wasted by rich countries, but [is] too expensive to be used as domestic fuel by the poor". The solution is simple: oil consumption in the rich countries should be taxed, while the use of liquefied petroleum gas or kerosene for fuel in the poor countries should be subsidised.[30]

Allowing the poor to ascend just one rung up the hierarchies of resource consumption requires a very moderate sacrifice by the rich. In the present climate, however, any proposal with even the slightest hint of redistribution would be shot down as smacking of "socialism". But this might change, as conflicts over consumption begin to sharpen, as they assuredly shall. Within countries, access to water, land, and forest and mineral resources will be fiercely fought over by contending groups. Between countries, there will be bitter arguments about the "environmental space" occupied by the richer nations.[31] As these divisions become more manifest, the global replicability of Western styles of living will be more directly and persistently challenged. Sometime in the middle decades of the twenty-first century, Galbraith's great unasked question, "How Much Should a Country Consume?", with its corollary, "How Much Should a Person Consume?", will come, finally, to dominate intellectual and political debate.

Notes

1. John Kenneth Galbraith, *The Affluent Society* (London: Hamish Hamilton, 1958), pp. 109–10.

2. Ibid., p. 96.

3. John Kenneth Galbraith, "How Much Should a Country Consume?", in *Perspectives on Conservation,* ed. Henry Jarret (Baltimore: Johns Hopkins University Press, 1958), pp. 91–2.

4. Carl Sauer, "Theme of Plant and Animal Destruction in Economic History" (1938), in his *Land and Life* (Berkeley: University of California Press, 1963), p. 154.

5. Galbraith, "How Much Should a Country Consume?", p. 97.

6. Samuel Hays, "From Conservation to Environment: Environmental Politics in the United States since World War Two", *Environmental Review* 6, no. 1 (1982), p. 21.

7. For details, see my essays, "Radical American Environmentalism and Wilderness Preservation: A Third World Critique", *Environmental Ethics* 11, no. 1 (spring 1989), and "The Two Phases of American Environmentalism: A Critical History", in *Decolonizing Knowledge,* ed. Stephen A. Marglin and Frederique Apffel-Marglin (Oxford: Clarendon Press, 1996).

8. Paul R. Ehrlich, *The Population Bomb* (New York: Ballantine Books, 1968), p. 15.

9. See Satyajit Singh, "Environment, Class and State in India: A Perspective on Sustainable Irrigation" (PhD dissertation, Delhi University, 1994).

10. Galbraith, "How Much Should a Country Consume?", p. 90.

11. Helmut Lippelt, "Green Politics in Progress: Germany", *International Journal of Sociology and Social Policy* 12, nos. 4–7 (1992), p. 197.

12. Rudolf Bahro, *From Red to Green: Interviews with New Left Review* (London: Verso, 1984), p. 184.

13. This paragraph is based on Werner Hülsberg, *The German Greens: A Social and Political Profile* (London: Verso, 1988); but see also Margit Mayer and John Ely, eds., *Between Movement and Party: The Paradox of the German Greens* (Philadelphia: Temple University Press, 1997), and Saral Sarkar, "The Green Movement in West Germany", *Alternatives* 11, no. 2 (1986).

14. Mahatma Gandhi, "Discussion with a Capitalist", *Young India*, 20 December 1928, in the *Collected Works of Mahatma Gandhi* (hereafter *CWMG*) [New Delhi: Publications Division, n.d.], vol. 38, p. 243.

15. "The Same Old Argument", *Young India*, 7 October 1926 (*CWMG*, vol. 31, p. 478).

16. "Choice before Us", *Young India*, 2 June 1927 (*CWMG*, vol. 33, pp. 417–8).

17. "No and Yes", *Young India*, 17 March 1927 (*CWMG*, vol. 33, p. 163).

18. See *Harijan*, 23 June 1946.

19. See especially the two *Citizens Reports on the Indian Environment*, published in 1982 and 1985 by the New Delhi–based Centre for Science and Environment. See also the magisterial essay by the centre's director, Anil Agarwal, "Human–Nature Interactions in a Third World Country", *Environmentalist* 6, no. 3 (1986).

20. The following paragraphs expand and elaborate on some ideas first presented in Madhav Gadgil and Ramachandra Guha, *Ecology and Equity: The Use and Abuse of Nature in Contemporary India* (London: Routledge, 1995).

21. See Pranab Bardhan, *The Political Economy of India's Development* (Oxford: Clarendon Press, 1984).

22. See Eenakshi Ganguly-Thukral, ed., *Big Dams, Displaced People* (New Delhi: Sage Publishers, 1992).

23. The environmentalist and social critic Wolfgang Sachs.

24. See, for example, Ashis Nandy, ed., *Science, Hegemony and Violence: A Requiem for Modernity* (New Delhi: Oxford University Press, 1989); Vandana Shiva, *Staying Alive: Women, Ecology and Development* (London: Zed Books, 1989).

25. See, for example, Arturo Escobar, *Encountering Development: The Making and Unmaking of the Third World* (Princeton, N.J.: Princeton University Press, 1995); James Scott, *Seeing Like a State: How Certain Schemes to Improve the Human Condition Have Failed* (New Haven: Yale University Press, 1998); and especially Wolfgang Sachs, ed., *The Development Dictionary: A Guide to Knowledge as Power* (London: Zed Books, 1992).

26. Majid Rahnema, ed., *The Post-Development Reader* (London: Zed Books, 1998).

27. And elaborated in more detail in Gadgil and Guha, *Ecology and Equity*.

28. Wolfgang Sachs et al., *Greening the North: A Post-Industrial Blueprint for Ecology and Equity* (London: Zed Books, 1998), on which the rest of this section is based. See also F. Schmidt-Beek, ed., *Carnoules Declaration: Factor 10 Club* (Wüppertal: WIKUE, 1994), which sets the target of a 90 percent reduction in material use by the industrialised countries.

29. Sachs et al., *Greening the North*, p. 159.

30. See Martinez-Alier's essay, "Poverty and the Environment", in Ramachandra Guha and Juan Martinez-Alier, *Varieties of Environmentalism: Essays North and South* (London: Earthscan, 1997). See also Juan Martinez-Alier, *Ecological Economics: Energy, Environment, Society*, rev. ed. (London: Basil Blackwell, 1991).

31. In this connection, see Anil Agarwal and Sunita Narain, *Global Warming in an Unequal World: A Case of Environmental Colonialism?* (New Delhi: Centre for Science and Environment, 1992).

Critical Thinking

1. Describe some of the potential global consequences of the "consumer society."

2. What would be the global environmental consequences (potential) of both India and China "developing" the way the United States has?

3. With regard to patterns of consumption, what is the difference between "omnivores" and "ecosystem people"?

4. Explain the idea of "inequalities of consumption between nations."

5. What are some implications this article has for global development? For feeding humanity? For a thirsty planet? For our quest for energy? Pick one and discuss.

6. Identify in this article three key terms, concepts, or principles that are used in your textbook (environmental science, economics, sociology, history, geography, etc,) or employed in the discipline you are currently studying. (Note: The terms, concepts. or principles may be implicit, explicit, implied, or inferred.)

RAMACHANDRA GUHA is a historian and anthropologist who lives in Bangalore. His paper is the product of a research and writing grant from the John D. and Catherine T. MacArthur Foundation.

Article

Why Do We Over-Consume?

Darek Gondor

Jared Diamond famously stated that "the biggest problems facing the world today are not at all beyond our control, rather they are all of our own making, and entirely in our power to deal with" when talking about his book *Collapse: How Societies Choose to Fail or Succeed.*

But why have human ingenuity, technology, knowledge, and wealth grown step in step with unsustainability? If you compare the Human Development Index with resource use, we can see that as soon as countries meet the development standard of "high human development" they inevitably cross the line of unsustainability.

Opponents of this view will say that human well-being has on average increased in the world. However, while this is true, the indicators for species extinctions, habitat loss, greenhouse gas emissions and resource depletion have all been negative for a prolonged period of time.

Personal consumption data is even more telling. When the richest 10% account for 60% of all private consumption, we have to ask ourselves if these top-tier consumers could possibly improve their well-being any further through material gains?

Back to Our Pre-Modern Roots

Researchers like E.O. Wilson explain this paradox with a theory rarely incorporated into decisions—evolution.

The characteristics of human behaviour that became fixed in our population through natural selection occurred over the 95% of our pre-modern existence where we lived in sparsely populated hunter-gatherer bands with local community connections. Then the resource problem was one of local access.

Early human societies had primitive and inefficient ways of collecting resources, so those that thrived were ones that developed high rates of consumption and new innovations for resource gathering. They also had built up strong identity with their own community and competitiveness with others, and short-term thinking (discounting the future).

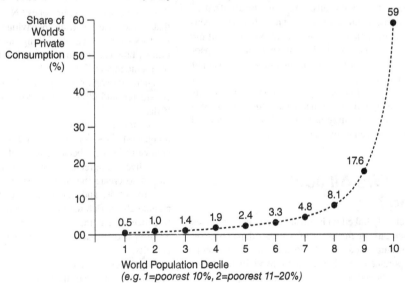

Inequality of Consumption, 2005

Share of World's Private Consumption (%)

World Population Decile
(e.g. 1=poorest 10%, 2=poorest 11–20%)

Source: World Bank Development Indicators 2008

Why Do We Always Need More Stuff?

Those characteristics endure today, in concrete but perhaps increasingly extraneous ways.

One of the basic human needs is food: the accumulation of which, along with other resources, is directly linked to the ability to reproduce and provide for a family. In pre-agricultural times, it was unlikely that a single family or tribe could gather enough food to make any further consumption undesirable, so there was little need for the evolution of a trait to limit consumption.

The second greatest human need was to secure a partner for reproduction. Unsurprisingly, it seems that those that could secure more resources through their hunting skills or status also had the best choice of mates. Research shows that women in all cultures, more than men, prefer partners with higher social status and that flaunting what you've got helps to seal the deal, so to speak.

Acquiring enough resources is not the end of it. Status is a comparative mark (dependent on one's immediate peers), and relates to competition. Often cited research by the likes of J.F. Helliwell shows that happiness levels peak at an income level of $10,000 per year in the US, after which happiness is determined by one's relative affluence.

That most of us want to earn more is therefore very well explained by sexual selection: the process of choosing a sexual partner. Some individual male birds—a species whose mating relationships most resemble humans—will spend a great deal of energy building elaborate, colourful and useless displays on the forest floor to attract females. But in doing so they signal to the female counterpart that they get along just fine nonetheless: a sign of a healthy, capable individual.

Researchers think that people buy yachts, numerous cars and expensive jewelry in the same way. This over-consumption pattern just gets more intense as we move up the social ladder, and seems to have little to do with satisfying living needs. That is, when we become successful enough to own yachts and expensive cars, the absolute amount of possessions does not dull the drive to consume—because we tend to hang out with other people who own yachts and expensive cars and they put a damper on our relative status.

Today, advertising and marketing professionals exploit this drive, as they do many traits of human nature, to keep the consumption train going. This may in part explain the continued wealth disparities between individuals.

Why Can't We All Just Get Along?

Competition is closely linked with consumption, as it produces social hierarchies among members of a group depending on their ability to secure resources. The idea of "us" and "them" was a very important one when humans lived in territorial bands and formed allegiances against common enemies.

Membership in a group provided security against aggression from other groups and means to cooperate. Internally, there was still a hierarchy that enabled the strong to control relationships and resources.

From the perspective of evolutionary fitness, the strongest individual had the opportunity to pass along the most genes, while receiving the protection of the group. Since evolutionary pressures act on individuals, competition and consumption do not have a shut-off point when the survival of the species is at stake, and there are many examples of human societies (think Easter Island) that likely competed themselves to extinction.

Today, we can look at political divisions to see how competing loyalties and different identities stall our efforts at cooperation. One reason why the United Nations organisation could not unanimously interfere in acts deplored by members (like genocide in Sudan or Rwanda) is that it is a collection of leaders whose allegiances lie elsewhere, such as with their in-group that provides security and shares commonalities like language, religion or culture.

In federal states like Canada, the national government has little power to enforce national policies in Alberta, where oil sand development is provincial jurisdiction, even though it may impact aboriginal communities falling under national protection. There inter-provincial and intergovernmental competition is a defining feature of that country's politics.

Is it any wonder we are just now beginning to attempt to halt carbon dioxide emissions, nearly 20 years after the need was demonstrated? How will any deal reached at COP15 in Copenhagen be implemented in countries with competing subnational identities?

With new global problems like poverty, climate change and biodiversity loss, we are now being asked to be global citizens, and care about those we have never met, and areas we will never visit. This runs counter to our evolutionary past.

Evolution of Culture and Ideas

But are we slaves to our genes? No serious biologist believes that is the case regarding behaviour, we simply have genetic predispositions to do some things and not others. So the question is: how can we put our ingrained traits to benefit, or even overcome them?

There are certainly ways that human characteristics can be considered and utilised in working towards sustainable future paths.

The melting Antarctic ice sheet—no matter how bleak the images on TV—does not seem able to provoke wide enough behaviour change, because most of us can all go back to our daily lives, unaffected. Our individual interests have to be tapped to create the political support for implementing progressive ideas, and one way to do this is with money. The recent call for rich nations to put up at least $10 billion a year to entice developing countries into an agreement at COP15 is a starter because dollars can easily be mentally translated into benefits.

Regulation can also be swallowed more easily with the aid of self-interest—like the very recent EPA announcement that GHGs are health dangers, clearing the way for laws restricting their release.

Other ways of playing to individual interests is through reputation—rewarding and shaming. Or by setting an extreme baseline for policy and then intermittently moving it back. For example, like closing the tuna fishery and then opening it back up slowly. Expectations for improvement from an undesirable baseline can be more acceptable than an unsustainable benefit with dire future predictions.

Another manner of influencing behaviour is perhaps the most obvious. Environmental education for the world's children, that builds on human-nature relationships, is indispensible to nurturing an identity that recognises the intrinsic value of nature and equality of cultures.

Such education is bound to pay off. We often point to that which makes humans unique—our language, intelligence, art and culture—as the root of cultural evolution. In other words, the development and passing down of ideas and values by societies that have lots of spare time after they have met their livelihood needs.

There is evidence that shows we increasingly live for ourselves, forego reproduction, enjoy life past reproductive age (thanks to the evolution of menopause), turn to cooperation over conflict, and choose partners based on humour and personality—traits that may not be indicators of reproductive success and survival.

Cultural evolution is quicker and can be more powerful than our ingrained instincts. Our modern environment has changed from locally centered to global, and biologically we have not caught up. Our ideas have to make up the difference.

Critical Thinking

1. How can the richest 10 percent possibly improve their well-being any further through material gain?

2. Why do we always need so much stuff? Why do you personally? Do all humans all over the world have the same desire to accumulate material wealth?

3. How long can we maintain this level of overconsumption as more and more countries become "middle class"?

4. How can education change a culture of overconsumption?

Unit 3

UNIT

Prepared by: Richard Eathorne, *Northern Michigan University*

Eating at the Whole Earth Café: The Daily Environmental Specials

The insufferable arrogance of human beings to think that Nature was made solely for their profit, as if it was conceivable that the sun had been set afire merely to ripen men's apples and head their cabbages.

Savinien deCryano de Bergerac, *États etempires de la lune*, 1656

Global population growth and changing consumption demands for Earth's resources over the last century are putting increasing strains on the planet's ability to provide for the needs, and desires, of the human species. Our consumption patterns of food, water, energy, and land are changing from the patterns of our early ancestors. The use of Earth's resources is moving from need to desire, functionality to fashion. As societies transition from rural agrarian to urban industrial, lifestyles transition as well. These new lifestyles bring with them new needs, and more importantly, they bring the luxury of new desires. These new lifestyles also increase the physical, social, and psychological distance between people and the earth's resources they consume. This combination of desire and distance are changing more and more of humanity's relationship to the earth. It is a relationship plagued with growing unfamiliarity, unawareness, and underappreciation of the planetary ecosystems that humbly provide for our needs and desires.

But alas, we must consume the earth to survive, and some of our most basic consumption needs are food, water, energy, land, and functioning ecosystems. One of our most fundamental needs, food, has experienced monumental pattern changes in the last several decades. Changing human lifestyles, energy, geopolitics, future trends in demand, and availability are presenting a cornucopia of 21st-century sustainability challenges. Consumption as a social process and consumerism as a social reality are contributing substantially to our food problems. For example, the global lifestyle changes are resulting in clustered worlds of energy use and food consumption. A growing global middle class consumes more meat every year. The problem is that meat production demands so many resources and results in so many environmental negative externalities.

The possibility of the changing consumption geopolitics of food supply and scarcity and how it may create a new food economy is fast approaching. This new food economy and future trends in food demand, availability, and consumption may lead to global political instability and increasing environmental pressures.

And we can't speak of food without speaking also of water. Water may become a crisis of such magnitude that unless we begin to address it now, the food debate may become a moot point, and attending to global conflict resulting from fresh water scarcity and changing geographic patterns of fresh water access will be the order of the day. Unlike food, fresh water provides for a myriad of human–Earth ecosystems needs. If water were simply called upon to slake our thirst (thus meeting our requisite biological functions) as food is essentially called upon to fill our bellies and provide for cellular respiration (giving us the energy needed to consume the earth), our freshwater issue may be simpler. Like food, the themes of the freshwater issue remain consistent: consumption, availability, access, use, and resource competition.

We will have to not only focus on managing freshwater sustainability, but on establishing a true value for it as well. Data is available that suggests that water can be ascribed a market value against which more sustainable consumption decisions and policies can be made. Without better understanding and appreciation of the linkages between access to and availability of fresh water, such a valuation can lead to inappropriate pricing and denied access. Our illusions of abundant water, likewise, contribute toward the tendency to undervalue it. Also, the "water footprints" of countries (i.e., the volume of water needed for the production of goods and services consumed by a nation's people) will increasing become part of the geopolitical discourse on water.

Finally, the complex "environmental science" linkages between the earth's hydrological cycle, climate change, fresh water availability, agriculture, politics, and conflict will have to be addressed. For example, glacial shrinkage and changing global precipitation patterns may become a very serious geopolitical issue. While places like the United States, Europe, and Latin America may not currently depend on glaciers for their water, other place likes India, China, and Pakistan do. And to make matters worse, these regions also have population growth stresses, which mean higher demands for food, resulting in an increasing demand for water. Locate this situation in an already contentious sociopolitical arena, and the majesty of glaciers takes on a whole new meaning.

Along with food and water, we consume copious amounts of nonrenewable energy. Our most current energy infatuation is fracking. Investors are now viewing shale gas extraction as an energy paradigm-shifting innovation. But according to critics, what we are really doing is literally shattering the bedrock of our nations and pumping it full of carcinogens in order to bring methane out of the earth. Such criticism suggests that we have hardly scratched the surface regarding our understanding of fracking's environmental and human health costs.

Humans also consume land, but first it must be transformed. And human transformation of the land has been taking place for millennia, to the point where studies indicate that now nearly 83 percent of the planet's ice-free land surface is influenced by humans in some way or another. Our two most popular kinds of transformation are urbanization and agriculture, and demand for these two "products" of our transformation is growing each year. We now have half the world's population living in cities, and over the next 25 years we will see another 1 million square kilometers of land transformed into urban space. The demands for agricultural land are rising as well. The paradox is that the land we need for agriculture is typically the land most prized for urban sprawl. This paradox,

however, has not gone unrecognized. Rich countries are now realizing the need for agricultural land and are buying up the agricultural rights to millions of hectares, mostly in developing countries.

Lastly, we need to consider our consumption needs and their impact on the lifeblood of the planet—its ecosystems. Ecosystems have contributed to our making substantial gains in human well-being and socioeconomic development, but gains have not come without their costs. When did humans begin consuming ecosystems—ecophagy? Scholars believe it was the period following modern agriculturalization and industrialization. They refer to this period as the "anthropocene," when humans finally became a global geoenvironmental force. The earth was being tamed and transformed for even more explosive growth of the human population. To meet the growing demands from these revolutions and population growth, we needed more products of the earth's ecosystems: food, fresh water, timber, fiber, minerals, ores, and fuel. Earth was consumed at faster and faster rates, and humanity spread into more and more ecosystems and biomes.

To survive as a species, we need food, water, energy, and the services of earth's ecosystem. But more importantly, we will have to redesign antiquated, unsustainable consumption habits into the kinds of nonlinear, sustainable home-cooked food webs that nature spent millions of years perfecting.

Article   Prepared by: Richard Eathorne, *Northern Michigan University*

2013 World Hunger and Poverty Facts and Statistics

WORLD HUNGER EDUCATION SERVICE

Learning Outcomes

After reading this article, you will be able to:

- Define hunger, world hunger, and protein-energy malnutrition.
- Describe the principal causes of hunger.
- Assess our ability to produce enough food for everyone.

Hunger Concepts and Definitions

Hunger is a term which has three meanings (Oxford English Dictionary 1971)

- the uneasy or painful sensation caused by want of food; craving appetite. Also the exhausted condition caused by want of food
- the want or scarcity of food in a country
- a strong desire or craving

World hunger refers to the second definition, aggregated to the world level. The related technical term (in this case operationalized in medicine) is either malnutrition, or, if malnutrition is taken to refer to both undernutrition and overnutrition, undernutrition. Both malnutrition and undernutrition refer to not having enough food.

Malnutrition (or undernutrition) is a general term that indicates a lack of some or all nutritional elements necessary for human health (Medline Plus Medical Encyclopedia).

There are two basic types of malnutrition. The first and most important is protein-energy malnutrition (PEM). It is basically a lack of calories and protein. Food is converted into energy by humans, and the energy contained in food is measured by calories. Protein is necessary for key body functions including provision of essential amino acids and development and maintenance of muscles. This is the most lethal form of malnutrition/hunger and is the type of malnutrition that is referred to when world hunger is discussed.

The second type of malnutrition, also very important, is micronutrient (vitamin and mineral) deficiency. This is not the type of malnutrition that is referred to when world hunger is discussed, though it is certainly very important.

Number of Hungry People in the World

The United Nations Food and Agriculture Organization (FAO) estimates that nearly 870 million people, or one in eight people in the world, were suffering from chronic undernourishment in 2010–2012. Almost all the hungry people, 852 million, live in developing countries, representing 15 percent of the population of developing countries. There are 16 million people undernourished in developed countries (FAO 2012).

The number of undernourished people decreased nearly 30 percent in Asia and the Pacific, from 739 million to 563 million, largely due to socio-economic progress in many countries in the region. The prevalence of undernourishment in the region decreased from 23.7 percent to 13.9 percent.

Latin America and the Caribbean also made progress, falling from 65 million hungry in 1990–1992 to 49 million in 2010–2012, while the prevalence of undernourishment dipped from 14.6 percent to 8.3 percent. But the rate of progress has slowed recently.

The number of hungry grew in Africa over the period, from 175 million to 239 million, with nearly 20 million added in the last few years. Nearly one in four are hungry. And in sub-Saharan Africa, the modest progress achieved in recent years up to 2007 was reversed, with hunger rising 2 percent per year since then.

Developed regions also saw the number of hungry rise, from 13 million in 2004–2006 to 16 million in 2010–2012, reversing a steady decrease in previous years from 20 million in 1990–1992 (FAO 2012).

The above is based on the new estimates of world hunger by the FAO using revised procedures. It is worth noting that the new estimates give a different answer than the old estimates (Lappe, 2013).

Children and Hunger

Children are the most visible victims of undernutrition. Children who are poorly nourished suffer up to 160 days of illness each year. Poor nutrition plays a role in at least half of the 10.9 million child deaths each year—five million deaths. Undernutrition magnifies the effect of every disease, including measles and malaria. The estimated proportions of deaths in which undernutrition is an underlying cause are roughly similar for diarrhea (61%), malaria (57%), pneumonia (52%), and measles (45%) (Black 2003, Bryce 2005). Malnutrition can also be caused by diseases, such as the diseases that cause diarrhea, by reducing the body's ability to convert food into usable nutrients.

According to the most recent estimate that Hunger Notes could find, malnutrition, as measured by stunting, affects 32.5 percent of children in developing countries—one of three (de Onis 2000). Geographically, more than 70 percent of malnourished children live in Asia, 26 percent in Africa and 4 percent in Latin America and the Caribbean. In many cases, their plight began even before birth with a malnourished mother. Undernutrition among pregnant women in developing countries leads to 1 out of 6 infants born with low birth weight. This is not only a risk factor for neonatal deaths, but also causes learning disabilities, mental retardation, poor health, blindness, and premature death.

Does the World Produce Enough Food to Feed Everyone?

The world produces enough food to feed everyone. World agriculture produces 17 percent more calories per person today than it did 30 years ago, despite a 70 percent population increase. This is enough to provide everyone in the world with at least 2,720 kilocalories (kcal) per person per day according to the most recent estimate that we could find (FAO 2002, p. 9). The principal problem is that many people in the world do not have sufficient land to grow, or income to purchase, enough food.

What Are the Causes of Hunger?

What are the causes of hunger is a fundamental question, with varied answers.

Poverty is the principal cause of hunger. The causes of poverty include poor people's lack of resources, an extremely unequal income distribution in the world and within specific countries, conflict, and hunger itself. As of 2008 (2005 statistics), the World Bank has estimated that there were an estimated 1,345 million poor people in developing countries who live on $1.25 a day or less.[1] This compares to the later FAO estimate of 1.02 billion undernourished people. Extreme poverty remains an alarming problem in the world's developing regions, despite some progress that reduced "dollar—now $1.25—a day" poverty from (an estimated) 1,900 million people in 1981, a reduction of 29 percent over the period. Progress in poverty reduction has been concentrated in Asia, and especially, East Asia, with the major improvement occurring in China. In Sub-Saharan Africa, the number of people in extreme poverty has increased.

The statement that 'poverty is the principal cause of hunger' is, though correct, unsatisfying. Why then are (so many) people poor? The next section summarizes Hunger Notes answer.

Harmful Economic Systems Are the Principal Cause of Poverty and Hunger

Hunger Notes believes that the principal underlying cause of poverty and hunger is the ordinary operation of the economic and political systems in the world. Essentially, control over resources and income is based on military, political, and economic power that typically ends up in the hands of a minority, who live well, while those at the bottom barely survive, if they do. We have described the operation of this system in more detail in our special section on harmful economic systems.

Conflict as a Cause of Hunger and Poverty

At the end of 2005, the global number of refugees was at its lowest level in almost a quarter of a century. Despite some large-scale repatriation movements, the last three years have witnessed a significant increase in refugee numbers, due primarily to the violence taking place in Iraq and Somalia. By the end of 2008, the total number of refugees under UNHCR's mandate exceeded 10 million. The number of conflict-induced internally displaced persons (IDPs) reached some 26 million worldwide at the end of the year. Providing exact figures on the number of stateless people is extremely difficult But, important, (relatively) visible though it is, and anguishing for those involved conflict is less important as poverty (and its causes) as a cause of hunger. (Using the statistics above 1.02 billion people suffer from chronic hunger while 36 million people are displaced [UNHCR 2008].)

Hunger Is Also a Cause of Poverty, and Thus of Hunger

By causing poor health, low levels of energy, and even mental impairment, hunger can lead to even greater poverty by reducing people's ability to work and learn, thus leading to even greater hunger.

Climate Change

Climate change is increasingly viewed as a current and future cause of hunger and poverty. Increasing drought, flooding, and changing climatic patterns requiring a shift in crops and farming practices that may not be easily accomplished are three key issues.

Progress in Reducing the Number of Hungry People

There are two sets of issues that must be considered in evaluating progress: estimations of hunger and goals set.

Estimations of hunger. As indicated above, the two FAO estimations differ. Specifically, since 1992, the earlier estimate has hunger going up, while the later has hunger going down.

Secondly, how do you evaluate progress—what goals have been set?

The target set at the 1996 World Food Summit was to halve the number of undernourished people by 2015 from their number in 1990–1992. The target set by the Millenium goals was to halve the proportion of hungry people by 2015.

World Food Summit target. The target set at the 1996 World Food Summit was to halve the number of undernourished people by 2015 from their number in 1990–1992. (FAO uses three year averages in its calculation of undernourished people.)

Progress using the old estimate of world hunger. The number of undernourished people in developing countries using the old estimate was 824 million in 1990–1992. In 2010–2012, the number had increased to 870 million people. So rather than being cut in half to 420, the number has increased to 870 million.

Using the new estimates of world hunger, the number of undernourished people was 1 billion in 1990–1992 and had decreased to 870 in 2010–2012, with the goal of 500 million people.

Millenium goal target. Using the old estimates, there were 824 million hungry people in 1990–1992 and the world population was 5,370 million (US census estimates for 1991). Thus the proportion was .143 and halving it would be .071. The current proportion (870 million hungry divided by 2013 world population of 7,095) is .122. Thus in 2013 the world is .051 of world population away from reaching this target, or 362 million people.

Using the new estimates, there were 1 billion hungry people in 1990–1992 and the world population was 5,370 million (US census estimates for 1991). Thus the proportion was .18 and halving it would be .09. The current proportion (870 million hungry divided by 2013 world population of 7,095) is .123. Thus in 2013, the world is .033 away, or 234 million people, from reaching this target.

Thus, in summary, the world is from 870 million to 234 million people away from reaching a hunger reduction goal, depending on which goal and which estimate is chosen.

Micronutrients

Quite a few trace elements or micronutrients—vitamins and minerals—are important for health. 1 out of 3 people in developing countries are affected by vitamin and mineral deficiencies, according to the World Health Organization. Three, perhaps the most important in terms of health consequences for poor people in developing countries, are:

Vitamin A Vitamin A deficiency can cause night blindness and reduces the body's resistance to disease. In children vitamin A deficiency can also cause growth retardation. Between 100 and 140 million children are vitamin A deficient. An estimated 250,000 to 500,000 vitamin A-deficient children become blind every year, half of them dying within 12 months of losing their sight (World Health Organization).

Iron Iron deficiency is a principal cause of anemia. Two billion people—over 30 percent of the world's population—are anemic, mainly due to iron deficiency, and, in developing countries, frequently exacerbated by malaria and worm infections. For children, health consequences include premature birth, low birth weight, infections, and elevated risk of death. Later, physical and cognitive development are impaired, resulting in lowered school performance. For pregnant women, anemia contributes to 20 percent of all maternal deaths (World Health Organization).

Iodine Iodine deficiency disorders (IDD) jeopardize children's mental health—often their very lives. Serious iodine deficiency during pregnancy may result in stillbirths, abortions and congenital abnormalities such as cretinism, a grave, irreversible form of mental retardation that affects people living in iodine-deficient areas of Africa and Asia. IDD also causes mental impairment that lowers intellectual prowess at home,

Notes

1. The table used to calculate this number.

Region	% in $1.25 a day poverty	Population (millions)	Pop. in $1 a day poverty (millions)
East Asia and Pacific	16.8	1,884	316
Latin America and the Caribbean	8.2	550	45
South Asia	40.4	1,476	596
Sub-Saharan Africa	50.9	763	388
Total Developing Countries	28.8	4673	**1345**
Europe and Central Asia	0.04	473	17
Middle East and North Africa	0.04	305	11
Total		5451	1372

Source: See World Bank PovcalNet "Replicate the World Bank's Regional Aggregation" at http://iresearch.worldbank.org/PovcalNet/povDuplic.html (accessed May 7, 2010). Also see World Bank "PovcalNet" at http://web.worldbank.org/WBSITE/EXTERNAL/EXTDEC/EXTRESEARCH/EXTPROGRAMS/EXTPO

at school, and at work. IDD affects over 740 million people, 13 percent of the world's population. Fifty million people have some degree of mental impairment caused by IDD (World Health Organization).

(Updated July 27, 2013)

Bibliography

Black RE, Morris SS, Bryce J. "Where and why are 10 million children dying every year?" *Lancet.* 2003 Jun 28; 361(9376):2226–34.

Black, Robert E, Lindsay H Allen, Zulfiqar A Bhutta, Laura E Caulfield, Mercedes de Onis, Majid Ezzati, Colin Mathers, Juan Rivera, for the Maternal and Child Undernutrition Study Group **Maternal and child undernutrition: global and regional exposures and health consequences.** (Article access may require registration) *The Lancet* Vol. 371, Issue 9608, 19 January 2008, 243–260.

Jennifer Bryce, Cynthia Boschi-Pinto, Kenji Shibuya, Robert E. Black, and the WHO Child Health Epidemiology Reference Group. 2005. **"WHO estimates of the causes of death in children."** *Lancet*; 365: 1147–52.

Cafiero, Carlo and Pietro Gennari. 2011. **The FAO indicator of the prevalence of undernourishment** FAO.

Caulfield LE, de Onis M, Blössner M, Black RE. **Undernutrition as an underlying cause of child deaths associated with diarrhea, pneumonia, malaria, and measles.** *American Journal of Clinical Nutrition* 2004; 80: 193–98.

Shaohua Chen and Martin Ravallion. June 2004. **"How have the world's poorest fared since the early 1980s?"** World Bank Policy Research Working Paper 3341 Washington: World Bank.

de Onis, Mercedes, Edward A. Frongillo and Monika Blossner. 2000. **"Is malnutrition declining? An analysis of changes in levels of child malnutrition since 1980."** *Bulletin of the World Health Organization* 2000: 1222–1233.

Food and Agriculture Organization, International Fund for Agricultural Development, World Food Program. 2002 **"Reducing Poverty and Hunger, the Critical Role of Financing for Food, Agriculture, and Rural Development."**

Food and Agriculture Organization. 2006. **State of World Food Insecurity 2006**.

Food and Agriculture Organization. 2010. The State of Food Insecurity in the World 2010 www.fao.org/docrep/013/i1683e/i1683e.pdf

Food and Agriculture Organization. 2012. "The State of Food Insecurity in the World 2012" www.fao.org/docrep/016/i3027e/i3027e00.htm

Headey, Derek. 2011. **"Was the Global Food Crisis Really a Crisis? Simulations versus Self-Reporting"**, IFPRI Discussion Paper 01087.

International Food Policy Research Institute. 2010. **2010 Global Hunger Index**

Frances Moore Lappé, Jennifer Clapp, Molly Anderson, Robin Broad, Ellen Messer, Thomas Pogge and Timothy Wise. 2013. **"How We Count Hunger Matters,"** *Ethics & International Affairs.*

Oxford University Press. 1971. *Oxford English Dictionary.* Definition for malnutrition.

Pelletier DL, Frongillo EA Jr, Schroeder D, Habicht JP. **The effects of malnutrition on child mortality in developing countries.** *Bulletin of the World Health Organization* 1995; **73:** 443–48.

United Nations High Commissioner on Refugees. 2007. *Statistical Yearbook 2006* "**Main Findings**"

UNHCR 2008 *Global Report 2008* "The Year in Review" www.unhcr.org/4a2d0b1d2.pdf

World Bank. **Understanding Poverty website**

World Health Organization **Comparative Quantification of Health Risks: Childhood and Maternal Undernutrition**

Critical Thinking

1. Why is malnutrition so prevalent in poor countries?

2. Who suffers most from hunger, and why?

3. How can we reduce global hunger and still achieve sustainability goals?

Create Central

www.mhhe.com/createcentral

Internet References

Sustainable Development.Org
www.sustainabledevelopment.org

The Hunger Project
www.thp.org

World Health Organization
www.who.int

Article

How to Feed 8 Billion People

Record grain shortages are threatening global food security in the immediate future. A noted environmental analyst shows how nations can better manage their limited resources.

LESTER R. BROWN

The world is entering a new food era. It will be marked by higher food prices, rapidly growing numbers of hungry people, and an intensifying competition for land and water resources that crosses national boundaries when food-importing countries buy or lease vast tracts of land in other countries. Because some of the countries where land is being acquired do not have enough land to adequately feed their own people, the stage is being set for future conflicts.

The sharp rise of grain prices in recent years underlines the gravity of the situation. From mid-2006 to mid-2008, world prices of wheat, rice, corn, and soybeans roughly tripled, reaching historic highs. It was not until the global economic crisis beginning in 2008 that grain prices began to level off and recede slightly.

The world has experienced several grain price surges over the last half century, but none like this. Earlier surges were event-driven, weather-related, and temporary—caused by monsoons, droughts, heat waves, etc.

The recent record surge in grain prices has been trend-driven. Working our way out of this tightening food situation means reversing the trends that are causing it, such as soil erosion, falling water tables, and rising carbon emissions.

As a result of persistently high food prices, hunger is spreading. In the mid-1990s, the number of hungry people had fallen to 825 million. But instead of continuing to decline, the number of people facing chronic food insecurity and undernourishment started to edge upward, jumping to more than 1 billion in 2009.

Rising food prices and the swelling ranks of the hungry are among the early signs of a tightening world food situation. More and more, food is looking like the weak link in our civilization, much as it was for the earlier ones whose archaeological sites we now study.

Food: The Weak Link

As the world struggles to feed all its people, farmers are facing some worrying trends. On the demand side of the food equation are three consumption-boosting trends: population growth, the growing consumption of grain-based animal protein, and, most recently, the massive use of grain to fuel cars.

Each year there are 79 million more people at the dinner table, and the overwhelming majority of these individuals are being added in countries where soils are eroding, water tables are falling, and irrigation wells are going dry.

Even as our numbers are multiplying, some 3 billion people are trying to add to their diets, consuming more meat and dairy products. At the top of the food-consumption ranking are the United States and Canada, where people consume on average 800 kilograms of grain per year, most of it indirectly as beef, pork, poultry, milk, and eggs. Near the bottom of this ranking is India, where people have less than 200 kilograms of grain each, and thus must consume nearly all of it directly, leaving little for conversion into animal protein.

The orgy of investment in ethanol fuel distilleries that followed the 2005 surge in U.S. gas prices doubled grain consumption to 40 million tons by 2008.

On the supply side, ongoing environmental trends are making it very difficult to expand food production fast enough. These include soil erosion, aquifer depletion, crop-shrinking heat waves, melting ice sheets and rising sea levels, and the melting of the mountain glaciers that feed major rivers and irrigation systems. In addition, three resource trends are affecting our food supply: the loss of cropland to non-farm uses, the diversion of irrigation water to cities, and the coming reduction in oil supplies.

Soil erosion is currently lowering the inherent productivity of some 30% of the world's cropland. In some countries, it has reduced grain production by half or more over the last three decades. Vast dust storms coming out of sub-Saharan Africa, northern China, western Mongolia, and Central Asia remind us that the loss of topsoil is not only continuing but expanding. Advancing deserts in China—the result of overgrazing, overplowing, and deforestation—have forced the complete or partial abandonment of some 24,000 villages and the cropland surrounding them.

The loss of topsoil began with the first wheat and barley plantings, but falling water tables are historically quite recent, simply because the pumping capacity to deplete aquifers has evolved only in recent decades. Water tables are now falling in countries that together contain half the world's people. An estimated 400 million people (including 175 million in India and

130 million in China) are being fed by over-pumping, a process that is by definition short term. Saudi Arabia has announced that, because its major aquifer, a nonreplenishable fossil aquifer, is largely depleted, it will be phasing out wheat production entirely by 2016.

An estimated 400 million people are being fed by overpumping water, a process that is by definition short term.

Climate change also threatens food security. For each 1°C rise in temperature above the norm during the growing season, farmers can expect a 10% decline in wheat, rice, and corn yields. Since 1970, the earth's average surface temperature has increased by 0.6°C. And the Intergovernmental Panel on Climate Change projects that the temperature will rise by up to 6°C during this century.

As the earth's temperature continues to rise, mountain glaciers are melting throughout the world. The projected melting of the glaciers on which China and India depend presents the most massive threat to food security that humanity has ever faced. China and India are the world's leading wheat producers and also dominate the world rice harvest. Whatever happens to the wheat and rice harvests in these two population giants will affect food prices everywhere.

The accelerating melting of the Greenland and West Antarctic ice sheets combined with thermal expansion of the oceans could raise sea level by up to six feet during this century. Every rice-growing river delta in Asia is threatened by the melting of these ice sheets. Even a three-foot rise would devastate the rice harvest in the Mekong Delta, which produces more than half the rice in Vietnam, the world's number-two rice exporter.

Three-fourths of oceanic fisheries are now being fished at or beyond capacity or are recovering from over-exploitation. If we continue with business as usual, many of these fisheries will collapse. We are taking fish from the oceans faster than they can reproduce.

With additional water no longer available in many countries, growing urban thirst can be satisfied only by taking irrigation water from farmers. Thousands of farmers in California find it more profitable to sell their irrigation water to Los Angeles and San Diego and leave their land idle. China's farmers are also losing irrigation water to the country's fast-growing cities.

If we paid the full cost of producing it—including the true cost of the oil used in producing it, the future costs of over-pumping aquifers, the destruction of land through erosion, and the carbon-dioxide emissions from land clearing—food would cost far more than we now pay for it in the supermarket.

The question—at least for now—is: Will the world grain harvest expand fast enough to keep pace with steadily growing demand? Food security will deteriorate further unless leading countries collectively mobilize to stabilize population, stabilize climate, stabilize aquifers, conserve soils, protect cropland, and restrict the use of grain to produce fuel for cars.

The Emerging Geopolitics of Food Scarcity

As world food security deteriorates, individual countries, acting in their narrowly defined self-interest, are banning or limiting grain exports.

In response, other countries have been trying to nail down long-term bilateral trade agreements that would lock up future grain supplies. Several have succeeded. Egypt, for example, has reached a long-term agreement with Russia for more than 3 million tons of wheat each year.

The more affluent food-importing countries have sought to buy or lease for the long term large blocks of land to farm in other countries. Libya, which imports 90% of its grain and has been worried about access to supplies, was one of the first to look abroad for land. After more than a year of negotiations, it reached an agreement to farm 100,000 hectares (250,000 acres) of land in Ukraine to grow wheat for its own people.

Countries selling or leasing their land are often low-income countries and, more often than not, those where chronic hunger and malnutrition are commonplace. A major acquisition site for Saudi Arabia and several other countries is Sudan—the site of the World Food Programme's largest famine relief effort.

The growing competition for land across national boundaries is also an indirect competition for water. In effect, land acquisitions are also water acquisitions. Land acquisitions in Sudan that tap water from the Nile, which is already fully utilized, may mean that Egypt will get less water from the river—making it even more dependent on imported grain.

Such bilateral land acquisitions raise many questions. To begin with, negotiations and the agreements they lead to tend to lack transparency. Typically, only a few high-ranking officials are involved, and the terms are confidential. Not only are many stakeholders such as farmers not at the table when the agreements are negotiated, they do not even learn about the deals until after they have been signed. And since there is rarely idle productive land in the countries where the land is being purchased or leased, the agreements suggest that many local farmers will be displaced. Their land may be confiscated or bought from them at a price over which they have little say.

This helps explain the public hostility that often arises within host countries. China, for example, signed an agreement with the Philippine government to lease more than a million hectares of land on which to produce crops that would be shipped home. Once word leaked out, the public outcry—much of it from Filipino farmers—forced the government to suspend the agreement. A similar situation developed in Madagascar, where South Korea's Daewoo Logistics had pursued rights to an area half the size of Belgium. The political furor led to a change in government and cancellation of the agreement.

Raising Land Productivity

There are many things that can be done in agriculture to raise land and water productivity. The challenge is for each country to fashion agricultural and economic policies that enable it to realize its unique potential.

Prior to 1950, expansion of the food supply came almost entirely from expanding cropland area. Then as frontiers disappeared and population growth accelerated after World War II, the world quickly shifted to raising land productivity. After several decades of rapid rise, however, it is now becoming more difficult to continue increasing productivity.

Gains in land productivity have come primarily from three sources: the growing use of fertilizer, the spread of irrigation, and the development of higher-yielding varieties of wheat, rice, and corn.

Among the three grains, corn is the only one where the yield is continuing to rise in high-yield countries. Even though fertilizer use has not increased since 1980, corn yields continue to edge upward as seed companies invest huge sums in corn breeding.

Despite dramatic past leaps in grain yields, it is becoming more difficult to expand world food output. There is little productive new land to bring under the plow. Expanding the irrigated area is difficult. Returns on the use of additional fertilizer are mostly diminishing. In the more arid countries of Africa, there is not enough rainfall to raise yields dramatically.

One way is to breed crops that are more tolerant of drought and cold. Another way to raise land productivity, where soil moisture permits, is to expand the area of land that produces more than one crop per year. Indeed, the tripling in the world grain harvest from 1950 to 2000 was due in part to widespread increases in multiple cropping in Asia. The spread of double cropping of winter wheat and corn on the North China Plain helped boost China's grain production to where it now rivals that of the United States.

A concerted U.S. effort to both breed earlier-maturing varieties and develop cultural practices that would facilitate multiple cropping could boost crop output. If China's farmers can extensively double crop wheat and corn, then U.S. farmers—at a similar latitude and with similar climate patterns—could do more if agricultural research and farm policy were reoriented to support it. Western Europe, with its mild winters and high-yielding winter wheat, might also be able to double crop more with a summer grain, such as corn, or an oilseed crop. Brazil and Argentina, which have extensive frost-free growing seasons, commonly multicrop wheat or corn with soybeans.

One encouraging effort to raise cropland productivity in Africa is the simultaneous planting of grain and leguminous trees. At first the trees grow slowly, permitting the grain crop to mature and be harvested; then the saplings grow quickly to several feet in height, dropping leaves that provide nitrogen and organic matter, both sorely needed in African soils. The wood is then cut and used for fuel. This simple, locally adapted technology, developed by scientists at the International Centre for Research in Agroforestry in Nairobi, has enabled farmers to double their grain yields within a matter of years as soil fertility builds.

Raising Water Productivity

Since it takes 1,000 tons of water to produce one ton of grain, it is not surprising that 70% of world water use is devoted to irrigation. Thus, raising irrigation efficiency is central to raising water productivity overall.

Data on the efficiency of surface water irrigation projects—that is, dams that deliver water to farmers through a network of canals—show that crop usage of irrigation water never reaches 100% because some irrigation water evaporates, some percolates downward, and some runs off. Water policy analysts have found that surface water irrigation efficiency is well below 50% in a number of countries, including India and Thailand.

Irrigation water efficiency is affected not only by the type and condition of irrigation systems but also by soil type, temperature, and humidity. In hot, arid regions, the evaporation of irrigation water is far higher than in cooler, humid regions. In a May 2004 meeting, China's Minister of Water Resources Wang Shucheng outlined for me in some detail the plans to raise China's irrigation efficiency from 43% in 2000 to 51% in 2010 and 55% in 2030. The steps he described included raising the price of water, providing incentives for adopting more irrigation-efficient technologies, and developing the local institutions to manage this process. Reaching these goals, he believes, would assure China's future food security.

Raising irrigation efficiency typically means shifting to overhead sprinklers or drip irrigation, the gold standard of irrigation efficiency. Switching to low-pressure sprinkler systems reduces water use by an estimated 30%, while switching to drip irrigation typically cuts water use in half.

A drip system also raises yields because it provides a steady supply of water with minimal losses to evaporation. Since drip systems are both labor-intensive and water-efficient, they are well suited to countries with a surplus of labor and a shortage of water. Israel (where the method was pioneered) and neighboring Jordan both rely heavily on drip irrigation. In contrast, among the big three agricultural producers, this more-efficient technology is used on roughly 3% of irrigated land in India and China and on roughly 4% in the United States.

In recent years, small-scale drip-irrigation systems—literally a bucket or drum with flexible plastic tubing to distribute the water—have been developed to irrigate small vegetable gardens. The containers are elevated slightly so that gravity distributes the water. Large-scale drip systems using plastic lines that can be moved easily are also becoming popular. These simple systems can pay for themselves in one year. By simultaneously reducing water costs and raising yields, they can dramatically raise incomes.

Shifting to more water-efficient crops wherever possible also boosts water productivity. Rice production is being phased out around Beijing because rice is such a thirsty crop. Similarly, Egypt restricts rice production in favor of wheat.

Strategic Reductions in the Demand for Grain

Although we seldom consider the climate effect of various dietary options, they are substantial, to say the least. A plant-based diet requires roughly one-fourth as much energy as a diet rich in red meat. Shifting to a vegetarian diet cuts greenhouse gas emissions almost as much as shifting from an SUV to a hybrid vehicle does. Shifting to less grain-intensive forms of animal protein such as poultry or certain types of fish can also reduce pressure on the earth's land and water resources.

Shifting to a vegetarian diet cuts greenhouse gas emissions almost as much as shifting from an SUV to a hybrid vehicle does.

When considering how much animal protein to consume, it is useful to distinguish between grass-fed and grain-fed products. For example, most of the world's beef is produced with grass. Even in the United States, with an abundance of feedlots, over half of all beef cattle weight gain comes from grass rather than grain. Grasslands are usually too steeply sloping or too arid to plow, and can contribute to the food supply only if used for grazing.

Beyond the role of grass in providing high-quality protein in our diets, it is sometimes assumed that we can increase the efficiency of land and water use by shifting from animal protein to high-quality plant protein, such as that from soybeans. It turns out, however, that since corn yields in the U.S. Midwest are three to four times those of soybeans, it may be more resource-efficient to produce corn and convert it into poultry or catfish at a ratio of two to one than to have everyone heavily reliant on soy.

The massive conversion of grain into biofuel began just a few years ago. If we are to reverse the spread of hunger, we will almost certainly have to cut back on ethanol production. Removing the incentives for converting food into fuel will help ensure that everyone has enough to eat. It will also lessen the pressures that lead to overpumping of groundwater and the clearing of tropical rain forests. If the U.S. government were to abolish the subsidies and mandates that are driving the conversion of grain into fuel, it would help stabilize grain prices and set the stage for relaxing the political tensions that have emerged within importing countries.

The Localization of Agriculture

In the United States, there has been a surge of interest in eating fresh local foods, corresponding with mounting concerns about the climate effects of consuming food from distant places. This is reflected in the rise in urban gardening, school gardening, and farmers' markets.

Food from more distant locations boosts carbon emissions while losing flavor and nutrition. A localized food economy reduces fossil fuel usage. Supermarkets are increasingly contracting with local farmers, and upscale restaurants are emphasizing locally grown food on their menus.

In school gardens, children learn how food is produced, a skill often lacking in urban settings, and they may get their first taste of freshly picked peas or vine-ripened tomatoes. School gardens also provide fresh produce for school lunches. California, a leader in this area, has 6,000 school gardens.

Many universities are now making a point of buying local food as well. Some universities compost kitchen and cafeteria food waste and make the compost available to the farmers who supply them with fresh produce.

Community gardens can be used by those who would otherwise not have access to land for gardening. Providing space for community gardens is seen by many local governments as an essential service.

Many market outlets are opening up for local produce. Perhaps the best known of these are the farmers' markets where local farmers bring their produce for sale. Many farmers' markets also now take food stamps, giving low-income consumers access to fresh produce that they might not otherwise be able to afford.

A survey of food consumed in Iowa showed conventional produce traveled on average 1,500 miles, not including food imported from other countries. In contrast, locally grown produce traveled on average 56 miles—a huge difference in fuel investment.

Concerns about the climate effects of transporting food long distances has led Tesco, the leading U.K. supermarket chain, to begin labeling products with their carbon footprint, indicating the greenhouse gas contribution of food items from the farm to supermarket shelf.

The shift from factory farm production of milk, meat, and eggs to mixed crop—livestock operations also facilitates nutrient recycling as local farmers return livestock manure to the land. The combination of high prices of natural gas, which is used to make nitrogen fertilizer, and of phosphate, as reserves are depleted, suggests a much greater future emphasis on nutrient recycling—an area where small farmers producing for local markets have a distinct advantage over massive feeding operations.

Costs and Solutions

If we cannot quickly cut carbon emissions, the world will face crop-shrinking heat waves that can massively and unpredictably reduce harvests. A hotter world will mean melting ice sheets, rising sea levels, and the inundation of the highly productive rice-growing river deltas of Asia. The loss of glaciers in the Himalayas and on the Tibetan Plateau will shrink wheat and rice harvests in both India and China, the world's most populous countries. Both are already facing water shortages driven by aquifer depletion and melting glaciers.

Since hunger is almost always the result of poverty, eradicating hunger depends on eradicating poverty. And where people are outrunning their land and water resources, this means stabilizing population.

Given that a handful of the more affluent grain-importing countries are reportedly investing some $20–30 billion in land acquisition, there is no shortage of capital to invest in agricultural development. Why not invest it across the board in helping low-income countries develop their unrealized potential for expanding food production, enabling them to export more grain?

We have a role to play as individuals. Whether we bike, bus, or drive to work will affect carbon emissions, climate change, and food security. The size of the car we drive to the supermarket and its effect on climate may indirectly affect the size of the bill at the supermarket checkout counter. If we are living high on the food-consumption chain, we can move down, improving our health while helping to stabilize climate. Food security is something in which we all have a stake—and a responsibility.

Critical Thinking

1. Sketch out a concept map illustrating the linkages between the three consumption-boosting trends the author suggests. Now describe the geographic location of the (1) population growth, (2) grain-based animal protein consumption, and (3) automobile driving. What are your observations?

2. The author states that food security will deteriorate further unless leading countries collectively mobilize to do several things. What are those actions?

3. Describe what is meant by the "localization of agriculture."

4. How might the promotion of "agricultural localization" have more global benefit and better environmental resiliency than large, commercial agricultural production operations?

5. Identify in this article three key terms, concepts, or principles that are used in your textbook (environmental science, economics, sociology, history, geography, etc.) or employed in the discipline you are currently studying. (Note: The terms, concepts, or principles may be implicit, explicit, implied, or inferred.)

LESTER R. BROWN is the founder and president of the Washington, D.C.-based nonprofit Earth Policy Institute. This article draws from his most recent book, *Plan B 4.0: Mobilizing to Save Civilization* (W.W. Norton and Co., 2009). For additional information, visit www .earth-policy.org.

Article   Prepared by: Richard Eathorne, *Northern Michigan University*

Climate Change: How a Warming World Is a Threat to Our Food Supplies

Global warming is exacerbating political instability as tensions brought on by food insecurity rise. With research suggesting the issue can only get worse, we examine the risks around the world.

JOHN VIDAL

Learning Outcomes

After reading this article, you will be able to:

- Explain how climate change contributes to global food security issues.

- Outline how climate change can impact food supplies differently in different countries.

When the Tunisian street vendor, Mohamed Bouazizi, set himself on fire on 17 December 2010, it was in protest at heavy-handed treatment and harassment in the province where he lived. But a host of new studies suggest that a major factor in the subsequent uprisings, which became known as the Arab spring, was food insecurity.

Drought, rocketing bread prices, food and water shortages have all blighted parts of the Middle East. Analysts at the Centre for American Progress in Washington say a combination of food shortages and other environmental factors exacerbated the already tense politics of the region. As the *Observer* reports today, an as-yet unpublished US government study indicates that the world needs to prepare for much more of the same, as food prices spiral and longstanding agricultural practices are disrupted by climate change.

"We should expect much more political destabilisation of countries as it bites," says Richard Choularton, a policy officer in the UN's World Food Programme climate change office. "What is different now from 20 years ago is that far more people are living in places with a higher climatic risk; 650 million people now live in arid or semi-arid areas where floods and droughts and price shocks are expected to have the most impact.

"The recent crises in the Horn of Africa and Sahel may be becoming the new normal. Droughts are expected to become more frequent. Studies suggest anything up to 200 million more food-insecure people by 2050 or an additional 24 million malnourished children. In parts of Africa we already have a protracted and growing humanitarian disaster. Climate change is a creeping disaster," he said.

The Mary Robinson climate justice foundation is hosting a major conference in Dublin this week. Research to be presented there will say that rising incomes and growth in the global population, expected to create 2 billion more mouths to feed by 2050, will drive food prices higher by 40–50%. Climate change may add a further 50% to maize prices and slightly less to wheat, rice and oil seeds.

"We know population will grow and incomes increase, but also that temperatures will rise and rainfall patterns will change. We must prepare today for higher temperatures in all sectors," said Gerald Nelson, a senior economist with the International Food Policy Research Institute in Washington.

All of the studies suggest the worst impacts will be felt by the poorest people. Robinson, the former Irish president, said: "Climate change is already having a domino effect on food and nutritional security for the world's poorest and most vulnerable people. Child malnutrition is predicted to increase by 20% by 2050. Climate change impacts will disproportionately fall on people living in tropical regions, and particularly on the most vulnerable and marginalised population groups. This is the injustice of climate change—the worst of the impacts are felt by those who contributed least to causing the problem."

But from Europe to the US to Asia, no population will remain insulated from the huge changes in food production that the rest of the century will bring.

Frank Rijsberman, head of the world's leading Cgiar crop research stations, said: "There's a lot of complacency in rich countries about climate change. We must understand that instability is inevitable. We already see a lot of refugees. Perhaps if a lot of people come over on boats to Europe or the US that would wake them up."

Asia and Oceania

China is relatively resilient to climate change. Its population is expected to decline by up 400 million people this century, easing demand on resources, and it has the capacity to buy in vast quantities of food.

But because more and more Chinese are changing to a more meat-based diet, its challenges will be land and cattle feed. Climate change will affect regions in different ways, but many crops are expected to migrate northwards.

Crop losses are increasingly being caused by extreme weather events, insect attacks and diseases. The 2011 drought lifted food prices worldwide. Wheat is becoming harder to grow in some northern areas of China as the land gets drier and warmer.

In southern China, droughts in recent years have replaced rainy seasons. The national academy of agricultural sciences expects basic food supplies to become insufficient around the year 2030.

A new study for US Aid expects most of Vietnam, Cambodia, Laos and Thailand to see 4–6C temperature rises by 2050. The Lower Mekong region of 100 million people, which is prone to weather extremes, could also see rainfall increase 20% or more in some areas, reducing the growth of rice and other staple crops. Many provinces will see food production decline significantly. The number of malnourished children in the region may increase by 9 to 11 million by 2050.

Extreme events will increasingly affect agriculture in Australia. Key food-growing regions in the south are likely to experience more droughts in the future, with part of western Australia having already experienced a 15% drop in rainfall since the mid-1970s.

The number of record-breaking hot days in Australia has doubled since the 1960s, also affecting food output.

Europe

Climate change affects agricultural production through its effects on the timing, intensity and variability of rainfall and shifts in temperatures and carbon dioxide concentrations.

Crops normally seen growing in the south of Europe will be able to be grown further north. This would allow more sweetcorn, grapes, sunflowers, soya and maize to be grown in Britain. In Scotland, livestock farming could become more suitable. At the higher latitudes warmer temperatures are predicted to lengthen and increase the intensity of the growing season. But more CO_2 and a major temperature rise could cut yields by around 10% later in the century.

Latest EU projections suggest the most severe consequences of climate change will not be felt until 2050. But significant adverse impacts are expected earlier from more frequent and prolonged heatwaves, droughts and floods. Many crops now grown in southern Europe, such as olives, may not survive high temperature increases. Southern Europe will have to change the way it irrigates crops.

In Europe's high and middle latitudes, global warming is expected to greatly expand the growing season. Crops in Russia may be able to expand northwards but yields will be much lower because the soils are less fertile. In the south, the climate is likely to become much drier which will reduce yields. In addition, climate change is expected to make water resources scarcer and encourage weeds and pests.

In 2011, Russia banned wheat and grain exports after a heatwave. Warming will increase forest fires by 30–40%. This will affect soil erosion and increase the probability of floods.

In the Middle East and north Africa, declining yields of up to 30% are expected for rice, about 47% for maize and 20% for wheat.

Americas

The US is expected to grow by 120 million people by 2050. Government scientists expect more incidents of extreme heat, severe drought, and heavy rains to affect food production. The warming is expected to continue without undue problems for 30 years but beyond 2050 the effects could be dramatic with staple crops hit.

According to the latest government report: "The rising incidence of weather extremes will have increasingly negative impacts on crop and livestock productivity, because critical thresholds are already being exceeded." Many agricultural regions of the US will experience declines.

California's central valley will be hard hit with sunflowers, wheat, tomato, rice, cotton and maize expected to lose 10–30% of their yields, especially beyond 2050. Fruit and nut crops which depend on "winter chilling" days may have to relocate. Animals exposed to many hot nights are increasingly stressed. Many vegetable crops will be hit when temperatures rise only a few degrees above normal.

Nearly 20% of all US food is imported, so climate extremes elsewhere will also have an effect. In 2011, 14.9% of US households did not have secure food supplies and 5.7% had very low food security.

Because few crops can withstand average temperature rises of more than 2C, Latin America expects to be seriously affected by a warming climate and more extreme weather. Even moderate 1–2C rises would cause significant damage to Brazil, one of the world's biggest suppliers of food crops. Brazilian production of rice, beans, manioc, maize and soya are all expected to decline, with coffee especially vulnerable.

Other studies suggest Brazil's massive soya crop, which provides animal feed for much of the world, could slump by more than 25% over the next 20 years.

Two major crops should do well: quinoa and potatoes.

Africa

Many African countries are already experiencing longer and deeper droughts, floods and cyclones. The continent is expected to suffer disproportionately from food insecurity, due to fast-growing vulnerable populations.

Egypt expects to lose 15% of its wheat crops if temperatures rise 2C, and 36% if the increase is 4C. Morocco expects crops to remain stable up to about 2030, but then to drop quickly later. Most north African countries traditionally import wheat and are therefore highly vulnerable to price shocks and droughts elsewhere.

A new study of 11 west African countries expects most to be able to grow more food as temperatures rise and rainfall increases. But demand from growing populations may double food prices. Climate change may mean Nigeria, Ghana and Togo can grow and export more sorghum, raised for grain.

Temperatures are expected to rise several degrees in regions close to the Sahel. In Burkina Faso, the sorghum crop is expected to decline by 25% or more, but maize yields may improve.

Other studies by IFPRI suggest crop yields across sub-Saharan Africa may decline 5–22% by 2050, pushing large numbers of people deeper into destitution.

A new UN study suggests climatic conditions in southern Africa will worsen. Climate models mostly predict an increase in annual maximum temperatures in the region of 1 to 2C by 2050. This will favour some crops but shift others to higher ground or further north.

Both of Africa's staple crops, maize and sorghum, are expected to be badly hit by increasing severity of weather.

Oxfam warns that small-scale farmers in the Horn of Africa will bear the brunt of the negative impacts of climate change. Unpredictable weather here has already left millions semi-destitute and dependent on food aid.

Critical Thinking

1. Why might the impacts of climate change be different now than 20 years ago? 20 years in the future?

2. Who will feel the worst impacts on food supply, and why?

3. If a nation cannot feed its people, what will happen to that nation and its people?

Create Central

www.mhhe.com/createcentral

Internet References

Alliance for Global Sustainability (AGS)
http://globalsustainability.org

National Geographic Society
www.nationalgeographic.com

People & Planet
www.peopleandplanet.org

SocioSite: Sociological Subject Areas
www.pscw.uva.nl/sociosite/TOPICS

Article   Prepared by: Richard Eathorne, *Northern Michigan University*

Could Food Shortages Bring Down Civilization?

The biggest threat to global stability is the potential for food crises in poor countries to cause government collapse. Those crises are brought on by ever worsening environmental degradation.

LESTER R. BROWN

Learning Outcomes

After reading this article, you will be able to:

• Discuss how food scarcity issues could push some countries into political, social, and economic chaos.

• Outline the environmental factors that could begin placing severe limits on global food production.

One of the toughest things for people to do is to anticipate sudden change. Typically we project the future by extrapolating from trends in the past. Much of the time this approach works well. But sometimes it fails spectacularly, and people are simply blindsided by events such as today's economic crisis.

For most of us, the idea that civilization itself could disintegrate probably seems preposterous. Who would not find it hard to think seriously about such a complete departure from what we expect of ordinary life? What evidence could make us heed a warning so dire—and how would we go about responding to it? We are so inured to a long list of highly unlikely catastrophes that we are virtually programmed to dismiss them all with a wave of the hand: Sure, our civilization might devolve into chaos—and Earth might collide with an asteroid, too!

For many years I have studied global agricultural, population, environmental and economic trends and their interactions. The combined effects of those trends and the political tensions they generate point to the breakdown of governments and societies. Yet I, too, have resisted the idea that food shortages could bring down not only individual governments but also our global civilization.

I can no longer ignore that risk. Our continuing failure to deal with the environmental declines that are undermining the world food economy—most important, falling water tables, eroding soils and rising temperatures—forces me to conclude that such a collapse is possible.

The Problem of Failed States

Even a cursory look at the vital signs of our current world order lends unwelcome support to my conclusion. And those of us in the environmental field are well into our third decade of charting trends of environmental decline without seeing any significant effort to reverse a single one.

In six of the past nine years world grain production has fallen short of consumption, forcing a steady drawdown in stocks. When the 2008 harvest began, world carryover stocks of grain (the amount in the bin when the new harvest begins) were at 62 days of consumption, a near record low. In response, world grain prices in the spring and summer of last year climbed to the highest level ever.

As demand for food rises faster than supplies are growing, the resulting food-price inflation puts severe stress on the governments of countries already teetering on the edge of chaos. Unable to buy grain or grow their own, hungry people take to the streets. Indeed, even before the steep climb in grain prices in 2008, the number of failing states was expanding [*see sidebar*]. Many of their problems stem from a failure to slow the growth of their populations. But if the food situation continues to deteriorate, entire nations will break down at an ever increasing rate. We have entered a new era in geopolitics. In the 20th century the main threat to international security was superpower conflict; today it is failing states. It is not the concentration of power but its absence that puts us at risk.

States fail when national governments can no longer provide personal security, food security and basic social services such as education and health care. They often lose control of part or all of their territory. When governments lose their monopoly

Failing States

Every year the Fund for Peace and the Carnegie Endowment for International Peace jointly analyze and score countries on 12 social, economic, political and military indicators of national well-being. Here, ranked from worst to better according to their combined scores in 2007, are the 20 countries in the world that are closest to collapse:

- Somalia
- Sudan
- Zimbabwe
- Chad
- Iraq
- Democratic Republic of the Congo
- Afghanistan
- Ivory Coast
- Pakistan
- Central African Republic
- Guinea
- Bangladesh
- Burma (Myanmar)
- Haiti
- North Korea
- Ethiopia
- Uganda
- Lebanon
- Nigeria
- Sri Lanka

SOURCE: "The Failed States Index 2008," by the Fund for Peace and the Carnegie Endowment for International Peace, in Foreign Policy; July/August 2008

on power, law and order begin to disintegrate. After a point, countries can become so dangerous that food relief workers are no longer safe and their programs are halted; in Somalia and Afghanistan, deteriorating conditions have already put such programs in jeopardy.

Failing states are of international concern because they are a source of terrorists, drugs, weapons and refugees, threatening political stability everywhere. Somalia, number one on the 2008 list of failing states, has become a base for piracy. Iraq, number five, is a hotbed for terrorist training. Afghanistan, number seven, is the world's leading supplier of heroin. Following the massive genocide of 1994 in Rwanda, refugees from that troubled state, thousands of armed soldiers among them, helped to destabilize neighboring Democratic Republic of the Congo (number six).

Our global civilization depends on a functioning network of politically healthy nationstates to control the spread of infectious disease, to manage the international monetary system, to control international terrorism and to reach scores of other common goals. If the system for controlling infectious diseases—such as polio, SARS or avian flu—breaks down, humanity will be in trouble. Once states fail, no one assumes responsibility for their debt to outside lenders. If enough states disintegrate, their fall will threaten the stability of global civilization itself.

A New Kind of Food Shortage

The surge in world grain prices in 2007 and 2008—and the threat they pose to food security—has a different, more troubling quality than the increases of the past. During the second half of the 20th century, grain prices rose dramatically several times. In 1972, for instance, the Soviets, recognizing their poor harvest early, quietly cornered the world wheat market. As a result, wheat prices elsewhere more than doubled, pulling rice and corn prices up with them. But this and other price shocks were event-driven—drought in the Soviet Union, a monsoon failure in India, crop-shrinking heat in the U.S. Corn Belt. And the rises were short-lived: prices typically returned to normal with the next harvest.

In contrast, the recent surge in world grain prices is trend-driven, making it unlikely to reverse without a reversal in the trends themselves. On the demand side, those trends include the ongoing addition of more than 70 million people a year; a growing number of people wanting to move up the food chain to consume highly grain-intensive livestock products [see "The Greenhouse Hamburger," by Nathan Fiala; Scientific American, February 2009]; and the massive diversion of U.S. grain to ethanol-fuel distilleries.

The extra demand for grain associated with rising affluence varies widely among countries. People in low-income countries where grain supplies 60 percent of calories, such as India, directly consume a bit more than a pound of grain a day. In affluent countries such as the U.S. and Canada, grain consumption per person is nearly four times that much, though perhaps 90 percent of it is consumed indirectly as meat, milk and eggs from grain-fed animals.

The potential for further grain consumption as incomes rise among low-income consumers is huge. But that potential pales beside the insatiable demand for crop-based automotive fuels. A fourth of this year's U.S. grain harvest—enough to feed 125 million Americans or half a billion Indians at current consumption levels—will go to fuel cars. Yet even if the entire U.S. grain harvest were diverted into making ethanol, it would meet at most 18 percent of U.S. automotive fuel needs. The grain required to fill a 25-gallon SUV tank with ethanol could feed one person for a year.

The recent merging of the food and energy economies implies that if the food value of grain is less than its fuel value, the market will move the grain into the energy economy. That double demand is leading to an epic competition between cars and people for the grain supply and to a political and moral issue of unprecedented dimensions. The U.S., in a misguided effort to reduce its dependence on foreign oil by substituting grain-based fuels, is generating global food insecurity on a scale not seen before.

Water Shortages Mean Food Shortages

What about supply? The three environmental trends I mentioned earlier—the shortage of freshwater, the loss of topsoil and the rising temperatures (and other effects) of global warming—are making it increasingly hard to expand the world's grain supply fast enough to keep up with demand. Of all those trends, however, the spread of water shortages poses the most immediate threat. The biggest challenge here is irrigation, which consumes 70 percent of the world's freshwater. Millions of irrigation wells in many countries are now pumping water out of underground sources faster than rainfall can recharge them. The result is falling water tables in countries populated by half the world's people, including the three big grain producers—China, India and the U.S.

Usually aquifers are replenishable, but some of the most important ones are not: the "fossil" aquifers, so called because they store ancient water and are not recharged by precipitation. For these—including the vast Ogallala Aquifer that underlies the U.S. Great Plains, the Saudi aquifer and the deep aquifer under the North China Plain—depletion would spell the end of pumping. In arid regions such a loss could also bring an end to agriculture altogether.

In China the water table under the North China Plain, an area that produces more than half of the country's wheat and a third of its corn, is falling fast. Overpumping has used up most of the water in a shallow aquifer there, forcing well drillers to turn to the region's deep aquifer, which is not replenishable. A report by the World Bank foresees "catastrophic consequences for future generations" unless water use and supply can quickly be brought back into balance.

As water tables have fallen and irrigation wells have gone dry, China's wheat crop, the world's largest, has declined by 8 percent since it peaked at 123 million tons in 1997. In that same period China's rice production dropped 4 percent. The world's most populous nation may soon be importing massive quantities of grain.

But water shortages are even more worrying in India. There the margin between food consumption and survival is more precarious. Millions of irrigation wells have dropped water tables in almost every state. As Fred Pearce reported in *New Scientist:*

> Half of India's traditional hand-dug wells and millions of shallower tube wells have already dried up, bringing a spate of suicides among those who rely on them. Electricity blackouts are reaching epidemic proportions in states where half of the electricity is used to pump water from depths of up to a kilometer [3,300 feet].

A World Bank study reports that 15 percent of India's food supply is produced by mining groundwater. Stated otherwise, 175 million Indians consume grain produced with water from irrigation wells that will soon be exhausted. The continued shrinking of water supplies could lead to unmanageable food shortages and social conflict.

Less Soil, More Hunger

The scope of the second worrisome trend—the loss of topsoil—is also startling. Topsoil is eroding faster than new soil forms on perhaps a third of the world's cropland. This thin layer of essential plant nutrients, the very foundation of civilization,

took long stretches of geologic time to build up, yet it is typically only about six inches deep. Its loss from wind and water erosion doomed earlier civilizations.

In 2002 a U.N. team assessed the food situation in Lesotho, the small, landlocked home of two million people embedded within South Africa. The team's finding was straightforward: "Agriculture in Lesotho faces a catastrophic future; crop production is declining and could cease altogether over large tracts of the country if steps are not taken to reverse soil erosion, degradation and the decline in soil fertility."

In the Western Hemisphere, Haiti—one of the first states to be recognized as failing—was largely self-sufficient in grain 40 years ago. In the years since, though, it has lost nearly all its forests and much of its topsoil, forcing the country to import more than half of its grain.

The third and perhaps most pervasive environmental threat to food security—rising surface temperature—can affect crop yields everywhere. In many countries crops are grown at or near their thermal optimum, so even a minor temperature rise during the growing season can shrink the harvest. A study published by the U.S. National Academy of Sciences has confirmed a rule of thumb among crop ecologists: for every rise of one degree Celsius (1.8 degrees Fahrenheit) above the norm, wheat, rice and corn yields fall by 10 percent.

In the past, most famously when the innovations in the use of fertilizer, irrigation and high-yield varieties of wheat and rice created the "green revolution" of the 1960s and 1970s, the response to the growing demand for food was the successful application of scientific agriculture: the technological fix. This time, regrettably, many of the most productive advances in agricultural technology have already been put into practice, and so the long-term rise in land productivity is slowing down. Between 1950 and 1990 the world's farmers increased the grain yield per acre by more than 2 percent a year, exceeding the growth of population. But since then, the annual growth in yield has slowed to slightly more than 1 percent. In some countries the yields appear to be near their practical limits, including rice yields in Japan and China.

Some commentators point to genetically modified crop strains as a way out of our predicament. Unfortunately, however, no genetically modified crops have led to dramatically higher yields, comparable to the doubling or tripling of wheat and rice yields that took place during the green revolution. Nor do they seem likely to do so, simply because conventional plant-breeding techniques have already tapped most of the potential for raising crop yields.

Jockeying for Food

As the world's food security unravels, a dangerous politics of food scarcity is coming into play: individual countries acting in their narrowly defined self-interest are actually worsening the plight of the many. The trend began in 2007, when leading wheat-exporting countries such as Russia and Argentina limited or banned their exports, in hopes of increasing locally available food supplies and thereby bringing down food prices domestically. Vietnam, the world's second-biggest rice exporter after

Thailand, banned its exports for several months for the same reason. Such moves may reassure those living in the exporting countries, but they are creating panic in importing countries that must rely on what is then left of the world's exportable grain.

In response to those restrictions, grain importers are trying to nail down long-term bilateral trade agreements that would lock up future grain supplies. The Philippines, no longer able to count on getting rice from the world market, recently negotiated a three-year deal with Vietnam for a guaranteed 1.5 million tons of rice each year. Food-import anxiety is even spawning entirely new efforts by food-importing countries to buy or lease farmland in other countries [*see sidebar*].

In spite of such stopgap measures, soaring food prices and spreading hunger in many other countries are beginning to break down the social order. In several provinces of Thailand the predations of "rice rustlers" have forced villagers to guard their rice fields at night with loaded shotguns. In Pakistan an armed soldier escorts each grain truck. During the first half of 2008, 83 trucks carrying grain in Sudan were hijacked before reaching the Darfur relief camps.

How Failed States Threaten Everyone

When a nation's government can no longer provide security or basic services for its citizens, the resulting social chaos can have serious adverse effects beyond that nation's own borders:

- Spreading disease
- Offering sanctuary to terrorists and pirates
- Spreading the sale of drugs and weapons
- Fostering political extremism
- Generating violence and refugees, which can spill into neighboring states

Side Bets in the Game of Food Politics

Anxious to ensure future grain supplies, several nations are quietly making deals with grain-producing countries for rights to farm there. The practice tightens supplies for other importing nations and raises prices. Some examples:

- **China:** Seeking to lease land in **Australia, Brazil, Burma (Myanmar), Russia** and **Uganda**
- **Saudi Arabia:** Looking for farmland in **Egypt, Pakistan, South Africa, Sudan, Thailand, Turkey** and **Ukraine**
- **India:** Agribusiness firms pursuing cropland in **Paraguay** and **Uruguay**
- **Libya:** Leasing 250,000 acres in **Ukraine** in exchange for access to Libyan oil fields
- **South Korea:** Seeking land deals in **Madagascar, Russia** and **Sudan**

No country is immune to the effects of tightening food supplies, not even the U.S., the world's breadbasket. If China turns to the world market for massive quantities of grain, as it has recently done for soybeans, it will have to buy from the U.S. For U.S. consumers, that would mean competing for the U.S. grain harvest with 1.3 billion Chinese consumers with fast-rising incomes—a nightmare scenario. In such circumstances, it would be tempting for the U.S. to restrict exports, as it did, for instance, with grain and soybeans in the 1970s when domestic prices soared. But that is not an option with China. Chinese investors now hold well over a trillion U.S. dollars, and they have often been the leading international buyers of U.S. Treasury securities issued to finance the fiscal deficit. Like it or not, U.S. consumers will share their grain with Chinese consumers, no matter how high food prices rise.

Plan B: Our Only Option

Since the current world food shortage is trend-driven, the environmental trends that cause it must be reversed. To do so requires extraordinarily demanding measures, a monumental shift away from business as usual—what we at the Earth Policy Institute call Plan A—to a civilization-saving Plan B.

Similar in scale and urgency to the U.S. mobilization for World War II, Plan B has four components: a massive effort to cut carbon emissions by 80 percent from their 2006 levels by 2020; the stabilization of the world's population at eight billion by 2040; the eradication of poverty; and the restoration of forests, soils and aquifers.

Net carbon dioxide emissions can be cut by systematically raising energy efficiency and investing massively in the development of renewable sources of energy. We must also ban deforestation worldwide, as several countries already have done, and plant billions of trees to sequester carbon. The transition from fossil fuels to renewable forms of energy can be driven by imposing a tax on carbon, while offsetting it with a reduction in income taxes.

Stabilizing population and eradicating poverty go hand in hand. In fact, the key to accelerating the shift to smaller families is eradicating poverty—and vice versa. One way is to ensure at least a primary school education for all children, girls as well as boys. Another is to provide rudimentary, village-level health care, so that people can be confident that their children will survive to adulthood. Women everywhere need access to reproductive health care and family-planning services.

The fourth component, restoring the earth's natural systems and resources, incorporates a worldwide initiative to arrest the fall in water tables by raising water productivity: the useful activity that can be wrung from each drop. That implies shifting to more efficient irrigation systems and to more water-efficient crops. In some countries, it implies growing (and eating) more wheat and less rice, a water-intensive crop. And for industries and cities, it implies doing what some are doing already, namely, continuously recycling water.

At the same time, we must launch a worldwide effort to conserve soil, similar to the U.S. response to the Dust Bowl of the 1930s. Terracing the ground, planting trees as shelterbelts against windblown soil erosion, and practicing minimum tillage—in which the soil is not plowed and crop residues are left on the field—are among the most important soil-conservation measures.

There is nothing new about our four interrelated objectives. They have been discussed individually for years. Indeed, we have created entire institutions intended to tackle some of them, such as the World Bank to alleviate poverty. And we have made substantial progress in some parts of the world on at least one of them—the distribution of family-planning services and the associated shift to smaller families that brings population stability.

For many in the development community, the four objectives of Plan B were seen as positive, promoting development as long as they did not cost too much. Others saw them as humanitarian goals—politically correct and morally appropriate. Now a third and far more momentous rationale presents itself: meeting these goals may be necessary to prevent the collapse of our civilization. Yet the cost we project for saving civilization would amount to less than $200 billion a year, a sixth of current global military spending. In effect, Plan B is the new security budget.

Time: Our Scarcest Resource

Our challenge is not only to implement Plan B but also to do it quickly. The world is in a race between political tipping points and natural ones. Can we close coal-fired power plants fast enough to prevent the Greenland ice sheet from slipping into the sea and inundating our coastlines? Can we cut carbon emissions fast enough to save the mountain glaciers of Asia? During the dry season their meltwaters sustain the major rivers of India and China—and by extension, hundreds of millions of people. Can we stabilize population before countries such as India, Pakistan and Yemen are overwhelmed by shortages of the water they need to irrigate their crops?

It is hard to overstate the urgency of our predicament. Every day counts. Unfortunately, we do not know how long we can light our cities with coal, for instance, before Greenland's ice

sheet can no longer be saved. Nature sets the deadlines; nature is the timekeeper. But we human beings cannot see the clock.

We desperately need a new way of thinking, a new mind-set. The thinking that got us into this bind will not get us out. When Elizabeth Kolbert, a writer for the *New Yorker*, asked energy guru Amory Lovins about thinking outside the box, Lovins responded: "There is no box."

There is no box. That is the mind-set we need if civilization is to survive.

Critical Thinking

1. What environment factors are contributing to "failing" states?

2. Explain Plan B and identify some assumptions it must make in order to succeed.

3. Why should the rich countries of the world care about potential global food shortages?

Create Central

www.mhhe.com/createcentral

Internet References

Global Footprint Network
http://footprints@footprintnetwork.org

People & Planet
www.peopleandplanet.org

The Hunger Project
www.thp.org

Lester R. Brown, in the words of the *Washington Post*, is "one of the world's most influential thinkers." The *Telegraph* of Calcutta has called him "the guru of the environmental movement." Brown is founder of both the Worldwatch Institute (1974) and the Earth Policy Institute (2001), which he heads today. He has authored or coauthored 50 books; his most recent is *Plan B 3.0: Mobilizing to Save Civilization.* Brown is the recipient of many prizes and awards, including 24 honorary degrees and a MacArthur Fellowship.

Article   Prepared by: Richard Eathorne, *Northern Michigan University*

Understanding Water Scarcity: Definitions and Measurements

CHRIS WHITE

Learning Outcomes

After reading this article, you will be able to:

- Explain what is meant by "water scarcity."

- Discuss the strengths and weaknesses of the "water stress index."

- Describe alternative ways of defining and measuring water scarcity.

Water scarcity, which can broadly be understood as the lack of access to adequate quantities of water for human and environmental uses, is increasingly being recognised in many countries as a serious and growing concern. As a result, the term 'water scarcity' is regularly used by the media, government reports, NGOs, international organisations such as the UN and OECD, as well as in the academic literature, to highlight areas where water resources are under pressure.

However, despite its frequent use, there is no consensus on how water scarcity should be defined or how it should be measured. Thus, a reference to water scarcity in one report may measure something different to other reports which use the same term. This can create confusion as to what exactly water scarcity means and lead to different answers to the question of which regions are under the most water stress.

In order to reduce this confusion, this article looks at some of the most commonly used methods of defining and measuring water scarcity, so that readers can understand what exactly is meant in each case.

One of the most commonly used measures of water scarcity is the 'Falkenmark indicator' or 'water stress index'. This method defines water scarcity in terms of the total water resources that are available to the population of a region; measuring scarcity as the amount of renewable freshwater that is available for each person each year. If the amount of renewable water in a country is below 1,700 m^3 per person per year, that country is said to be experiencing water stress; below 1,000 m^3 it is said to be experiencing water scarcity; and below 500 m^3, absolute water scarcity[1].

The water stress index method is commonly used because it is straightforward, easy to use, and the data needed is readily available. However, such a simplistic approach has its limitations:

1. It ignores important regional differences in water availability, only measuring water scarcity at a country level;

2. It fails to account for whether or not those water resources are accessible, for example, some of the freshwater resources of a country may be stored deep underground or may be heavily polluted;

3. It does not include man-made sources of freshwater such as desalination plants which increase water availability beyond what is naturally available;

4. It does not account for the fact that different countries, and regions within countries, use different amounts of water, in Australia for example, most of the demand for water is focused around the major urban and agricultural centres in the Murray-Darling Basin, with much less used in the sparsely populated centre[2].

An alternative way of defining and measuring water scarcity is to use a criticality ratio. This approach relaxes the assumption that all countries use the same amount of water, instead defining water scarcity in terms of each country's water demand compared to the amount of water available; measuring scarcity as the proportion of total annual water withdrawals relative to total available water resources[3]. Using this approach, a country is said to be water scarce if annual withdrawals are between 20–40% of annual supply, and severely water scarce if they exceed 40%.

Suggested Citation: White, C.2072, 'Understanding water scarcity: Definitions and measurements', GWF Discussion Paper 1217, Global Water Forum, Canberra, Australia. Available online at http://www.globalwaterforum.org/2012/05/07/understanding-water-scarcity-definitions-and-measurements/

While this approach avoids the overly simplistic assumption that all countries have the same demand for water, it also has its limitations:

1. It does not consider man-made increases in water supply (such as desalination);
2. It ignores water withdrawals that are recycled and reused;
3. It doesn't consider the capacity of countries to adapt to lower water availability through changing behaviour or new technology[2].

A third measure of water scarcity was developed by the International Water Management Institute (IWMI). This approach attempts to solve the problems listed above by including: each country's water infrastructure, such as water in desalination plants, into the measure of water availability; including recycled water by limiting measurements of water demand to consumptive use rather than total withdrawals; and measuring the adaptive capacity of a country by assessing its potential for infrastructure development and efficiency improvements[5].

Using this approach, the IWMI classifies countries that are predicted to be unable to meet their future water demand without investment in water infrastructure and efficiency as economically water scarce; and countries predicted to be unable to meet their future demand, even with such investment, as physically water scarce[6].

While the IWMI measure of water scarcity is more sophisticated, its complexity means that it requires significant amounts of time and resources to estimate. This approach also fails to consider the ability of people within countries to adapt to reduced water availability by importing food grown in other countries, or by using water saving devices. The ability to adapt also depends on the economic resources available in countries as a whole, as well as to individuals within a country. For instance, wealthy residents in rich countries are more likely to be able to adapt to reduced water availability than poor people in developing countries.

A fourth approach to measuring water scarcity is the 'water poverty index'. This approach attempts to take into account the role of income and wealth in determining water scarcity by measuring: (1) the level of access to water; (2) water quantity, quality, and variability; (3) water used for domestic, food, and productive purposes; (4) capacity for water management; and (5) environmental aspects[7]. The complexity of this approach, however, means that it is more suited for analysis at a local scale, where data is more readily available, than on a national level.

There is, therefore, no single definition of water scarcity; different measurements capture different aspects of the pressures on water resources, and there isn't one measure which captures them all. This point is illustrated in Figure 1 which shows two different measures of water scarcity for Africa and Western Europe; one which accounts for the impact access to water technology can have on water scarcity, and one which does not.

First, by using a criticality ratio, the authors estimate the level of water scarcity based on a number of stressors (Incident HWS Threat). Since this measure does not include the impact that investment in technological development can have on improving water security, they then estimate an 'investment benefits factor' which measures the investment capabilities of each country. They then include the investment benefits factor to the measure of water scarcity to estimate an adjusted measure of water scarcity when technological capacity is taken into account (Adjusted HWS Threat)[8].

The way in which water scarcity is defined and measured has direct, and sometimes contradictory, implications on how serious the issue is perceived to be in different regions. As a result, relying on a single indicator may give a misleading impression about water scarcity issues. It is therefore important when discussing 'water scarcity', to be clear how the term is defined and which aspects of water scarcity it measures and to recognise that one measure by itself is not enough to give the whole picture.

References

1. Falkenmark, M., J. Lundquist and C. Widstrand (1989), "Macro-scale Water Scarcity Requires Micro-scale Approaches: Aspects of Vulnerability in Semi-arid Development", Natural Resources Forum, Vol. 13, No. 4, pp. 258–267.

2. Rijsberman, F.R. (2006), "Water Scarcity: Fact or Fiction?", Agricultural Water Management, Vol. 80, pp. 5–22.

3. Raskin, P. et al. (1997), Water Futures: Assessment of Long-range Patterns and Prospects, Stockholm Environment Institute, Stockholm, Sweden.

4. OECD (2009), Managing Water for All: An OECD Perspective on Pricing and Financing, OECD, Paris, France.

5. Seckler, D. et al. (1998), World Water Demand and Supply, 1990 to 2025: Scenarios and Issues, International Water Management Institute (IWMI) Research Report 19, IWMI, Colombo, Sri Lanka.

6. Molden, D. (ed.) (2007), Water for Food, Water for Life: A Comprehensive Assessment of Water Management in Agriculture, Earthscan/International Water Management Institute, London, UK.

7. Sullivan, C.A. et al. (2003), "The Water Poverty Index: Development and Application at the Community Scale", Natural Resources Forum, Vol. 27, pp. 189–199.

8. Vorosmarty, C.J et al. (2010), "Global Threats to Human Water Security and River Biodiversity", Nature, Vol. 467, pp. 555–561.

Critical Thinking

1. What is the broadly understood traditional idea of water scarcity?

2. Why does there need to be more accurate ways of understanding water scarcity?

3. List the alternative ways of measuring water scarcity. What is the benefit to having multiple measurement approaches?

Create Central

www.mhhe.com/createcentral

Internet References

Freshwater Society
www.freshwater.org

National Geographic Society
www.nationalgeographic.com

Natural Resources Defense Council
http://nrdc.org

The World's Water
www.worldwater.org

CHRIS WHITE is an editor of the *Global Water Forum*. The Global Water Forum (GWF) is an initiative of the UNESCO Chair in Water Economics and Transboundary Governance at the Australian National University. The GWF presents knowledge and insights from some of the world's leading water researchers and practitioners. The contributions generate accessible and evidence-based insights towards understanding and addressing local, regional, and global water challenges. The principal objectives of the site are to: support capacity building through knowledge sharing; provide a means for informed, unbiased discussion of potentially contentious issues; and, provide a means for discussion of important issues that receive less attention than they deserve. To reach these goals, the GWF seeks to: present fact and evidence-based insights; make the results of academic research freely available to those outside of academia; investigate a broad range of issues within water management; and, provide a more in-depth analysis than is commonly found in public media.

Article

The World's Water Challenge

If oil is the key geopolitical resource of today, water will be as important—if not more so—in the not-so-distant future.

Erik R. Peterson and Rachel A. Posner

Historically, water has meant the difference between life and death, health and sickness, prosperity and poverty, environmental sustainability and degradation, progress and decay, stability and insecurity. Societies with the wherewithal and knowledge to control or "smooth" hydrological cycles have experienced more rapid economic progress, while populations without the capacity to manage water flows—especially in regions subject to pronounced flood-drought cycles—have found themselves confronting tremendous social and economic challenges in development.

Tragically, a substantial part of humanity continues to face acute water challenges. We now stand at a point at which an obscenely large portion of the world's population lacks regular access to fresh drinking water or adequate sanitation. Water-related diseases are a major burden in countries across the world. Water consumption patterns in many regions are no longer sustainable. The damaging environmental consequences of water practices are growing rapidly. And the complex and dynamic linkages between water and other key resources—especially food and energy—are inadequately understood. These factors suggest that even at current levels of global population, resource consumption, and economic activity, we may have already passed the threshold of water sustainability.

An obscenely large portion of the world's population lacks regular access to fresh drinking water or adequate sanitation.

A major report recently issued by the 2030 Water Resources Group (whose members include McKinsey & Company, the World Bank, and a consortium of business partners) estimated that, assuming average economic growth and no efficiency gains, the gap between global water demand and reliable supply could reach 40 percent over the next 20 years. As serious as this world supply-demand gap is, the study notes, the dislocations will be even more concentrated in developing regions that

account for one-third of the global population, where the water deficit could rise to 50 percent.

It is thus inconceivable that, at this moment in history, no generally recognized "worth" has been established for water to help in its more efficient allocation. To the contrary, many current uses of water are skewed by historical and other legacy practices that perpetuate massive inefficiencies and unsustainable patterns.

The Missing Links

In addition, in the face of persistent population pressures and the higher consumption implicit in rapid economic development among large populations in the developing world, it is noteworthy that our understanding of resource linkages is so limited. Our failure to predict in the spring of 2008 a spike in food prices, a rise in energy prices, and serious droughts afflicting key regions of the world—all of which occurred simultaneously—reveals how little we know about these complex interrelationships.

Without significant, worldwide changes—including more innovation in and diffusion of water-related technologies; fundamental adjustments in consumption patterns; improvements in efficiencies; higher levels of public investment in water infrastructures; and an integrated approach to governance based on the complex relationships between water and food, water and economic development, and water and the environment—the global challenge of water resources could become even more severe.

Also, although global warming's potential effects on watersheds across the planet are still not precisely understood, there can be little doubt that climate change will in a number of regions generate serious dislocations in water supply. In a June 2008 technical paper, the Intergovernmental Panel on Climate Change (IPCC) concluded that "globally, the negative impacts of climate change on freshwater systems are expected to outweigh the benefits." It noted that "higher water temperatures and changes in extremes, including droughts and floods, are projected to affect water quality and exacerbate many forms of water pollution."

Climate change will in a number of regions generate serious dislocations in water supply.

As a result, we may soon be entering unknown territory when it comes to addressing the challenges of water in all their dimensions, including public health, economic development, gender equity, humanitarian crises, environmental degradation, and global security. The geopolitical consequences alone could be profound.

Daunting Trends

Although water covers almost three-quarters of the earth's surface, only a fraction of it is suitable for human consumption. According to the United Nations, of the water that humans consume, approximately 70 percent is used in agricultural production, 22 percent in industry, and 8 percent in domestic use. This consumption—critical as it is for human health, economic development, political and social stability, and security—is unequal, inefficient, and unsustainable.

Indeed, an estimated 884 million people worldwide do not have access to clean drinking water, and 2.5 billion lack adequate sanitation. A staggering 1.8 million people, 90 percent of them children, lose their lives each year as a result of diarrheal diseases resulting from unsafe drinking water and poor hygiene. More generally, the World Health Organization (WHO) estimates that inadequate water, sanitation, and hygiene are responsible for roughly half the malnutrition in the world.

In addition, we are witnessing irreparable damage to ecosystems across the globe. Aquifers are being drawn down faster than they can naturally be recharged. Some great lakes are mere fractions of what they once were.

And water pollution is affecting millions of people's lives. China typifies this problem. More than 75 percent of its urban river water is unsuitable for drinking or fishing, and 90 percent of its urban groundwater is contaminated. On the global scale, according to a recent UN report on world water development, every day we dump some 2 million tons of industrial waste and chemicals, human waste, and agricultural waste (fertilizers, pesticides, and pesticide residues) into our water supply.

Over the past century, as the world's population rose from 1.7 billion people in 1900 to 6.1 billion in 2000, global fresh water consumption increased six-fold—more than double the rate of population growth over the same period. The latest "medium" projections from the UN's population experts suggest that we are on the way to 8 billion people by the year 2025 and 9.15 billion by the middle of the century.

The contours of our predicament are clear-cut: A finite amount of water is available to a rapidly increasing number of people whose activities require more water than ever before. The UN Commission on Sustainable Development has indicated that we may need to double the amount of freshwater available today to meet demand at the middle of the century—after which time demand for water will increase by 50 percent with each additional generation.

Why is demand for water rising so rapidly? It goes beyond population pressures. According to a recent report from the UN Food and Agriculture Organization, the world will require 70 percent more food production over the next 40 years to meet growing per capita demand. This rising agricultural consumption necessarily translates into higher demand for water. By 2025, according to the water expert Sandra Postel, meeting projected global agricultural demand will require additional irrigation totaling some 2,000 cubic kilometers—roughly the equivalent of the annual flow of 24 Nile Rivers or 110 Colorado Rivers.

Consumption patterns aside, climate change will accelerate and intensify stress on water systems. According to the IPCC, in coming decades the frequency of extreme droughts will double while the average length of droughts will increase six times. This low water flow, combined with higher temperatures, not only will create devastating shortages. It will also increase pollution of fresh water by sediments, nutrients, pesticides, pathogens, and salts. On the other hand, in some regions, wet seasons will be more intense (but shorter). In underdeveloped communities that lack capture and storage capacity, water will run off and will be unavailable when it is needed in dry seasons, thus perpetuating the cycle of poverty.

Climatic and demographic trends indicate that the regions of the world with the highest population growth rates are precisely those that are already the "driest" and that are expected to experience water stress in the future. The Organization for Economic Cooperation and Development has suggested that the number of people in water-stressed countries—where governments encounter serious constraints on their ability to meet household, industrial, and agricultural water demands—could rise to nearly 4 billion by the year 2030.

The Geopolitical Dimension

If oil is the key geopolitical resource of today, water will be as important—if not more so—in the not-so-distant future. A profound mismatch exists between the distribution of the human population and the availability of fresh water. At the water-rich extreme of the spectrum is the Amazon region, which has an estimated 15 percent of global runoff and less than 1 percent of the world's people. South America as a whole has only 6 percent of the world's population but more than a quarter of the world's runoff.

At the other end of the spectrum is Asia. Home to 60 percent of the global population, it has a freshwater endowment estimated at less than 36 percent of the world total. It is hardly surprising that some water-stressed countries in the region have pursued agricultural trade mechanisms to gain access to more water—in the form of food. Recently, this has taken the form of so-called "land grabs," in which governments and state companies have invested in farmland overseas to meet their countries' food security needs. *The Economist* has estimated that, to date, some 50 million acres have been remotely purchased or leased under these arrangements in Africa and Asia.

Although freshwater management has historically represented a means of preventing and mitigating conflict between countries with shared water resources, the growing scarcity of water will likely generate new levels of tension at the local, national, and even international levels. Many countries with limited water availability also depend on shared water, which increases the risk of friction, social tensions, and conflict.

The Euphrates, Jordan, and Nile Rivers are obvious examples of places where frictions already have occurred. But approximately 40 percent of the world's population lives in more than 260 international river basins of major social and economic importance, and 13 of these basins are shared by five or more countries. Interstate tensions have already escalated and could easily intensify as increasing water scarcity raises the stakes.

Within countries as well, governments in water-stressed regions must effectively and transparently mediate the concerns and demands of various constituencies. The interests of urban and rural populations, agriculture and industry, and commercial and domestic sectors often conflict. If allocation issues are handled inappropriately, subnational disputes and unrest linked to water scarcity and poor water quality could arise, as they already have in numerous cases.

Addressing the Challenge

Considering the scope and gravity of these water challenges, responses by governments and nongovernmental organizations have fallen short of what is needed. Despite obvious signs that we overuse water, we continue to perpetuate gross inefficiencies. We continue to skew consumption on the basis of politically charged subsidies or other supports. And we continue to pursue patently unsustainable practices whose costs will grow more onerous over time.

The Colorado River system, for example, is being overdrawn. It supplies water to Las Vegas, Los Angeles, San Diego, and other growing communities in the American Southwest. If demand on this river system is not curtailed, there is a 50 percent chance that Lake Mead will be dry by 2021, according to experts from the Scripps Institution of Oceanography.

Despite constant reminders of future challenges, we continue to be paralyzed by short-term thinking and practices. What is especially striking about water is the extent to which the world's nations are unprepared to manage such a vital resource sustainably. Six key opportunities for solutions stand out.

First, the global community needs to do substantially more to address the lack of safe drinking water and sanitation. Donor countries, by targeting water resources, can simultaneously address issues associated with health, poverty reduction, and environmental stewardship, as well as stability and security concerns. It should be stressed in this regard that rates of return on investment in water development—financial, political, and geopolitical—are all positive. The WHO estimates that the global return on every dollar invested in water and sanitation programs is $4 and $9, respectively.

Consider, for example, how water problems affect the earning power of women. Typically in poor countries, women and girls are kept at home to care for sick family members inflicted with water-related diseases. They also spend hours each day walking to collect water for daily drinking, cooking, and washing. According to the United Nations Children's Fund, water

and sanitation issues explain why more than half the girls in sub-Saharan Africa drop out of primary school.

Second, more rigorous analyses of sustainability could help relevant governments and authorities begin to address the conspicuous mismanagement of water resources in regions across the world. This would include reviewing public subsidies—for water-intensive farming, for example—and other supports that tend to increase rather than remove existing inefficiencies.

Priced to Sell

Third, specialists, scholars, practitioners, and policy makers need to make substantial progress in assigning to water a market value against which more sustainable consumption decisions and policies can be made. According to the American Water Works Association, for example, the average price of water in the United States is $1.50 per 1,000 gallons—or less than a single penny per gallon. Yet, when it comes to the personal consumption market, many Americans do not hesitate to pay prices for bottled water that are higher than what they pay at the pump for a gallon of gasoline. What is clear, both inside and outside the United States, is that mechanisms for pricing water on the basis of sustainability have yet to be identified.

Fourth, rapid advances in technology can and should have a discernible effect on both the supply and demand sides of the global water equation. The technology landscape is breathtaking—from desalination, membrane, and water-reuse technologies to a range of cheaper and more efficient point-of-use applications (such as drip irrigation and rainwater harvesting). It remains to be seen, however, whether the acquisition and use of such technologies can be accelerated and dispersed so that they can have an appreciable effect in offsetting aggregate downside trends.

From a public policy perspective, taxation and regulatory policies can create incentives for the development and dissemination of such technologies, and foreign assistance projects can promote their use in developing countries. Also, stronger links with the private sector would help policy makers improve their understanding of technical possibilities, and public-private partnerships can be effective mechanisms for distributing technologies in the field.

Fifth, although our understanding of the relationship between climate change and water will continue to be shaped by new evidence, it is important that we incorporate into our approach to climate change our existing understanding of water management and climate adaptation issues.

Sixth, the complex links among water, agriculture, and energy must be identified with greater precision. An enormous amount of work remains to be done if we are to appreciate these linkages in the global, basin, and local contexts.

In the final analysis, our capacity to address the constellation of challenges that relate to water access, sanitation, ecosystems, infrastructure, adoption of technologies, and the mobilization of resources will mean the difference between rapid economic development and continued poverty, between healthier populations and continued high exposure to water-related diseases, between a more stable world and intensifying geopolitical tensions.

Critical Thinking

1. In what way will the geopolitical patterns of water resources and consumption be different than the geopolitical patterns of oil resources and consumption?

2. Why does "an obscenely large portion of the world's population lack regular access to fresh water and sanitization"?

3. Refer to your map, and map out the "profound mismatch between the distribution of the human population and the availability of fresh water." Make some critical observations regarding that pattern.

4. How might climate change make the world's future water challenge even more challenging?

5. How might the water challenges of the industrialized world be different than the challenges facing "developing" nations?

ERIK R. PETERSON is senior vice president of the Center for Strategic and International Studies and director of its Global Strategy Institute. **RACHEL A. POSNER** is assistant director of the CSIS Global Water Futures project.

Article   Prepared by: Richard Eathorne, *Northern Michigan University*

Global Water Crisis: Too Little, Too Much, or Lack of a Plan?

The global water crisis—caused by drought, flood, and climate change—is less about supply than it is about recognizing water's true value, using it efficiently, and planning for a different future, say experts.

WILLIAM WHEELER

Learning Outcomes

After reading this article, you will be able to:

- Outline the issues regarding the current global water crisis.
- Explain why climate change is expected to play a critical role with regard to the crisis.
- Discuss why the consequences of regional water shortages can have global effects.

For most of history, thirsty humans made do with what moisture fell from above: The sun warmed the salty seas, pure water evaporated into the air and then cooled and fell to the earth as precipitation. There it clung to glaciers, froze and thawed in lakes, was absorbed by plant roots, coursed through fractured bedrock, and seeped slowly through soil, into aquifers. Most of it returned to sea and sky all over again. There is as much of that water on the planet today as when the first amphibian flopped ashore; as much as when the ancient Greeks divined the future in the babble of brooks.

So why do experts in science, economics, and development warn that a "global water crisis" threatens the stability of nations and the health of billions?

From space, the idea of a global water crisis may seem perplexing: 75 percent of the planet's surface is blue. But usable fresh water is a tiny fraction of what we see—only 2.5 percent of the water on Earth. And two-thirds of that fresh water is locked away in glaciers, icecaps, and permanent snow. Of the stock of accessible fresh water, 99 percent is in underground aquifers—some are nonrenewable; and in some that are replenishable, ground water is slurped up faster by a growing population than it can be replaced.

But even so, say experts, the problem is perhaps more an issue of recognizing water's true value, using it efficiently and planning for the lean times, than it is a lack of overall supply.

The ongoing historic American drought, with its cascade effect on food and utility prices at home and food costs abroad, is an example of scarcity's effect.

But superstorm Sandy's deluge and flooding, says Geoff Dabelko, an environmental expert at Ohio University in Athens, is an example of how the term "global water crisis" can be misleading. It tends to imply that there's just one kind of crisis—a water shortage.

"The kind of dead-cow-carcass-in-the-desert image that global 'water crisis' evokes is very real for some people," Professor Dabelko says. "But there are so many dimensions." Too much water—whether from flooding, sea level rise, or more extreme storms—can be just as deadly as too little.

While the balance between water supplies and the demands of a burgeoning population are further complicated by the effect of climate change on delicate hydrological margins, there are those who say there is enough water, if nations learn to plan for a different future—one in which past abundance is no guide.

The Growing Thirst for Water

Water is a part of everything we do: It feeds crops, powers cities, cools computer servers, and is key to the manufacturing of everything from clothes to cars. The billion more people expected on the planet by 2025 will increase water demand for all of those functions. And just to feed those people, water withdrawals for agriculture are expected to increase by about half.

But it's not only about the additional mouths to feed; it's also the growth of new appetites. Much of the growth in demand will emerge from the swelling sprawl of bustling, slum-pocked metropolises across the developing world. For the first time in history, the share of the global population living in cities recently surpassed 50 percent—on its way to 75 percent expected by 2050.

With each step up the economic ladder, people demand more water for sanitation, industry, hydroelectric power, and water-intensive diets—such as preferring beef to wheat, a shift that requires 10 times as much water per kilogram to produce. Urban-rural competition for water has already pushed countries to import grains—"virtual water"— or, in the case of wealthier countries like China, South Korea, and Saudi Arabia, to lease land in developing countries.

By 2030, the Water Resources Group forecasts, global water requirements may outstrip sustainable use by 40 percent. And almost half the world's people will be living under severe water stress, predicts the Organization for Economic Cooperation and Development (OECD).

Already, water stress—where the reliable water supply is being used up more quickly than it can be replenished—is widespread and is expected to increase significantly in the years ahead, particularly in North Africa, the Middle East, and Asia. By 2050, according to the UN's Food and Agriculture Organization, 1 in 5 developing countries will face water shortages.

Too Many Straws in the Glass

In 2009, twin NASA satellites—orbiting 300 miles above Earth, measuring changes in the mass of underground water in northern India—yielded disturbing data: Excessive irrigation practices were sucking the region dry. Even though rainfall had been slightly above average, millions of tube wells—like too many straws in the glass—were draining groundwater levels by as much as a foot per year, threatening farm output in the country's fertile breadbasket and raising the risk of a major water crisis. Over the past seven years, an amount equivalent to nearly three times the water in Lake Mead, America's largest water reservoir, had been lost.

"If measures are not taken to ensure sustainable groundwater usage," NASA scientists concluded, "the consequences for the 114 million residents of the region may include a collapse of agricultural output and severe shortages of potable water."

If renewable water supplies—rainfall in lakes, streams, and rivers—are like an annually replenished checking account, then ground water and deep aquifers are the savings. A few thousand years ago, when civilizations first branched out from rivers, they populated areas where they could draw from that savings in the form of ground water 20 to 30 feet below the surface. Globally, this was the norm until the 1950s, when fossil fuel energy became widely available to allow pumping water from ever-deeper depths. Ever since, humanity has increasingly lived beyond the margins of its renewable water supply.

In ancient fossil aquifers—in the Great Plains of the United States, the North China Plain, or Saudi Arabia—water levels are not recharged by rainfall. Elsewhere, as in northern India, ground water is used faster than it can be replenished. According to the United Nations, ground-water extraction globally has tripled in the past 50 years, during which time India and China's ground-water use has risen 10-fold.

As a result, half of the global population lives in countries where water tables are rapidly falling. These supply problems are compounded by new land use patterns, like deforestation and soil grading, as well as leakage from poorly maintained infrastructure in cities.

Climate Complications

To make things worse, climate change is expected to cause water shortages in many parts of the world, making ground water all the more important as a buffer.

The spike in global grain prices caused by the US drought last summer, on the heels of an epic winter drought in Spain and summer heat waves in southern Europe, showed the cascade effect of the sort of droughts that the Intergovernmental Panel on Climate Change expects will multiply in the decades ahead.

Not surprisingly, the greatest impact is on the poor. While American households spend, on average, 13 percent of their budgets on food, that expenditure is often 50 percent or more in the developing world. So a spike in food prices can trigger explosive riots like those that erupted there in the past five years.

According to Richard Seager, a drought specialist at Columbia University in New York, the recent US drought was mostly a result of naturally occurring weather patterns. But it's probably influenced by a background of unprecedented record-high temperatures that reflect an already warming environment. A significant recent development in climate research is that scientists have begun linking climate change to the probability of individual weather events. Professor Seager's own research predicts that, owing to climate change, the aridity levels experienced in parts of America during the Dust Bowl of the 1930s and again in the 1950s will be the new normal in the American Southwest by midcentury.

Seager says that climate change exacerbated the impact of superstorm Sandy, as well—contributing to higher sea levels: "We've known forever that hurricanes of this intensity can get up to New York City. Nothing there that couldn't be due to just natural variability. But it's happening with sea levels higher, and sea levels are still going up. So when these things happen, they can do extra damage because it's easier to breach the sea wall protections."

He says Gov. Andrew Cuomo and New York City Mayor Michael Bloomberg have accurately gauged the threat climate change poses to the city. "The sea levels are going to continue to go up. So, boy, do we have a problem. There's no reason to believe this won't happen again in the next two decades."

Climate change increases variability, says Dabelko: "That's the challenge that we have to [face] as individuals, as societies, as governments, as businesses . . . to understand that it's going to change. It's going to be bigger swings. And some people may benefit . . . and many are not going to be well adapted . . ."

There's also another misconception about the global water crisis, he says, which is the assumption that "it's somebody else's problem, on the presumption that we're wealthy enough to just deal.

"[S]o climate change, it's Bangladesh. Global water crisis, it's the Horn of Africa. It's somebody else's problem, and those [who] can't afford something are going to be the ones that suffer. Rather than understanding, 'Yes, it's global. Yes, it's a crisis. But it's also very meaningful for us even if we can insulate ourselves from the changes in food prices.'"

Consequences Don't Respect Borders

"During the next 10 years, many countries important to the United States will almost certainly experience water problems—shortages, poor water quality, or floods—that will contribute to the risk of instability and state failure, and increased regional tensions," predicted the federal government's National Intelligence Council in an assessment of global water security earlier this year.

Annual river runoff and water availability in some high altitudes and in some wet tropical areas will actually increase 20 to 40 percent by midcentury, while it will decrease 10 to 30 percent in some already waterstressed dry regions in the mid-latitudes and in the dry tropics, according to the Intergovernmental Panel on Climate Change (IPCC). This may affect water resources in many arid and semiarid areas in the Mediterranean Basin, western US, Southern Africa, northeast Brazil, and much of Australia.

Over the next century, climate change will reduce the runoff from melting glaciers that feed major rivers, affecting water availability in important regions. More than one-sixth of the world's population relies on the meltwater from receding glaciers and snowpacks, including tens of millions of people in the Andes and hundreds of millions who depend on meltwater from the Hindu Kush and the Himalayas.

These supply problems will be exacerbated by bad water management, including the over-pumping of ground-water supplies, wasteful irrigation practices, deforestation, soil grading, leaking urban infrastructure, and faulty economic models that don't account for the true value of water, according to the National Intelligence Council.

In light of these changes, the OECD predicts that, by 2030, nearly half of the world's population will be living under severe water stress.

The problem is more than just water shortages. The risk of drought and flood would increase by the end of the century, according to the IPCC, and rising sea levels and deteriorating coastal buffers will increase vulnerability to coastal storms over the next few decades. While vulnerability will be greatest in urban areas of the developing world, where flood control structures are often poorly maintained, "at times water flows will be severe enough to overwhelm the water control infrastructures of even developed countries, including the United States," predicts the National Intelligence Council. Developing countries without the resources or ability to solve their water problems risk destabilizing social disruptions, even state failure, the report concludes, especially if the population believes the government is responsible.

While interstate conflict over water is unlikely within 10 years, beyond that time frame, water will increasingly be used as economic and political leverage between states and could even become a weapon, using dams to choke off water supplies to downstream neighbors or to flood them. Dams, desalinization facilities, canals, and pipelines may also make appealing targets for terrorist attacks.

If these problems are not managed, food supplies could decline, the risk of waterborne diseases could increase, and energy shortages might hamper growth. (More than 15 countries rely on hydropower to generate at least 80 percent of their electricity. And, in the US, nuclear, hydroelectric, coal-fired, and gas-fired power plants account for half of water withdrawals.)

Pessimistic Scenarios May Be Averted

But the picture may not be as bad as it seems. While the projections about the growing global water crisis drastically underestimate how bad things really are, says Upmanu Lall, director of the Water Center at Columbia University, they also underestimate the scale of waste and the water efficiency improvements that could make adaptation easier.

"Things could actually be worse than what these guys are putting out," says Professor Lall. "They are too optimistic about the current situation compared to what it actually is. And they're too pessimistic about the situation for the future . . . I do see a way to get there."

That's what he's learned from much of his work on water issues in India, which he calls "a basket case for water." He adds: "You could actually eliminate water stress in India if you were just a little bit smarter about which places you were procuring which crops from."

Science, he says, is part of the solution: Agricultural efficiency can be drastically improved with a better mix of what is grown where, accounting for geography, water constraints, and income; governments will have a role to play in setting economic signals to promote conservation and the right mix of crops, and regulation to ensure access in urban and rural areas; cheap soil-moisture sensors could improve agricultural water efficiency by 10 to 15 percent by reducing waste in irrigation systems; recycled waste water could save in the billions of dollars that the US spends purifying water up to drinking quality even though only 10 percent is used for drinking and cooking; flood-control systems can be repurposed to store water.

But most important, says Lall, "the economics of it has to be sorted out." Water allocations for personal consumption and ecological preservation should be protected, he said, but about 75 percent of water consumed globally should be subject to more competitive pricing. In a sense, he argues, water should be treated like oil, allowing developers a guaranteed allocation as an incentive to develop it. About a quarter of water supplies should be protected to ensure people have water for drinking and to preserve ecology, he says. But everyone—from the home-owner watering the lawn to big industry and agriculture—should pay more for water.

Instability, conflict, and economic stagnation may be the prod societies need before they adapt, says Lall.

He deems the US system for allocating water rights as "not too bad." Where those rights were not tradable, he says, "things are a mess."

Some states—Arizona, California, Idaho, and Texas—have water banks that facilitate leases between rights-holders and users. But since these water banks don't incorporate forecasting, they fail to make deals until a drought begins. What the US needs, says Lall, is a national water policy that incorporates forecasts, trading mechanisms, options, and the coordinated use of both surface and ground-water resources.

While the tools and strategies exist to cope with the impending pressures of a warmer and more populous planet, Lall says, "the question is, will we do it right?"

Critical Thinking

1. What will accelerate the growth in demand for water?

2. How does climate change complicate predicting where water shortages will occur in the future?

3. In what ways could the global water issue impact the United States?

Create Central

www.mhhe.com/createcentral

Internet References

Freshwater Society
www.freshwater.org
The World's Water
www.worldwater.org
United Nations Environment Program (UNEP)
www.enep.ch

Article

The Big Melt

BROOK LARMER

Glaciers in the high heart of Asia feed its greatest rivers, lifelines for two billion people. Now the ice and snow are diminishing.

The gods must be furious.

It's the only explanation that makes sense to Jia Son, a Tibetan farmer surveying the catastrophe unfolding above his village in China's mountainous Yunnan Province. "We've upset the natural order," the devout, 52-year-old Buddhist says. "And now the gods are punishing us."

On a warm summer afternoon, Jia Son has hiked a mile and a half up the gorge that Ming-yong Glacier has carved into sacred Mount Kawagebo, looming 22,113 feet high in the clouds above. There's no sign of ice, just a river roiling with silt-laden melt. For more than a century, ever since its tongue lapped at the edge of Mingyong village, the glacier has retreated like a dying serpent recoiling into its lair. Its pace has accelerated over the past decade, to more than a football field every year—a distinctly unglacial rate for an ancient ice mass.

"This all used to be ice ten years ago," Jia Son says, as he scrambles across the scree and brush. He points out a yak trail etched into the slope some 200 feet above the valley bottom. "The glacier sometimes used to cover that trail, so we had to lead our animals over the ice to get to the upper meadows."

Around a bend in the river, the glacier's snout finally comes into view: It's a deathly shade of black, permeated with pulverized rock and dirt. The water from this ice, once so pure it served in rituals as a symbol of Buddha himself, is now too loaded with sediment for the villagers to drink. For nearly a mile the glacier's once smooth surface is ragged and cratered like the skin of a leper. There are glimpses of blue-green ice within the fissures, but the cracks themselves signal trouble. "The beast is sick and wasting away," Jia Son says. "If our sacred glacier cannot survive, how can we?"

It is a question that echoes around the globe, but nowhere more urgently than across the vast swath of Asia that draws its water from the "roof of the world." This geologic colossus—the highest and largest plateau on the planet, ringed by its tallest mountains—covers an area greater than western Europe, at an average altitude of more than two miles. With nearly 37,000 glaciers on the Chinese side alone, the Tibetan Plateau and its surrounding arc of mountains contain the largest volume of ice outside the polar regions. This ice gives birth to Asia's largest

and most legendary rivers, from the Yangtze and the Yellow to the Mekong and the Ganges—rivers that over the course of history have nurtured civilizations, inspired religions, and sustained ecosystems. Today they are lifelines for some of Asia's most densely settled areas, from the arid plains of Pakistan to the thirsty metropolises of northern China 3,000 miles away. All told, some two billion people in more than a dozen countries—nearly a third of the world's population—depend on rivers fed by the snow and ice of the plateau region.

But a crisis is brewing on the roof of the world, and it rests on a curious paradox: For all its seeming might and immutability, this geologic expanse is more vulnerable to climate change than almost anywhere else on Earth. The Tibetan Plateau as a whole is heating up twice as fast as the global average of 1.3°F over the past century—and in some places even faster. These warming rates, unprecedented for at least two millennia, are merciless on the glaciers, whose rare confluence of high altitudes and low latitudes make them especially sensitive to shifts in climate.

For thousands of years the glaciers have formed what Lonnie Thompson, a glaciologist at Ohio State University, calls "Asia's freshwater bank account"—an immense storehouse whose buildup of new ice and snow (deposits) has historically offset its annual runoff (withdrawals). Glacial melt plays its most vital role before and after the rainy season, when it supplies a greater portion of the flow in every river from the Yangtze (which irrigates more than half of China's rice) to the Ganges and the Indus (key to the agricultural heartlands of India and Pakistan). But over the past half century, the balance has been lost, perhaps irrevocably. Of the 680 glaciers Chinese scientists monitor closely on the Tibetan Plateau, 95 percent are shedding more ice than they're adding, with the heaviest losses on its southern and eastern edges. "These glaciers are not simply retreating," Thompson says. "They're losing mass from the surface down."

The ice cover in this portion of the plateau has shrunk more than 6 percent since the 1970s—and the damage is still greater in Tajikistan and northern India, with 35 percent and 20 percent declines respectively over the past five decades. The rate of melting is not uniform, and a number of glaciers in the Karakoram Range on the western edge of the plateau are actually advancing. This anomaly may result from increases in snowfall in the higher latitude—and therefore colder—Karakorams, where snow and ice are less vulnerable to small temperature increases. The gaps in scientific knowledge are still great, and in the Tibetan Plateau they are deepened by the region's remoteness and political sensitivity—as well as by the inherent complexities of climate science.

Though scientists argue about the rate and cause of glacial retreat, most don't deny that it's happening. And they believe the worst may be yet to come. The more dark areas that are exposed by melting, the more sunlight is absorbed than reflected, causing temperatures to rise faster. (Some climatologists believe this warming feedback loop could intensify the Asian monsoon, triggering more violent storms and flooding in places such as Bangladesh and Myanmar.) If current trends hold, Chinese scientists believe that 40 percent of the plateau's glaciers could disappear by 2050. "Full-scale glacier shrinkage is inevitable," says Yao Tandong, a glaciologist at China's Institute of Tibetan Plateau Research. "And it will lead to ecological catastrophe."

The potential impacts extend far beyond the glaciers. On the Tibetan Plateau, especially its dry northern flank, people are already affected by a warmer climate. The grasslands and wetlands are deteriorating, and the permafrost that feeds them with spring and summer melt is retreating to higher elevations. Thousands of lakes have dried up. Desert now covers about one-sixth of the plateau, and in places sand dunes lap across the highlands like waves in a yellow sea. The herders who once thrived here are running out of options.

Along the plateau's southern edge, by contrast, many communities are coping with too much water. In alpine villages like Mingyong, the glacial melt has swelled rivers, with welcome side effects: expanded croplands and longer growing seasons. But such benefits often hide deeper costs. In Mingyong, surging meltwater has carried away topsoil; elsewhere, excess runoff has been blamed for more frequent flooding and landslides. In the mountains from Pakistan to Bhutan, thousands of glacial lakes have formed, many potentially unstable. Among the more dangerous is Imja Tsho, at 16,400 feet on the trail to Nepal's Island Peak. Fifty years ago the lake didn't exist; today, swollen by melt, it is a mile long and 300 feet deep. If it ever burst through its loose wall of moraine, it would drown the Sherpa villages in the valley below.

This situation—too much water, too little water—captures, in miniature, the trajectory of the overall crisis. Even if melting glaciers provide an abundance of water in the short run, they portend a frightening endgame: the eventual depletion of Asia's greatest rivers. Nobody can predict exactly when the glacier retreat will translate into a sharp drop in runoff. Whether it happens in 10, 30, or 50 years depends on local conditions, but the collateral damage across the region could be devastating. Along with acute water and electricity shortages, experts predict a plunge in food production, widespread migration in the face of ecological changes, even conflicts between Asian powers.

The nomads' tent is a pinprick of white against a canvas of green and brown. There is no other sign of human existence on the 14,000-foot-high prairie that seems to extend to the end of the world. As a vehicle rattles toward the tent, two young men emerge, their long black hair horizontal in the wind. Ba O

and his brother Tsering are part of an unbroken line of Tibetan nomads who for at least a thousand years have led their herds to summer grazing grounds near the headwaters of the Yangtze and Yellow Rivers.

Inside the tent, Ba O's wife tosses patties of dried yak dung onto the fire while her four-year-old son plays with a spool of sheep's wool. The family matriarch, Lu Ji, churns yak milk into cheese, rocking back and forth in a hypnotic rhythm. Behind her are two weathered Tibetan chests topped with a small Buddhist shrine: a red prayer wheel, a couple of smudged Tibetan texts, and several yak butter candles whose flames are never allowed to go out. "This is the way we've always done things," Ba O says. "And we don't want that to change."

But it may be too late. The grasslands are dying out, as decades of warming temperatures—exacerbated by overgrazing—turn prairie into desert. Watering holes are drying up, and now, instead of traveling a short distance to find summer grazing for their herds, Ba O and his family must trek more than 30 miles across the high plateau. Even there the grass is meager. "It used to grow so high you could lose a sheep in it," Ba O says. "Now it doesn't reach above their hooves." The family's herd has dwindled from 500 animals to 120. The next step seems inevitable: selling their remaining livestock and moving into a government resettlement camp.

Across Asia the response to climate-induced threats has mostly been slow and piecemeal, as if governments would prefer to leave it up to the industrialized countries that pumped the greenhouse gases into the atmosphere in the first place. There are exceptions. In Ladakh, a bone-dry region in northern India and Pakistan that relies entirely on melting ice and snow, a retired civil engineer named Chewang Norphel has built "artificial glaciers"—simple stone embankments that trap and freeze glacial melt in the fall for use in the early spring growing season. Nepal is developing a remote monitoring system to gauge when glacial lakes are in danger of bursting, as well as the technology to drain them. Even in places facing destructive monsoonal flooding, such as Bangladesh, "floating schools" in the delta enable kids to continue their education—on boats.

But nothing compares to the campaign in China, which has less water than Canada but 40 times more people. In the vast desert in the Xinjiang region, just north of the Tibetan Plateau, China aims to build 59 reservoirs to capture and save glacial runoff. Across Tibet, artillery batteries have been installed to launch rain-inducing silver iodide into the clouds. In Qinghai the government is blocking off degraded grasslands in hopes they can be nurtured back to health. In areas where grasslands have already turned to scrub desert, bales of wire fencing are rolled out over the last remnants of plant life to prevent them from blowing away.

Along the road near the town of Madoi are two rows of newly built houses. This is a resettlement village for Tibetan nomads, part of a massive and controversial program to relieve pressure on the grasslands near the sources of Chinas three major rivers—the Yangtze, Yellow, and Mekong—where nearly half of Qinghai Province's 530,000 nomads have traditionally lived. Tens of thousands of nomads here have had to give up their way of life, and many more—including, perhaps, Ba O—may follow.

The subsidized housing is solid, and residents receive a small annual stipend. Even so, Jixi Lamu, a 33-year-old woman in a traditional embroidered dress, says her family is stuck in limbo, dependent on government handouts. "We've spent the $400 we had left from selling off our animals," she says. "There was no future with our herds, but there's no future here either." Her husband is away looking for menial work. Inside the one-room house, her mother sits on the bed, fingering her prayer beads. A Buddhist shrine stands on the other side of the room, but the candles have burned out.

It is not yet noon in Delhi, just 180 miles south of the Himalayan glaciers. But in the narrow corridors of Nehru Camp, a slum in this city of 16 million, the blast furnace of the north Indian summer has already sent temperatures soaring past 105 degrees Fahrenheit. Chaya, the 25-year-old wife of a fortune-teller, has spent seven hours joining the mad scramble for water that, even today, defines life in this heaving metropolis—and offers a taste of what the depletion of Tibet's water and ice portends.

Chaya's day began long before sunrise, when she and her five children fanned out in the darkness, armed with plastic jugs of every size. After daybreak, the rumor of a tap with running water sent her stumbling in a panic through the slum's narrow corridors. Now, with her containers still empty and the sun blazing overhead, she has returned home for a moment's rest. Asked if she's eaten anything today, she laughs: "We haven't even had any tea yet."

Suddenly cries erupt—a water truck has been spotted. Chaya leaps up and joins the human torrent in the street. A dozen boys swarm onto a blue tanker, jamming hoses in and siphoning the water out. Below, shouting women jostle for position with their containers. In six minutes the tanker is empty. Chaya arrived too late and must move on to chase the next rumor of water.

Delhi's water demand already exceeds supply by more than 300 million gallons a day, a shortfall worsened by inequitable distribution and a leaky infrastructure that loses an estimated 40 percent of the water. More than two-thirds of the city's water is pulled from the Yamuna and the Ganges, rivers fed by Himalayan ice. If that ice disappears, the future will almost certainly be worse. "We are facing an unsustainable situation," says Diwan Singh, a Delhi environmental activist. "Soon—not in thirty years but in five to ten—there will be an exodus because of the lack of water."

The tension already seethes. In the clogged alleyway around one of Nehru Camp's last functioning taps, which run for one hour a day, a man punches a woman who cut in line, leaving a purple welt on her face. "We wake up every morning fighting over water," says Kamal Bhate, a local astrologer watching the melee. This one dissolves into shouting and finger-pointing, but the brawls can be deadly. In a nearby slum a teenage boy was recently beaten to death for cutting in line.

As the rivers dwindle, the conflicts could spread. India, China, and Pakistan all face pressure to boost food production to keep up with their huge and growing populations. But climate change and diminishing water supplies could reduce cereal yields in South Asia by 5 percent within three decades. "We're going to see rising tensions over shared water resources,

including political disputes between farmers, between farmers and cities, and between human and ecological demands for water," says Peter Gleick, a water expert and president of the Pacific Institute in Oakland, California. "And I believe more of these tensions will lead to violence."

The real challenge will be to prevent water conflicts from spilling across borders. There is already a growing sense of alarm in Central Asia over the prospect that poor but glacier-heavy nations (Tajikistan, Kyrgyzstan) may one day restrict the flow of water to their parched but oil-rich neighbors (Uzbekistan, Kazakhstan, Turkmenistan). In the future, peace between Pakistan and India may hinge as much on water as on nuclear weapons, for the two countries must share the glacier-dependent Indus.

The biggest question mark hangs over China, which controls the sources of the region's major rivers. Its damming of the Mekong has sparked anger downstream in Indochina. If Beijing follows through on tentative plans to divert the Brahmaputra, it could provoke its rival, India, in the very region where the two countries fought a war in 1962.

For the people in Nehru Camp, geopolitical concerns are lost in the frenzied pursuit of water. In the afternoon, a tap outside the slum is suddenly turned on, and Chaya, smiling triumphantly, hauls back a full, ten-gallon jug on top of her head. The water is dirty and bitter, and there are no means to boil it. But now, at last, she can give her children their first meal of the day: a piece of bread and a few spoonfuls of lentil stew. "They should be studying, but we keep shooing them away to find water," Chaya says. "We have no choice, because who knows if we'll find enough water tomorrow."

Fatalism may be a natural response to forces that seem beyond our control. But Jia Son, the Tibetan farmer watching Mingyong Glacier shrink, believes that every action counts— good or bad, large or small. Pausing on the mountain trail, he makes a guilty confession. The melting ice, he says, may be his fault.

When Jia Son first noticed the rising temperatures—an unfamiliar trickle of sweat down his back about a decade ago—he figured it was a gift from the gods. Winter soon lost some of its brutal sting. The glacier began releasing its water earlier in the summer, and for the first time in memory villagers had the luxury of two harvests a year.

Then came the Chinese tourists, a flood of city dwellers willing to pay locals to take them up to see the glacier. The Han tourists don't always respect Buddhist traditions; in their gleeful hollers to provoke an icefall, they seem unaware of the calamity that has befallen the glacier. Still, they have turned a poor village into one of the region's wealthiest. "Life is much easier now," says Jia Son, whose simple farmhouse, like all in the village, has a television and government-subsidized satellite dish. "But maybe our greed has made Kawagebo angry."

He is referring to the temperamental deity above his village. One of the holiest mountains in Tibetan Buddhism, Kawagebo has never been conquered, and locals believe its summit—and its glacier—should remain untouched. When a Sino-Japanese expedition tried to scale the peak in 1991, an avalanche near the top of the glacier killed all 17 climbers. Jia Son remains convinced the deaths were not an accident but an act of divine retribution. Could Mingyong's retreat be another sign of Kawagebo's displeasure?

Jia Son is taking no chances. Every year he embarks on a 15-day pilgrimage around Kawagebo to show his deepening Buddhist devotion. He no longer hunts animals or cuts down trees. As part of a government program, he has also given up a parcel of land to be reforested. His family still participates in the village's tourism cooperative, but Jia Son makes a point of telling visitors about the glacier's spiritual significance. "Nothing will get better," he says, "until we get rid of our materialistic thinking."

It's a simple pledge, perhaps, one that hardly seems enough to save the glaciers of the Tibetan Plateau—and stave off the water crisis that seems sure to follow. But here, in the shadow of one of the world's fastest retreating glaciers, this lone farmer has begun, in his own small way, to restore the balance.

Critical Thinking

1. Sketch a concept map of the linkages between Asia's population centers, location of glaciers, and their agricultural regions. Locate potential areas for conflict over water resources.

2. If water resources (via glaciers) became too scarce, how will Asia feed its people?

3. What other environmental impacts in the region may also result from glacial loss?

Article   Prepared by: Richard Eathorne, *Northern Michigan University*

Michael Pollan on the Links between Biodiversity and Health

Author Michael Pollan has often written about people's relationship to the natural world. In a *Yale Environment 360* interview, he talks about researching his latest book and what he learned about the connections between ecology and human health.

JACK HITT

Learning Outcomes

After reading this article, you will be able to:

- Describe author Pollan's argument about the connection between biodiversity and human health.
- Explain why the trend toward a more monoculture type of agriculture presents threats to human health.

It was an odd paradox that led author Michael Pollan to write a book about cooking: How was it, he wondered, that in an era when Americans were buying more and more prepackaged, ready-to-eat food, they were spending more time watching programs about cooking on television?

That question led to his new book, *Cooked,* which like his previous books, delves into issues relating to the connections between the environment and what we eat, and, more broadly, to humanity's relationship to the natural world. Pollan argues that taking control of cooking may be the single most important step an individual can take to help make the American food system healthier and more sustainable.

In an interview with *Yale Environment 360* contributor Jack Hitt, Pollan talked about how his research led him on a journey that ranged from the monoculture fields of U.S. commodity agriculture to the bacterial world inside the human body. And he noted the fundamental importance of biodiversity—in the landscape and the farm field, as well as in people's diets. "This may prove to be the key legacy of ecology—what it teaches us about health," Pollan said. "Who would have thought?"

Yale Environment 360: In your new book, *Cooked,* you head to the stove, where previously you had been in the garden or the feed lot or a cornfield. Has taking your observations indoors changed the way you think about the big outdoors?

Michael Pollan: I would say it has. Like most journalists I tended to gravitate toward exotic places, places my reader hadn't been—like the feedlot or the laboratory. That's one of the things we do—we're kind of these designated inquirers. And it was my experience on the feedlot and other sites of industrialized agriculture that sent me into the kitchen. Because I came to realize that the way we cook, or whether we cook or not, or who's doing the cooking, is creating that other landscape. And it really was the industrializing of cooking—which we call food processing, done by corporations, of course—which drove the industrialization of our farming.

It's McDonald's that gives us the giant monocultures of Russet Burbank potatoes that I wrote about in *Botany of Desire,* or the feed lots that I wrote about in *Omnivore's Dilemma.* And I came to realize that you couldn't understand those landscapes without reference to these everyday decisions we make about whether we're going to cook or whether we're going to go out to McDonald's. That they were linked. I never expected to write a book about a landscape as familiar as my kitchen, or anyone's kitchen. But that's of course the great lesson of ecology—these things are connected.

e360 Recently you've described yourself as a "superorganism." What do you mean?

Pollan: One of the byways of this book was learning about fermentation, and meeting these "fermentos" as I call them—these passionate fermentation geeks who have a completely different relationship to bacteria than most of us do. And they taught me a different way to think about bacteria. Learning about these external fermentations, whether you're talking about tea or beer or bread, very quickly gets you into its mirror image, which is the fermentation within, the fermentation in your own large intestine, and what those bacteria are up to.

So I followed this path into the microbiology of the gut and was amazed to learn that first, we are only 10 percent human, if you're counting cells, and 90 percent bacterial. And those bacteria have a profound impact on your health, on your mood, on your immune system, on your metabolism, and whether you're going to become infected by bad bacteria or not. And it turns out that health—which we think of as a property of us, the human cells in our body—turns out to be a collective property of the whole community. That community consists of these microbes. You can't be healthy if they're not . . . That's a radical rethinking of who we are.

e360 At one point you referred to "the impoverished westernized microbiome," and you posed the question of whether the human body needs what some microbiologists call "restoration ecology." So you're applying environmental metaphors to the human body. How might this kind of language make us think in a new way about our bodies?

Pollan: I think when you bring the concepts of ecology into your body, that's a revolutionary new paradigm for medicine and for the philosophy of human identity. It breaks down the "us and them" attitude we bring to nature. It's a very direct implication of the natural world in the body. We know when we eat we're always taking nature into us. But the idea that we're a host to an ecological community and that that ecological community is obviously shaped by what's going on in the world—whether we're talking about toxins, antibiotics—you're really breaking down that barrier between us and nature *out there*. Nature is passing through us. I didn't tease out these implications, but I think it does have important implications for how you think about nature. It definitely brings it home.

e360 And also how you think about what you eat?

Pollan: Yes. If it doesn't necessarily change your diet, it does change your attitude toward the various chemical compounds that poison this environment. We've understood that feeding antibiotics to livestock is a public health risk because of the rise of superbugs and antibiotic-resistant microbes, and that's the reason people have campaigned to remove them. But it turns out there's another reason to remove them, and that is that these antibiotics are poisoning and cutting down on the biodiversity inside you. So there are implications of knowing this that go beyond diet.

e360 How was it that scientists recently came to start talking about the human microbiome?

Pollan: There are two tools that have allowed for this wilderness to be explored. One is this new sequencing technology. But the other was theories of ecology. It was when scientists began thinking, "Hey, what if we ask the questions that ecosystems scientists ask?" Which was radical for medicine. Medicine doesn't usually think that way. And that really opened it up. And they started using terms like community dynamics and invasion resistance. And exotic species. And resilience. So there was an intellectual tool and there was a technical tool. And they were both required to make the breakthroughs we're starting to make.

e360 Wow, that's cool. So there really was a kind of theoretical borrowing?

Pollan: Yes. And this may be prove to be a key legacy of ecology—what it teaches us about health. Who would have thought?

e360 What might the last 50 years of environmental action policy and environmental education teach us as we begin to discover the Amazonian rainforest that resides in our gut?

Pollan: We know that we're connected and that there are links between soil and health, and water and health. This is just another way to draw those links.

I was really struck by how many of the microbiologists were concerned about very common food additives. Xanthan gum and polysorbate 80, these emulsifiers, which seem like one of the least toxic of food additives—these are just chemicals that allow water and oil to be held in solution so they don't come apart. And if you're making processed food, that's really important because it looks really nasty when the sauce in your frozen, I don't know, beef Stroganoff, starts separating.

These [emulsifiers] are very important in processed food. But it turns out that they may be damaging the lining of the gut. And that's not what the FDA [U.S. Food and Drug Administration] ever tested for . . . So we really have to rethink toxicology in light of the microbiome.

e360 These microbes evolve really, really fast. As you point out, some of them take 20 minutes a generation. That's crazy—it's so at odds with everything we know about life out here on the megafauna scale of existence, where evolution is slow, really slow. Is there any evidence that this microbial speed will advantage us in some way as we all adapt to say global warming?

Pollan: One of the questions I've struggled with in writing about the gut and writing about fermentation in the book is how weird it is to outsource very important functions of life to microbes and not have evolved our own systems for dealing with metabolism, temperament, immunity. I mean, it is a huge outsourcing of a critical life function.

One case I thought was absolutely fascinating is this difference in the gut of Japanese people and Americans. There's a very common bacteria that we all share, that all humans have in their gut, and it's involved in digesting polysaccharides of complex carbohydrates and plants. And the Japanese version of it has a gene that allows it to break down seaweed that we can't break down. When you eat seaweed in a Japanese restaurant, you're not getting the nutritional value from it that a Japanese person is getting. And they actually traced the source of that gene, and it came from the bacteria that hang out on seaweed in the ocean. In other words, the bacteria who first learned how to digest seaweed. Through the eating of enough seaweed, this bacteria that is common in the gut of the Japanese borrowed this bit of genetic information and uses it now to digest seaweed. And so now it's a permanent part of the genome of that bug.

There's an example of how the microbiome evolved to take advantage of a change in the environment—i.e., Japanese eating of seaweed—probably because they needed to. And the same thing is true with, say, dealing with a new toxin, detoxifying, and other changes in our environment. It's kind of evolution on fast forward. That's probably critical to our ability to adapt to change, and it may become more critical as we face more rapid and radical environmental changes.

e360 You've written in the past about arguments over preserving "pristine" nature or humans intervening to "garden" nature. How does that apply the human microbiome?

Pollan: Well, if you want to adjust to changes in the environment, you need the genetic resources. This ability to adapt probably depends on high levels of biodiversity, and that's precisely what we have damaged with the Western diet and the Western overuse of antibiotics and other antimacrobials. As scientists have pointed out to me, if you damage the biodiversity enough, the various genes you need to cope will not be there. And the microbiome will come up empty-handed in meeting the challenges it faces.

So that's an argument for restoring the biodiversity of the gut, gardening it, if you will, introducing more species. That may turn out to be the value of these pristine microbiomes, that the genetic resources we need may exist there. We may have to culture those and reintroduce those. We don't know enough to say exactly how to garden the microbiome, but we may need to. We may need to just give it enough biodiversity to be resilient to change. And you see, I'm using all the words we use when we're talking about a farm or any land.

e360 So now that you're very intimate with the alchemy of cooking and fire, water, air, and earth, how would you change America's farm policy if you could, right now?

Pollan: Well, I would try to create incentives that drive diversification. I still feel that the great evil of American agriculture is monoculture. It really does contribute to so many problems at the level of the field and the pests, but also at the level of the diet. The thing you learn is the importance of diversity in what you eat, and to the extent you would drive diversity [in farm policy] you would also be creating raw materials for cooking rather than raw materials for processed food, which are mostly corn and soy.

I love this term "specialty crop." That's what the USDA [U.S. Department of Agriculture] lingo is for anything you grow that you could actually eat—fruits and vegetables. Corn and soy and rice and wheat, these are commodity crops—in the case of rice you do eat it directly, but everything else has to be heavily processed first. Right now, we actually have laws that prohibit farmers receiving subsidies to grow commodity crops from growing specialty crops. They get fined. If you're growing corn and soy, and you want to put in 20 acres of tomatoes because somebody's doing some local canning deal in your county and you want to get in on it and diversify, you get fined. I know farmers who have been fined forty or fifty thousand dollars for doing that. That's unconscionable. We should be encouraging farmers to diversify, for both economic and ecological reasons.

Critical Thinking

1. What does Pollan mean by describing himself as a "superorganism"?

2. Why is monoculture agriculture a threat to human health?

3. Explain why biodiversity in nature is "good" for human health.

Create Central

www.mhhe.com/createcentral

Internet References

Endangered Species
www.endangeredspecie.com

Smithsonian Institution Website
www.si.edu

United Nations Environment Programme (UNEP)
www.unep.ch

World Wildlife Federation (WWF)
www.wwf.org

JACK HITT, who conducted this interview for *Yale Environment 360*, is a contributing writer to the *New York Times Magazine* and author of the book, *Bunch of Amateurs: A Search for the American Character.* He is an occasional contributor to the public radio program, "This American Life," and his writing has appeared in *Harper's, Rolling Stone, Wired,* and *The Best of the Best of American Science Writing.*

Article

The Human Factor

E. O. Wilson talks to Elizabeth Kolbert about ants, habitat, and the threat of mass extinction.

ELIZABETH KOLBERT

If you could talk to any scientist in the world, who would it be? For me, the choice is pretty easy: E. O. Wilson. Wilson is one of the natural world's keenest observers and, at the same time, probably its most eloquent spokesman. As much as any one person can, he has tried to save what's left of the astonishing diversity of life.

Now 81, Wilson began his career as a naturalist when he was barely out of elementary school. As a 13-year-old Boy Scout, in 1942, he noticed some peculiar ant colonies in a vacant lot near his house, in Mobile, Alabama. In this way, he discovered that the imported red fire ant, a native of South America, had invaded the United States. (The Department of Agriculture's attempt to eradicate the ants in the 1950s would become a case study in misguided pesticide application, chronicled by Rachel Carson and dubbed by Wilson the "Vietnam of entomology.") Twenty-five years after his first boyhood discoveries, as a zoology professor at Harvard, Wilson cowrote one of the seminal books in ecology, *The Theory of Island Biogeography*, and in 1975, more or less singlehandedly, he created a whole new field of inquiry: sociobiology—the concept that behavior, including human behavior, has a basis in evolution. Wilson also became one of the first scientists to warn about what has since become known as the biodiversity crisis.

"The worst thing that can happen, will happen," he wrote in 1980.

> *Not energy depletion, economic collapse, limited nuclear war, or conquest by a totalitarian government. As terrible as these catastrophes would be for us, they can be repaired within a few generations. The one process ongoing in the 1980s that will take millions of years to correct is the loss of genetic and species diversity by the destruction of natural habitats. This is the folly our descendants are least likely to forgive us.*

In 1991, Wilson and his coauthor, Bert Hölldobler, won a Pulitzer Prize—Wilson's second—for their book *The Ants*. Though he is now retired from teaching, he is still writing; he published his first novel, *Anthill*, to generally positive reviews

in 2010. He is also still studying ants and still speaking out about the threat that one species—ours—poses to the millions of others on the planet.

I met up with Wilson in his office, which is above Harvard's Museum of Comparative Zoology and right across the hall from the university's ant collection. In the 1970s, Wilson's concept of sociobiology caused so much controversy at Harvard that he briefly considered decamping to another university; however, he has said, he could not bear to leave behind the school's ant collection, which contains nearly 1,000,000 individual ants, representing more than 6,000 species. After we had talked for a while, Wilson showed me around the collection. Many of the ants Wilson gathered himself on trips to, among other places, Brazil, Cuba, Fiji, and New Guinea. Each ant—some were so small I could barely make them out—was marked with a tiny label bearing its name in almost microscopic print. Wilson's office is decorated with pieces of ant-related art, which friends and colleagues have given him, and also with three hominid skulls, which, he likes to tell visitors, belonged to former grad students.

In his 1994 autobiography, *Naturalist*, Wilson described himself as "a happy man in a terrible century." By his own account, he places "great store in civility and good manners." Both in person and in his writing, he is courtly and good-humored. But he's blunt about the damage that humans are causing.

"It seems like almost on an annual basis now we have another really massive biodiversity problem to worry about," he told me. "We've reached the point where global catastrophes are getting to be the norm. We were just hacking down parts of the natural world in pieces here and there, but now things are getting global and they are coming right home." I spoke to Wilson about his early scientific career, his turn to environmental advocacy, and the future of biodiversity. One of the first topics we spoke about was Wilson's fieldwork in the 1950s and 1960s.

E. O. Wilson: When you went out into the field, say in Veracruz, Mexico, or Fiji, when I first got there, you didn't have somebody take you in a four-wheel drive to a field station that was all set up and give you a cot. I would get into a town somewhere and make myself comfortable and I almost always collected alone. I prefer that actually. Then someone would tell me there's a nice patch of rainforest if you go 30 kilometers up the road. And I would get a ride out there.

The next thing you'd do is get out of the car, pry apart a barbed wire fence, and step through. You'd walk among the cows, watching out not to get your feet gummy with cow manure. Then there it is: good-looking vegetation, and it's on an incline. So you know probably the reason it hasn't been cut was because it's on a slope. Before you get there the land dips down into a stream and a bog. You have to get through another barbed wire fence and cross the stream, getting yourself muddy, and then finally you are climbing your way up and starting to collect. That was so typical of those days. So many islands were like this. There were not many active field biologists in those days, but most of us became aware, especially those of us who were going into tropical areas, that entire ecosystems were being wiped out.

In 1967 Wilson and Robert MacArthur, a biology professor at Princeton, published The Theory of Island Biogeography, *their landmark work in ecology. The book attempted to explain why certain islands are species-rich, while others are species-poor. One of the key variables is size: all other things being equal, larger islands will be home to more species than smaller ones. The ratio, Wilson and MacArthur found, tends to follow a consistent mathematical formula: roughly speaking, the number of species doubles with every tenfold increase in area. The formula also works in reverse, so that if an island's area is reduced by 90 percent, the number of species that can survive will drop by half. I asked Wilson about the development of the theory and how it applied to "islands" of habitat in a fragmented landscape.*

Wilson: Islands are the laboratories of species formation and extinction. Islands are separate experiments in what species can get there and what species turn into new species, which then go extinct, and so on. That's why islands have always been so important. They were important to Darwin and much more important to Alfred Russel Wallace, who founded biogeography.

In 1959 I got together with Robert MacArthur. We were two young, ambitious biologists. I was much more the naturalist and data person and Robert was a brilliant mathematical modeler. The idea was to use islands as our laboratory to understand how species spread and how and why they become extinct. On islands the patterns became much clearer than on the mainland. It also turns out that islands have the highest rates of human-induced extinctions. They are the real disaster areas. Hawaii is the extinction capital of America and one of the hot spots of the world.

Then we realized that the same principles apply to anything that is broken into fragments—for example, bodies of freshwater, from rivers to streams to springs to lakes to ponds.

In the 1970s Wilson's interest in extinction ceased to be academic. He began to speak out and to rethink his assumptions about what it means to be a scientist. I asked him about this transition.

Wilson: In the 1960s it was sort of just in my peripheral vision that what we were doing was relevant to understanding the extinction process. I thought that what we should be doing was finding out the information needed. At that time, oddly, in the scientific culture it was regarded as unseemly that scientists speak up or take an activist role. And being at Harvard, with all the devotion I felt to the purity of science, I certainly could see the problem, but my duty was to stay with science and just get the theory and facts right. And that I shouldn't say anything. After all, there was the World Wildlife Fund and the International Union for the Conservation of Nature, all those great people, and they were taking care of that.

By 1970 there was a significant burgeoning of conservation awareness and the early stages of the new conservation movement, which was also becoming increasingly scientific in its basis. I give credit to Paul Ehrlich [now president of Stanford University's Center for Conservation Biology] and to Peter Raven [now president emeritus of the Missouri Botanical Garden], who were first-rate scientists. They were yelling their heads off by that time, and nobody was calling them exhibitionists or loudmouths. So I thought probably they were an example to be followed. In 1974 I published a hard-hitting article in *Harvard Magazine* on species extinction and the desperate need to have a global conservation movement. That's how I got into it.

Wilson often compares humans with ants and termites. Social insects, like humans, cooperate in ways that are enormously empowering. I asked him why it is that ants don't, at least as far we know, drive other species to extinction.

Wilson: Ants and termites today make up very roughly three-quarters of the total insect biomass. A lot of people might think that's amazing because there are only some 15,000 ant species, whereas there are over 900,000 known species of insects. In terms of biomass, they own the world. But in terms of the damage they've done? Have the ants taken over the world? No. Why? Because—and this tells us the significance of the human story—ants came into existence in the Mesozoic, more than 100 million years ago. We have fossils now and we know what they looked like and how they appeared. In the beginning they were rather scarce. It was only after tens of millions of years of evolution, occasionally rushing out and stinging the feet of dinosaurs who were clumsy enough to step on their nests, that they diversified a good deal and probably had advanced societies. But they still were not the most abundant insects. That didn't occur until the beginning of the age of mammals.

We know that by 15 million years ago ants had taken over. Their habitats had tens of millions of years to evolve and accommodate the ants as they became more and more prevalent. There are vast numbers of insects that make their living off of ants, and the ants make their living off of other insects, particularly sap-sucking insects, with which they share nutrients. Many, many species of plants have special structures that they developed so that ants could live in them, and the ants in turn could offer them protection. After this long period of evolution, ants eased into their preeminent position, which they have held for 15 million years. Not bad.

Now considering humanity, good lord . . . When *Homo erectus* began to evolve a million years ago, they too were quite scarce. Then kaboom. *Homo sapiens* became prominent, maybe 200,000 years ago. Out of Africa they spread, maybe 60,000 years ago. And they began to have an impact. They wiped out the megafauna wherever they went, animals of maybe 100 pounds or more. Then kaboom, kaboom, kaboom. Neolithic agriculture. Villages and towns and technology. We hit the world's fauna and flora with a sucker punch, if I could use ordinary language like that. They just weren't ready for us. We really got on the scene big time 10,000 years ago. No way to coadapt. The ants gave them at least 30 million years, and we gave them 10,000 years. We're too darn good at it.

So what about us? I asked Wilson why it was that humans seem to be so good at driving other organisms extinct. Are we just very good competitors, or are we somehow qualitatively different from other organisms?

Wilson: This is a very rough figure, but before modern humans came along, especially before the Neolithic period 10,000 years ago, the extinction rate was, as close as we can tell, about one species going extinct per million per year. And the rate at which species were being created before humanity plunked down in the middle of things was the same. So you had very roughly an equilibrium. Even though species were coming and going, it was a very slow turnover. We have now upped the extinction rate by at least 1,000 times. It could easily go to 10,000. We have eliminated so much natural habitat that we now have places all around the world where we've cut everything down to 10 percent or 20 percent of the original cover. That's what you see in the Philippines, in Madagascar, in Hawaii. Substantial parts of Indonesia are going that way fast. Another very rough figure: if you reduce an area by 90 percent, so you have only 10 percent of the original forest left, for example, whatever the habitat is, you can expect to sustain only about half the species. Half of them, roughly, will go extinct. This is what we learned from our theory of island biogeography, and it happens pretty quick.

We are also reducing the birthrate—the cradles are disappearing. Now, why would I say that if we're not very careful we could easily take it from 1,000 up to 10,000 times the pre-human extinction rate? Because it's so easy to knock out the land that remains. That's why I think we can use those high figures. Some experts might be more conservative, but that's where we're at now. That's why we have to create preserves all around the world, make them as large as possible, and also connect them up with one another. Most scientists working in conservation and biology would agree. We need corridors, particularly in the face of climate change.

In other words, humans are unique as destroyers. There's never been anything like humans before on a global scale.

Wilson has said that "the pattern of human population growth in the twentieth century was more bacterial than primate." I asked him how this pattern has been sustained.

Wilson: We need to realize that up until this point we have saved our own species with technology, new developments in agriculture, opening new land—and therefore of course destroying large numbers of other species. We've always found a way

around our exponential population growth through technology. When it comes to energy extraction, we've had to develop very high technology and complex systems, and they're getting more complex all the time. We've reached a point where what we have wrought is so complicated and ill planned that we can't handle a lot of it. That takes us to a point where we have to recognize that we're not going to have any kind of livable planet for ourselves unless we make our environment sustainable— and that includes the living environment. We have to slam on the brakes before we wreck the planet. Which we're about to do.

I'm exasperated by the professional optimists, who say, "These bad things are happening, but human genius and the resources this good earth has given us will allow us to keep on doing pretty much what we've been doing. So don't worry about it." There is a huge flaw in that reasoning. You may be familiar with the famous French riddle of the 29th day of lily pads, which everybody should know. Most of the things that should be worrying us are happening exponentially. With each interval that passes, the impact is more serious. There comes a time when the next interval is devastating, and here comes the riddle of the 29th day.

There is a pond with one lily pad. The number of lily pads doubles every day. The pond will fill up by the 30th day. On what day is the pond half full? The 29th day. That's the whole point. Okay, let's take the optimists' argument. Let's assume that the lily pads are getting really worried. They point out, Hey guys, we've got one short period left and then we're all going to be fighting over the same nutrients and choking each other out. Not to worry: some of the lily pads are technological geniuses. They'll figure out a way to get around this. They announce to every lily pad's joy that they have found an opening now to another empty pond of the same size, so you don't have to change your patterns and way of life, fellow lily pads, we can go on. Okay. When does that new pond fill up? On the 31st day. That's the problem with humanity today, and I don't care if we spend a huge amount of money to shoot people off into space toward Mars. I don't care if we figure out a way to do fusion or find some other energy source. We can't go on like this.

In his book The Diversity of Life, *Wilson writes about the five "mass extinction" events that have been identified in the geologic record. The most recent of these took place 65 million years ago, when an asteroid seven and a half miles wide hit the Earth, killing off not just the dinosaurs, but also the pterosaurs, plesiosaurs, and mosasaurs. I asked Wilson if he thought we were in the midst of another mass extinction event.*

Wilson: Sure we are. We're in the early stages but it's coming on fast. Compared with a giant meteorite strike, of course, it's taking longer, but that only means a few centuries, and we're coming up to where it will get up to those catastrophic levels within this century. Unless we can somehow stop it.

Population is going to peak at around 9 billion or 10 billion, 40 percent more than we have now. We can manage this if we make the necessary changes. We can't just go on using the usual nonrenewable energy and planting the same old crops. We have to develop dryland agriculture in areas that have run out of groundwater. That agriculture has to be based on—I will just say it right out—genetically modified crops that can produce high yields without sucking up the world's remaining groundwater. At the same time, we've got to save what's left—biological diversity. That's basically it. We can do it with reserves, with a lot more knowledge of what the species are and what they need. This is the reason, incidentally, why I put a lot of my time in the last 10 years into helping to get the Encyclopedia of Life started. [See Alan Burdick, "The (New) Web of Life," *OnEarth,* Fall 2009.] We need to be putting a lot more scientific and technical effort into mapping the world's biodiversity. We only know fewer than 10 percent of species. We're really flying blind.

Wilson has written that we are a product of our own evolutionary history, that we evolved to be shortsighted, kin-concerned creatures, and that this is no longer serving us very well. But how do you get beyond your own evolutionary history?

Wilson: We are ill equipped by instinct to control ourselves. Even with our tremendous intellect, we have a deep propensity for group conflict. Look at our defense expenditures, the way we glorify the constant expansion of human settlement and human growth, our archaic religions, which give us nothing but grief because they are essentially tribal. Our religions are ill equipped to handle our present problems, especially when they start trying to discredit what we can find out and prove with science.

However, we are adaptable. I think that when we get enough really serious knocks, we can start treating our problems as problems and not as the evil machinations of conspiracies—which is the way we tend to think about them. Our problems come from the fact that we are a *Star Wars* civilization. When you think about *Star Wars,* those movies reflect what we are: people blowing up whole planets. We have Paleolithic emotions, Stone Age emotions—we've inherited those nice and pure. We have medieval institutions. And we have godlike technology. Put those three together and you have a very dangerous mix. So, somehow I think we ought to develop a new kind of self-understanding, self-reflection, and self-imaging. Then we might be able to actually get somewhere together.

NRDC: A Continent of Riches

Latin America is home to some of the most biodiverse ecosystems on the planet. Costa Rica immediately comes to mind. Its rainforests, mountains, and coasts simply pulse with life. Just a few minutes in a Costa Rican rainforest is enough to notice the complex networks among the variety of species there. At the southern end of the continent, in Chile's Patagonia, there are remarkable terrestrial and riparian ecosystems along the Baker River. This nutrient-rich river, which originates in Andean glaciers, ultimately feeds the biodiverse marine fjord system near the Pacific coast. The Baker is another tangible illustration of the connections in nature—in this case among the area's glaciers, temperate rainforests, swamps, and marine life.

Critical Thinking

1. According to E.O. Wilson, what may be the greatest environmental catastrophe looming ahead? Why is it so terrible?

2. Why is it, according to Wilson, that humans seem to be so good at driving other organisms extinct?

Article

The End of a Myth

We thought the sea was infinite and inexhaustible. It is not. Exploring a new vision for Earth's greatest wilderness.

JULIA WHITTY

At dawn on a remote beach along Mexico's Baja California Peninsula, in a world of pink and red desert and forests of *cardón* cactus, I come upon an unlikely mass stranding of Portuguese man-of-wars, or bluebottles. They've come ashore in the night and their blue sails are as bright and shiny as living tissue, as if the beach were strewn with thousands of excised lungs. Their tentacles lie hopelessly tangled around them, reminiscent of dissected blood vessels, giving the otherwise peaceful morning the feel of the abattoir, as if many animals have been butchered and their larger parts consumed.

Vision is the art of seeing things invisible, wrote Jonathan Swift. And sometimes the invisible is a huge, dominant, virtually omnipotent presence in our world, the feature for which our planet should have been named, and may well be named by distant intelligent beings with the means to peer farther than we can at present. The ocean is our blind spot: a deep, dark, distant, and complex realm covering 70.8 percent of Earth's surface. We have better maps of the surface of Mars than of our own sea floor. Yet under our skin, we're a plasma ocean, so entwined with the outer seas that we can't easily know either ourselves or our water world.

This ocean is the largest wilderness on Earth, home to wildlife in staggering multispecies aggregations, and with a lineage of life three billion years older than anything above sea level. Its three-dimensional realm comprises 99 percent of all habitable space and is so embedded with life as to be largely composed of life, with an ounce of seawater home to as many as 30 billion microorganisms—and counting. Honing our technological eyesight, we begin to observe what was once too small to be seen, in an exercise that mirrors infinity.

For most of our time on Earth, most of what we've known of the ocean has been its dead oddities on the beach. The Portuguese man-of-wars must once have seemed the leftovers of immortals, stamped with the teethmarks of Oceanus, Varuna, or Tangaroa. Modern explanations are likewise riddled with paradox, since science reveals the man-of-war to be not a jellyfish but a siphonophore, not a single body but a collection of bodies, a colony of as many as 1,000 polyps. The blue bottle

bobbing at the surface, the pneumatophore, functions as an upside-down sailboat keeping the colony afloat, its inflatable sail rigged to navigate wind and waves. The nearly invisible tentacles, the dactylozooids, trail scores of feet below the boat and fish for prey with built-in stinging harpoons. The digestive polyps, the gastrozooids, cook up the catch and serve it to the pneumatophore, the dactylozooids, and the last members of the colony, the gonozooids, whose job it is to reproduce the man-of-war. Combined, the team is as integrated as a single animal. Yet absent of leadership, insight, or foresight, these strange conglomerates—we don't know if they function as one or many beings—beach, often in blue fleets by the dozens or hundreds. As we might if our legs were separate entities from our heads, our stomachs and sex organs separate again.

But we are not jellyfish. And we see the alarms, the messages inside the man-of-wars' blue bottles joining a host of other distress signals washing ashore these days from oil spills, fish kills, slain cetaceans, washed-up seabirds composed in part of lethally indigestible plastic. Some are silent sirens: the disappearing seashells and horseshoe crabs, the missing sea turtles and their eggs, the vanished egg casings of sharks and rays, the lost coral debris, the dwindling beach-spawning grunion, and the anguillid eels, those long-distance travelers that migrate thousands of miles from ocean to river and back again, and appear to be evaporating from the face of the earth.

Only of late have we learned to see the ocean's surprising vulnerabilities. That it's neither infinite nor inexhaustible. That it's the beleaguered terminus of all our downstream pollutants, part of a dynamic system intensely interactive with land and atmosphere and everything we do there. Only in the past decade has science discovered the ocean to be fragile in the way only really enormous things are fragile: with resilience teetering on the brink of collapse. Yet our behavior lags far behind our understanding, and the ocean awaits our enlightened action.

One in seven people on Earth depend on food from the sea as their primary source of protein. Yet one of the more optimistic assessments calculates that we've depleted up to a third of all the world's fisheries, with 7 percent to 13 percent of stocks collapsed, perhaps never to recover. These declines happen in our lifetime: bluefin tuna, once cheap, becomes exorbitant; species once scorned become market favorites.

The ocean is Earth's last frontier and its fish stocks are the bison we're currently obliterating with trawlers, longliners, purse seiners, and gillnets. Modern fisheries target not only the ocean's herbivores but also its carnivores—the apex predators such as tuna, sharks, and billfish, the marine equivalent of wolves, mountain lions, and grizzlies. Of late, we've begun large-scale hunting of the field mice of the sea, the forage fish, such as sardines and anchovies, which form the ecological backbone of many marine food webs and which, as we've learned from examples off California, Peru, Japan, and Namibia, collapse catastrophically whenever the stresses of climate change intersect with the stresses of overfishing. Worse, we're turning our guns on the ocean's primary consumers, like krill, which, one or three trophic links removed, feed most everything else that lives in or makes its living from the sea, including us.

It's not easy to calculate the magnitude of our appetites. We visit the ocean and look forward to eating the food of the sea, even those of us who would not in our wildest dreams consider eating elephants, lions, or leopards on our visit to a dry wilderness in Africa or India. Yet it's about more than the cost of eating wildlife. It's also about suffering. We hook, bludgeon, net, drown, and drag to death seabirds, sea turtles, seals, dolphins, and whales in the course of hunting seafood. We blindly assume that fish feel no pain—though many scientists firmly believe otherwise—and leave unquestioned the inhumane business of slaughtering them by the billions in the wild with truly cold-blooded detachment.

Life cycles in the sea are more complex than those of terrestrial life. Virtually all species that spend their adulthood anchored to the sea floor, such as corals, oysters, and sponges, spend their youth adrift: a two-part life history that allows them to disperse before becoming immobile. Most swimming species, such as swordfish and tuna, spend their embryo-like larval lives as translucent plankton-pickers no bigger than fingernail clippings afloat on currents. This fundamental difference in strategy between marine and terrestrial development magnifies our impacts in frightening ways. We hunt adults in one part of the ocean and destroy the nursery grounds of their larvae in another part and poison the habitat of their juveniles somewhere else while tangentially depleting the species they depend on for food at each stage.

Consider the Atlantic bluefin tuna, an endangered species on the Red List of the International Union for Conservation of Nature (IUCN). Overfishing contributes to its decline, yet pollutants inflict an insidious, often invisible toll. In 2010, tuna spawning partially converged in time and space with the *Deepwater Horizon* catastrophe in the Gulf of Mexico, one of its only two known breeding areas. We don't know the effects of 206 million gallons of oil and almost two million gallons of chemical dispersant on adult fish that came to spawn that year, or will come the next, or the next. We don't know the outcome of unprecedented levels of pollution on delicate eggs, and therefore on entire generations of an endangered species. We may not know for years, decades, or ever. Add to that ongoing

debacle the other ongoing calamities in the Gulf: the disappearing wetlands; the channelization of the Mississippi River; the overfertilization of America's breadbasket, which downriver fuels the world's second-largest oceanic dead zone; the laying of 36,000 miles of offshore pipeline; the drilling of 52,000 offshore wells; the thousands of rigs left abandoned. Most of what undermines the Gulf has been done with little or no consideration of its waters and wildlife, in marked contrast to our developing attitudes toward the land. In this, the battered Gulf of Mexico is a microcosm of the global ocean.

Meanwhile the international body of the IUCN estimated that Atlantic bluefin tuna has declined by as much as 51 percent in only three tuna generations as a result of overfishing of adult fish by longlines, drift nets, traps, bait boats, and purse seines. Its demise may also be hastened by unregulated recreational fisheries that impose no limits on the catch of juvenile tuna, as well as, increasingly, by their capture for tuna farms. We don't know much about the status of Atlantic bluefin tuna as larvae, when it dwells among zooplankton communities in warm surface waters. We do know that the mid-ocean gyres are now rife with plastic debris that breaks down at sea into tiny pieces, which are eaten and passed up the food web, starting with zooplankton, to endure seemingly forever, the modern immortals. We do know that phytoplankton—the microscopic organisms fueling zooplankton—which produce half of all plant matter on Earth, have declined an average of 1 percent a year since 1950, for a staggering total of 40 percent worldwide, according to one study. If nearly half of all wild and cropped plants disappeared from the terrestrial world, all animals, including humans, would likewise suffer severe depopulations. Humble phytoplankton. These are the microscopic organisms that perform on a global scale what we can't even manage on a village scale, namely, turning sunlight into food. They are the keystone players not just of the sea but of all the planet. Through the process of photosynthesis, they produce half the oxygen we breathe, mitigate the carbon dioxide we unleash into the air, and support all marine life. Their demise stems from a different kind of pollution, that of atmospheric carbon dioxide and other greenhouse gases, which produce a warming, more stratified ocean, with less mixing between layers and less stirring up of nutrients from the depths to support phytoplankton on the surface. In a real sense, the ocean begins to petrify and phytoplankton to starve.

A warming ocean also threatens to reroute the travels of drifting species, like the Portuguese man-of-war, as well as all that follow them, like endangered leatherback and loggerhead turtles. Man-of-wars meander tropical and subtropical seas, adrift on wind-driven currents. But changes in global temperature can send more rain and fresh meltwater into the ocean, altering the saltiness of seawater and therefore its density and changing the force of the powerful underwater rivers embedded in the depths. In one of the most exciting scientific investigations of the twentieth century, oceanographers mapped these saltwater rivers to discover they form a system connecting all the oceans of the world into one World Ocean. They called this system the ocean conveyor because it transports the rainfall from one ocean basin through subsurface currents around the world. More important, the conveyor also carries heat, drawing warmth from equatorial waters to the high latitudes—a crucial global thermostat. But now a warmer ocean, freshened by melting icecaps and glaciers, threatens to disrupt the oceanic rivers and upend one of our most critical climate regulators.

That's not the worst of it. We know that the ocean currently sequesters about a third of our atmospheric carbon dioxide emissions—yet another seemingly inexhaustible service performed by these seemingly inexhaustible waters. As we tally the true cost of this mitigation we see what was largely invisible even a decade ago—the other CO_2 problem, of rising carbon dioxide in the ocean unleashing a complex series of chemical reactions that make seawater more acidic. The ocean has, since the onset of the Industrial Revolution, become about 30 percent more acidic—a gargantuan change in chemistry that has also reduced carbonate ion concentrations in seawater by 16 percent. Carbonate ions are needed for marine life to make their shelters, their reefs and shells, which means that rising acidity threatens the survival of entire ecosystems, starting with phytoplankton and including coral communities, Antarctic systems reliant on sea urchins, and many human food webs, from oyster beds to salmon fisheries. Nor will mobile species escape. Pteropods, or sea butterflies, the swimming snails that flap through open waters and are important fuel for temperate herring, salmon, whales, and seabirds, are threatened with an acidic extinction even before the forecast rise of an ocean that will be two and a half times more acidic by 2100. The latest research shows that fish eggs and larvae are far more vulnerable to rising acidity than scientists had imagined.

Seen through a myopic lens, changes in the ocean's pH are a threat to our dinner plates and wallets. Seen through the telescope of history, acidification may have been one of the primary "kill mechanisms" behind the grimmest of all extinctions, 252 million years ago, when nearly all life on Earth—in the seas and on the land—perished. Recovery from the Great Dying took an astonishing 30 million years and required a near-total reboot of life. In our modern ocean, beset by dwindling phytoplankton, warming waters, melting ice, rising acidity, corroding reefs, dying shellfish beds, and collapsing food webs, life itself threatens to sputter out.

Underwater off a beach along Australia's Great Barrier Reef I come upon a living Portuguese man-of-war drifting into the winds on the crimped wonton of its blue sail. The retractable fishing line, the dactylozooid, dangles beneath, bouncing with the waves to connect the chattery surface with the silent parade of floating zooplankton 15 feet below. Tucked fringelike under the sail are the digestive polyps and the reproductive polyps. They are such a pale blue as to be nearly invisible and are as reactive as exposed nerves, flinching at things I can't see.

And then I can see, attached to one squirming polyp, the strange creature known as a blue dragon—a floating sea slug that makes its living eating venomous man-of-wars. It's a fantastically beautiful creature, about an inch and a half long, that looks something like a swimming lizard with winglike legs tipped with feathery toes. It lives upside down at the surface, buoyed by a swallowed air bubble, and not only endures the stinging tentacles that would send you or me screaming from the water but also eats the most venomous of them, which it doesn't digest but stores inside special sacs in its "fingertips." Armed by its own prey—as if you or I could eat pork and grow boar's tusks—blue dragons are themselves formidably venomous creatures.

As far as we know, the man-of-war has no choice but to suffer this nibbling thief that steals its limbs and its weapons. Onward it meanders, an ethereally lethal self-contained society of captain, fishermen, harpoonists, cooks, and procreators, adrift in seemingly perpetual orbit through a blue emptiness. Yet even as it's being eaten, it eats, reeling in on its fishing line a nearly transparent juvenile fish. Still alive, but paralyzed by venom, the tiny victim stares unblinkingly at the approaching sail of the bluebottle, at the digestive polyps wriggling like blind tongues as they reach out to latch on, to form little mouths that combine into one large mouth. When the fish is enveloped, the man-of-war begins to digest its meal in a bath of corrosive enzymes.

Blind and rudderless, the enmeshed trio drifts, prodded by waves building into surf that somersaults against the beach. The current sweeps under them. The wind tips the bluebottle's sail landward. Since I am not a jellyfish, I can gaze both underwater and topside toward shore, where the future of their all-consuming promenade seems clear. Yet not one of them appears to anticipate the invisible shoal ahead, the shipwreck onto a world without ocean.

Critical Thinking

1. What is the magnitude of our appetite for the ocean's resources? How much of it have we eaten so far? Can that rate of consumption be continued? Discuss.

2. List the threats to our oceans the author discusses. Which of these four threats do you think will become the most critical and difficult to address in the next 50 years? Explain.

3. Who should be most responsible and bear most of the cost burden that will be necessary to protect and preserve our oceans? (*Hint:* Construct a concept map of the ecosystem services the oceans provide and make linkages to the geographical locations of the human groups that depend on the services.)

Whitty, Julia. From *OnEarth Magazine*, February 12, 2012, pp. 1–6. Copyright © 2012 by Natural Resources Defense Council. Reprinted by permission. http://www.onearth.org/article/the-end-of-a-myth.

Article

Rich Countries Launch Great Land Grab to Safeguard Food Supply

States and companies target developing nations, small farmers at risk from industrial-scale deals.

JULIAN BORGER

Rich governments and corporations are triggering alarm for the poor as they buy up the rights to millions of hectares of agricultural land in developing countries in an effort to secure their own long-term food supplies.

The head of the UN Food and Agriculture Organisation, Jacques Diouf, has warned that the controversial rise in land deals could create a form of "neo-colonialism", with poor states producing food for the rich at the expense of their own hungry people.

Rising food prices have already set off a second "scramble for Africa". This week, the South Korean firm Daewoo Logistics announced plans to buy a 99-year lease on a million hectares in Madagascar. Its aim is to grow 5m tonnes of corn a year by 2023, and produce palm oil from a further lease of 120,000 hectares (296,000 acres), relying on a largely South African workforce. Production would be mainly earmarked for South Korea, which wants to lessen dependence on imports.

"These deals can be purely commercial ventures on one level, but sitting behind it is often a food security imperative backed by a government," said Carl Atkin, a consultant at Bidwells Agribusiness, a Cambridge firm helping to arrange some of the big international land deals.

Madagascar's government said that an environmental impact assessment would have to be carried out before the Daewoo deal could be approved, but it welcomed the investment. The massive lease is the largest so far in an accelerating number of land deals that have been arranged since the surge in food prices late last year.

"In the context of arable land sales, this is unprecedented," Atkin said. "We're used to seeing 100,000-hectare sales. This is more than 10 times as much."

At a food security summit in Rome, in June, there was agreement to channel more investment and development aid to African farmers to help them respond to higher prices by producing more. But governments and corporations in some cash-rich but land-poor states, mostly in the Middle East, have opted not to wait for world markets to respond and are trying to guarantee their own long-term access to food by buying up land in poorer countries.

According to diplomats, the Saudi Binladin Group is planning an investment in Indonesia to grow basmati rice, while tens of thousands of hectares in Pakistan have been sold to Abu Dhabi investors.

Arab investors, including the Abu Dhabi Fund for Development, have also bought direct stakes in Sudanese agriculture. The president of the UEA, Khalifa bin Zayed, has said his country was considering large-scale agricultural projects in Kazakhstan to ensure a stable food supply.

Even China, which has plenty of land but is now getting short of water as it pursues breakneck industrialisation, has begun to explore land deals in southeast Asia. Laos, meanwhile, has signed away between 2m–3m hectares, or 15% of its viable farmland. Libya has secured 250,000 hectares of Ukrainian farmland, and Egypt is believed to want similar access. Kuwait and Qatar have been chasing deals for prime tracts of Cambodia rice fields.

Eager buyers generally have been welcomed by sellers in developing world governments desperate for capital in a recession. Madagascar's land reform minister said revenue would go to infrastructure and development in flood-prone areas.

Sudan is trying to attract investors for almost 900,000 hectares of its land, and the Ethiopian prime minister, Meles Zenawi, has been courting would-be Saudi investors.

"If this was a negotiation between equals, it could be a good thing. It could bring investment, stable prices and predictability to the market," said Duncan Green, Oxfam's head of research. "But the problem is, [in] this scramble for soil I don't see any place for the small farmers."

Alex Evans, at the Centre on International Cooperation, at New York University, said: "The small farmers are losing out already. People without solid title are likely to be turfed off the land."

Details of land deals have been kept secret so it is unknown whether they have built-in safeguards for local populations.

Steve Wiggins, a rural development expert at the Overseas Development Institute, said: "There are very few economies of scale in most agriculture above the level of family farm because managing [the] labour is extremely difficult." Investors might also have to contend with hostility. "If I was a political-risk adviser to [investors] I'd say 'you are taking a very big risk'. Land is an extremely sensitive thing. This could go horribly wrong if you don't learn the lessons of history."

Critical Thinking

1. Why is it not a good idea for rich countries to buy up agricultural land in poor countries?

2. Aside from the obvious increase in the hunger issue in poor countries, how can this "land grab" contribute to other global problems?

3. If, however, the United States is buying up some of this land to ensure our food security, why should we say "no"?

Article

Global Urbanization: Can Ecologists Identify a Sustainable Way Forward?

Robert I. McDonald

The year 2007 was the first year in which more than half of humanity lived in cities. Over the next 25 years, the world will see the addition of nearly one million km² of urban area, occurring in tens of thousands of cities around the globe. The form these new neighborhoods take will affect our planet's ecology profoundly. Here, I highlight the connection between urban form and ecosystem service generation and consumption, I also discuss how urban form controls energy use, and hence oil security and climate change. I argue that only by directly addressing the implications of urban growth as a research subject will ecologists meet their responsibility to provide a foundation for a sustainable biosphere, a mandate of the Ecological Society of America.

—*Front Ecol Environ* 2008; 6(2):

In a nutshell:

- Urban growth in both the developed and developing world will be the main obstacle to achieving sustainable development
- The form of new urban areas will determine per capita resource use, now and for decades to come
- Urbanization in developing countries could dramatically increase oil consumption, with implications for global warming and energy security
- Conducting multiple before-and-after assessments of urban sustainability projects may be the greatest contribution ecologists can make to sustainable development

Sometime in 2007, humanity crossed a momentous milestone: for the first time ever, the majority of humans are living in cities (UNPD 2005a). In the next 25 years, 1.7 billion new people will move into urban areas (UNPD 2005b), and new settlements in the developing world will spread to cover an area the size of California (Angel *et al.* 2005). Most of these settlements will be in the developing world (UN-HABITAT 2006), where new-found urban lifestyles and increased affluence could lead to dramatically increased resource use. This resource use, especially of oil and other fossil fuels, will have implications for global warming and the security of nations. Humanity is building the equivalent of a city the size of Vancouver—about 600 000 people—twice every week (Peñalosa 2006 . . .). What does the form of these new cities mean for the goal of sustainable development? And what role can ecologists play in helping to realize that goal?

The Coming Urbanization

The ongoing process of urbanization occurring in the world's poorer countries is the result of a predictable demographic shift: as a country's development proceeds, an increasing proportion of its population lives in urban areas. The increase in urban population is partly due to natural growth—the greater number of births than deaths among people already living in cities—and partly due to migration from rural areas to urban areas (NRC 2003). Lack of employment or safety sometimes pushes migrants from rural areas, while the increased economic and personal opportunities in cities can also attract migrants (eg Ma 2002). The precise mix of drivers for rural-urban migration seems to vary by region, and is still the subject of much debate (eg Roy *et al.* 1992; deHaan 1997).

The best quantitative source of global data on urbanization comes from the UN Population Division, although some concerns remain about the varying definitions of "urban" used by different member countries (Cohen 2004). These data show that urbanization has already largely ceased in the US (80.1% urban), Europe (72.2% urban), Latin America and the Caribbean (77.4% urban), and South America (81.6% urban). However, Africa (38.3% urban) and countries in Southeast Asia, such as China (40.4% urban) and India (28.7% urban), are just beginning their shift, and will undergo rapid urbanization over the next several decades. Global urban population is predicted to increase from 3.2 billion to 4.9 billion over the next 25 years (UNPD 2005b). For comparison, the population of Europe in 2000 was 729 million (US Census Bureau, Population

Division nd) and average household size was around 2.5 people per household (UNECE 2005), which means that there were approximately 291 million housing units. A 1.7 billion increase in urban dwellers, assuming five persons per household (typical for developing countries), would mean that more housing units will be built in the next 25 years than currently exist in all of Europe. . . .

Recent work by the World Bank allows us to translate urban population growth to urban area growth. In a survey of more than 120 cities from around the world, Angel *et al.* (2005) found that the biggest single variable controlling the per capita growth in area of a city was its income. On average, each new resident in a city adds 355 m^2 of developed area in a rich country, 125 m^2 in a middle-income country, and 85 m^2 in a poor country. As with any estimate of urban area, the values obtained are dependent on the definition of "urban" used in the particular study. However, if we accept this definition of "urban", and assume the current shift toward lower urban population density continues at the same rate, a reasonable estimate of total new urban area by 2030 is around 900 000 km^2. This will be split fairly evenly between the developed and developing nations, although its causes are quite different in each case: in the former, the driver is predominantly low-density settlement patterns (Jackson 1985), while in the latter, the driver is predominantly urban population growth (UN-HABITAT 2006). It is also important to note that around 46% of all urban population growth will occur in relatively small cities, with populations of fewer than 500 000 people (UNPD 2005b). Urbanization is therefore a fundamentally dispersed process, occurring in tens of thousands of cities.

Total urban area will remain a relatively small fraction of the Earth's terrestrial surface, from 0.3% today to 1% in 2030 (Angel *et al.* 2005). However, the ecological footprint of these cities will encompass an area many hundreds of times larger (eg Rees 1999; McGranahan and Satterthwaite 2003). Humanity will be entering a new world, a world of the city, by the city, and for the city. Urbanization will be the main obstacle to, and opportunity for, sustainable development.

Urban Form Matters

Humanity is building the grand cities of the 21st century, and their design, good or bad, is fundamentally a human decision. Even in capitalist economies, where urban development decisions are made by millions of different landowners, the pattern of development is largely a result of specific human plans, a joint consequence of topography (eg Muller 2001), zoning law (eg Munroe *et al.* 2005), and the geography of highways, rail lines, and mass transit (Handy 2005). This overall pattern of development can be referred to generally as urban form, and quantified using landscape metrics (cf Alberti 2005) of land-use intensity (eg people ha^{-1}), land-use heterogeneity (eg the number of different functional land uses), and land-use connectivity (eg degree of aggregation of land uses).

There is abundant evidence in the literature to show that urban form affects resource use (eg Folke *et al.* 1997; Pickett *et al.* 2001), although the exact relationship between the two

seems to vary substantially, depending on the resource in question and the socioeconomic context of the city. In general, there is a great need for high-quality, municipal-level data that can be used to build mechanistic models of how resource use responds to changes in urban form (Pataki *et al.* 2006). The form of the new cities in the developing world is doubly important, because of the tendency for patterns of past urban development to remain locked in the future. Past patterns tend to persist because major infrastructure (eg a road corridor) creates a physical imprint that lasts for decades. Moreover, past development patterns tend to condition the shape of new development. Therefore, the form of urban development today will control resource use for generations to come. Below, I focus on one particular facet: the link between urban form and energy use. . . .

One crucial way in which urban form affects energy use is through its control of, and mutual relationship with, the transportation sector (Banister *et al.* 1997). In developing countries, migration from the countryside to the city is typically associated with an increase in income, which in turn generates an increase in per-capita environmental consumption rates. If we control for the level of economic development, we can examine more closely how, at a given income level, alternative urban forms result in different resource utilization rates. For example, the average resident of Tokyo drives one-sixth as many kilometers per year as the average resident of Sacramento, despite having similar incomes (Kenworthy and Laube 1999). Personal automobile use is usually correlated with the density of an urban region, with use increasing dramatically at densities below 30 people per ha (Cameron *et al.* 2004). Finally, more energy-efficient public transportation systems require a density above a similar minimum threshold to be successful (Badoe and Miller 2000; Bento *et al.* 2005). While the empirical correlation between density and energy efficiency of transportation is clear, the exact mechanisms underlying this correlation are still uncertain (eg Anderson *et al.* 1996; Alberti 1999; Mindali *et al.* 2004).

Another way in which urban form affects energy use is through the heating and cooling of buildings (Steemers 2003). Heating a single-family, detached home in Oslo usually consumes 10 000 KW hr^{-1} per person per year, whereas heating an apartment in a larger building usually costs 7000 KW hr^{-1} per person per year, (Holden and Norland 2005). Generally, heating and cooling a single-family, detached home is less efficient than for row houses or multi-unit buildings. The quality of building construction also has an important influence on per-capita energy use, based on numerous factors, including building orientation, insulation, and choice of heating/cooling system. For example, new homes in Oslo consume 3000 fewer kW hr^{-1} annually than older homes in Oslo, correcting for house size, presumably because of improvements in some of the design components (Holden and Norland 2005).

Ecological Ramifications

Energy use in cities generally results in CO_2 emissions in one form or another. Essentially all motorized personal transport burns gasoline or diesel; US oil use alone accounts for 10% of global emissions (EIA 2006). Most heating and cooling of homes is either directly powered by fossil fuels or by electricity from power plants that burn fossil fuels. Given this link between urban form, energy use, and CO_2 emissions, it is clear that the urban form of cities in the developing world has serious implications for global warming. Although the Kyoto Protocol does not set binding emissions reduction targets for developing countries, it creates one of the first working examples of a payment-for-ecosystem-services scheme, via the Clean Development Mechanism (CDM). The CDM allows carbon trading between First World countries (ie Annex 1 countries) and the developing world. If countries exceed their quota of greenhouse-gas emissions, they can purchase carbon credits from a developing country that has implemented some project to reduce their emissions. For example, Dhakal (2003) shows that a modest increase in electric vehicle use in Kathmandu, converting all three-wheeled passenger travel to electric motors and 20% of the bus-travel to trolley buses run on overhead electric lines, would save 20 400 tons of CO_2 annually. As this upgrade could claim credit for several years' worth of decreases in emissions, the value of the project on the global carbon market could be in excess of US$500 000, which would cover a sizeable portion of the cost of the project.

Urbanization in the developing world, along with rising incomes, may dramatically increase the number of potential oil consumers (Riley 2002), raising concerns about global oil security. Most discussions about oil security focus on the potential supply of oil, which is key for oil price and availability over the short term (Cleveland and Kaufmann 2003). It seems reasonable, however, to examine not just supply-side issues but demand-side issues as well, and the aggregate effect on oil prices (cf Awerbuch and Sauter 2006). While oil-industry forecasts are notoriously uncertain, there is general agreement that, over the medium to long term, demand will grow faster than supply for the simple reason that, while desire for oil may increase without bound, oil supply is limited, in part by geologic constraints (for a pessimistic view on this issue, see Bentley [2002]). If the price of oil rises in response (cf Skeer and Wang 2007), some new sources of oil, such as oil shales, will become economically viable, and demand will abate somewhat; however, these adjustments will probably not alter the general long-term trend toward higher oil prices (IEA 2006). It is important to realize that the rise in global energy consumption is not preordained, but depends on the energy efficiency of rapidly growing cities, particularly their density and use of public transit (Kenworthy and Laube 1999). It is not far-fetched, therefore, to argue that the oil demand created by rapidly urbanizing countries is of great importance in terms of security, because it threatens to drive oil prices upward and to increase the likelihood of conflicts over oil supply.

Urbanization will also profoundly affect ecosystem services and the underlying biodiversity that maintains them (McGranahan et al. 2006). For example, the spatial concentration of humanity in cities results in the surrounding sources of freshwater being partially or fully appropriated for urban use. Over time, cities in many parts of the world may have to search farther afield to find sufficient freshwater (cf MA 2005), often constructing major hydrological diversions in the process

(eg Righter 2005). Similarly, the concentration of people in cities inevitably leads to increases in the concentration of the pollution they generate as well (eg Van der Zee et al. 1998), surpassing the ability of natural ecosystems to successfully absorb pollutants without becoming degraded (Pouyat et al. 1995). The political power of cities also often means that residents' desire for aesthetic and recreational pursuits substantially affects nearby natural resource management practices (eg Rothman 2004). Finally, the expansion of urban area has impacts on biodiversity that, while localized to a small portion of the Earth's surface, can cumulatively be quite considerable (McDonald et al. in review).

Payment for Sustainable Urbanization

The form of urban development is fundamentally a local decision, both for democratic and pragmatic reasons. Local citizens have the right to shape their city's development and the local knowledge necessary to make wise decisions. Many policy responses to urbanization, such as zoning and tax regimes, must be decided at this local level. However, the developed nations have a role to play in fostering sustainable development. First, they have a moral responsibility to help alleviate extreme poverty and environmental degradation. Second, there is a subset of sustainable development issues in which developed country aid appears to be a win-win scenario. Economists might call this an example of Coasian bargaining, in which a negative environmental externality is averted by a payment from another group affected by the externality. A classic example is when a downstream user of water pays an upstream polluter to stop polluting. Conservation NGOs have taken to calling it "payment for ecosystem service" (PES). The rapidly urbanizing countries, which have a legal and moral right to develop, as defined in the UN Declaration on the Right to Development, are creating substantial environmental "externalities". The developed countries could produce environmental benefits for themselves and reduce this "externality" by paying to promote more responsible urbanization in the rapidly urbanizing countries.

PES schemes have become increasingly common, with one review documenting more than 287 examples of payment for forest ecosystem services (Landell-Mills and Porras 2002). Lessons can be learned from these past markets (Salzman 2005) and applied to future PES schemes involving urbanization and the environment. First, it is important to clearly define what ecosystem services are important, how much service provision is needed, and who will ultimately pay for it. Given the vast difference in wealth, it is likely that developed countries will pay developing countries for more sustainable urban development (ie the beneficiary pays rather than the polluter). Second, the spatial scale of a particular ecosystem service, as well as the governance structure, will determine if PES is feasible and desirable (Chan et al. 2006). For ecosystem services that must be generated close to those receiving the service, it may be fairly easy to establish PES, as fewer institutions will be involved in the administration of the scheme, However, these local PES schemes may not have much potential in cities with few financial resources. For example, day-to-day recreation opportunities can best be provided by local governments responding to their citizens' desires, but in poorer countries, adequate funds for the purchase of parklands may be lacking. On the other hand, for ecosystem services that may be generated far from those receiving them, it may be difficult to set up a PES scheme due to the large number of institutions involved, as well as the consensual nature of international environmental treaties. However, PES schemes at this larger spatial scale may generate a far more active market between developed and undeveloped countries. For example, an increase in sequestration of CO_2 is of global value, in that everyone is affected by global warming, and it may therefore be relatively well-funded as a PES scheme. However, a working international market like the Clean Development Mechanism has been very difficult to construct due to the many groups involved in the negotiations.

The dispersed nature of future urbanization means that technologies or strategies aimed at increasing urban sustainability must have several characteristics. First, they must be scalable, that is, feasible to implement in thousands of cities. Second, they must be flexible, able to be adapted to myriad local circumstances. Third, they must be fairly inexpensive, within the budget of most developing countries. This may seem a tall order, but numerous projects seeking sustainable solutions are currently underway.

Treating Sustainable Development Projects as Experiments

One way for ecologists and environmental scientists to make a major contribution to sustainable urban development would be to view particular sustainability projects as experiments. This, while perhaps difficult for ecologists used to studying the workings of "natural" ecosystems, is quite similar in spirit to the new paradigm of evidence-based development work (Banerjee 2007), evidence-based conservation (Sutherland *et al.* 2004), and adaptive experimentation (Cook *et al.* 2004). Before any sustainability project is undertaken, assessments should be made of the current ecosystem services at the project site and at a set of similar control sites. After implementation, the effect on ecosystem services at the project site can be compared with the change in ecosystem services at control sites. In this way, sustainability science can move beyond a plethora of case studies of specific places and topics to a more solid scientific understanding of the measured benefits of sustainability projects.

This evidence-based philosophy will require ecologists and conservation biologists to change their focus from the elaboration of theories internal to their field to a more inherently collaborative venture. These sustainability projects will require a team of ecologists, economists, policy makers, and development advocates. While pleas for interdisciplinary collaboration are now commonplace in ecology, much further integration is needed. Only then will the scientific community begin to play its crucial role, describing how practical changes in urban forms can make future urbanization compatible with the dream

of sustainable development. Sustainability is currently a policy goal and a platitude—it needs to be transformed into an evidence-based and empirically grounded science, with close links to ecology and the study of ecosystem services.

References

Alberti M. 1999. Urban patterns and environmental performance: what do we know? *J Plan Educ Res* **19**: 151–63.

Alberti M. 2005. The effects of urban patterns on ecosystem function, *Int Regional Sci Rev* **28**: 168–92.

Anderson WP, Kanaroglou PS, and Miller EJ. 1996. Urban form, energy, and the environment: a review of issues, evidence, and policy. *Urban Stud* **33**: 7–35.

Angel S, Sheppard S, Civco D, *et al.* 2005. The dynamics of global urban expansion. Washington, DC: Transport and Urban Development Department, World Bank.

Awerbuch S and Sauter R. 2006. Exploiting the oil-GDP effect to support renewables deployment. *Energ Policy* **34**: 2805–19.

Badoe DA and Miller EJ. 2000. Transportation-land-use interaction: empirical findings in North America, and their implications for modeling. *Transport Res D-Tr E* **5**: 235–63.

Banerjee A. 2007. Making aid work. Cambridge, MA: MIT Press.

Banister D, Watson S, and Wood C. 1997. Sustainable cities: transport, energy, and urban form. *Environ Plana B* **24**: 125—43.

Bentley RW. 2002. Global oil and gas depletion: an overview. *Energ policy* **30**: 189–205.

Bento AM, Cropper ML, Mobarak AM, and Vinha K. 2005. The effects of urban spatial structure on travel demand in the United States. *Rev Econ Stat* **87**. 466–78.

Cameron I, Lyons T, and Kenworthy J. 2004. Trends in vehicle kilometers of travel in world cities, 1960–1990: underlying drivers and policy responses. *Transport Policy* **11**: 287–98.

Chan K, Shaw M, Cameron D, *et al.* 2006. Conservation planning for ecosystem services. *PLOS Biol* **4**: 2138–52.

Cleveland CJ and Kaufmann RK. 2003. Oil supply and oil politics: deja vu all over again. *Energ Policy* **31**: 485–89.

Cohen B. 2004. Urban growth in developing countries: a review of current trends and a caution regarding existing forecasts. *World Dev* **32**: 23–51.

Cook WM, Casagrande D, Hope D, *et al.* 2004. Learning to roll with the punches: adaptive experimentation in human-dominated systems. *Front Ecol Environ* **2**: 467–74.

deHaan A. 1997. Rural-urban migration and poverty: the case of India. *IDS Bull-l Dev Stud* **28**: 35–47.

Dhakal S. 2003. Implications of transportation policies on energy and environment in Kathmandu Valley, Nepal, *Energ Policy* **31**; 1493–1507.

EIA (Energy Information Administration). 2006. Emissions of green house gases in the United States 2005. Washington, DC: Energy Information Administration, US Department of Energy.

Folke C, Jansson A, Larsson J, and Costanza R. 1997. Ecosystem appropriation by cities. *Ambio* **26**: 167–72.

Handy S. 2005. Smart growth and the transportation-land use connection; what does the research tell us? *Int Regional Sci Rev* **28**: 146–67.

Holden E and Norland IT. 2005. Three challenges for the compact city as a sustainable urban form: household consumption of energy and transport in eight residential areas in the greater Oslo region. *Urban Stud* **42**: 2145–66.

IEA (International Energy Agency). 2006. World energy outlook 2006. Paris, France; International Energy Agency.

Jackson K. 1985. Crabgrass frontier. New York, NY: Oxford University Press.

Kenworthy J and Laube F. 1999. Patterns of automobile dependence in cities: an international overview of key physical and economic dimensions with some implications for urban policy. *Transport Res A-Pol* 33: 691–723.

Landell-Mills N and Porras I. 2002. Silver bullet or fool's gold? A global review of markets for forest environmental services and their impact on the poor. London, UK: International Institute for Environment and Development.

Ma L. 2002. Urban transformation in China, 1949–2000: a review and research agenda. *Environ Plana A* **34;** 1545–69.

McDonald RI, Kareiva P, and Forman R. The implications of urban growth for global protected areas and biodiversity conservation. *Nature*. In review.

McGranahan G, Marcotullio P, Bai X, *et al.* 2006. Urban systems. In: Hassan R, Scholes R, and Ash N (Eds). Ecosystems and human well-being: current state and trends. Washington, DC: Island Press.

McGranahan G and Satterthwaite D. 2003. Urban centers; an assessment of sustainability. *Annu Rev Environ Resour* 28: 243–74.

MA (Millenium Ecosystem Assessment). 2005. Ecosystems and human well-being: wetlands and water synthesis. Washington, DC: World Resources Institute.

Mindali O, Raveh A, and Salomon I. 2004. Urban density and energy consumption: a new look at old statistics. *Transport Res A-Pol* **38**: 143–62.

Muller EK. 2001. Industrial suburbs and the growth of metropolitan Pittsburgh, 1870–1920. *J Hist Geogr* **27;** 58–73.

Munroe DK, Croissant C, and York AM. 2005. Land-use policy and landscape fragmentation in an urbanizing region: assessing the impact of zoning. *Appl Geogr* **25:** 121–41.

NRC (National Research Council). 2003. Cities transformed: demographic change and its implication in the developing world. Washington, DC: National Academies Press.

Pataki DE, Alig RJ, Fung AS, *et al.* 2006. Urban ecosystems and the North American carbon cycle. *Global Change Biol* **12:** 2092–2102.

Peñalosa E. 2006. Plenary speech at the World Urban Forum. In: Report of the third session of the World Urban Forum; 2006 June 22; Vancouver, Canada. New York, NY: UN-Habitat.

Pickett STA, Cadenasso ML, Grove JM, *et al.* 2001. Urban ecological systems: linking terrestrial ecological, physical, and socioeconomic components of metropolitan areas. *Annu Rev Ecol Syst* **32;** 127–57.

Pouyat RV, McDonnell MJ, and Pickett STA. 1995. Soil characteristics of oak stands along an urban-rural land-use gradient. *J Environ Qual* 24: 516–26.

Rees WE. 1999. The built environment and the ecosphere: a global perspective. *Build Res Inf* **27;** 206–20.

Righter R. 2005. The battle over Hetch Hetchy; America's most controversial dam and the birth of modern environmentalism. New York, NY: Oxford University Press.

Riley K. 2002. Motor vehicles in China: the impact of demographic and economic changes. *Popui Environ* **23**: 479–94.

Rothman H. 2004. The new urban park: Golden Gate National Recreation Area and civic environmentalism. Lawrence, KS: University Press of Kansas.

Roy KC, Tisdell C, and Alauddin M. 1992. Rural-urban migration and poverty in south Asia, *J Contemp A* **22**: 57–72.

Salzman J. 2005, Creating markets for ecosystem services: notes from the field. *New York U Law Rev* **80**: 870–961.

Skeer J and Wang YJ. 2007. China on the move: oil price explosion? *Energ Policy* **35**: 678–91.

Steemers K. 2003. Energy and the city: density, buildings, and transport. *Energ Buildings* **35**: 3–14.

Sutherland WJ, Pullin AS, Dolman PM, and Knight TM. 2004. The need for evidence-based conservation. Trends *Ecol Evol* **19**: 305–08.

UN-HABITAT (UN Human Settlements Programme). 2006. State of the world's cities. New York, NY: UN Human Settlements Programme.

UNECE (United Nations Economic Commission for Europe). 2005. UNECE Trends 2005 Thematic Database. www.unece.org/stats/trends2005/Welcome.html. Viewed 15 Feb 2007.

UNPD (UN Population Division). 2005a. Population challenges and development goals. New York, NY: UN Population Division.

UNPD (UN Population Division). 2005b. World urbanization prospects: the 2005 revision. New York, NY: UN Population Division.

US Census Bureau, Population Division. US Census Bureau International Database. www.census.gov/ipc/www/idb/index.html. Viewed 15 Feb 2007.

Van der Zee SC, Hoek G, Harssema H, and Brunekreef B. 1998. Characterization of particulate air pollution in urban and non-urban areas in the Netherlands. *Atmos Environ* **32**: 3717–29.

Critical Thinking

1. This article says that urban growth in both the developed and developing world will be the main obstacle to achieving sustainable development. Why?

2. What does the author mean by "urban form matters"? Try to explain this in terms of "consuming the land."

3. According to the author, briefly describe the connections between urban form and ecosystem service generation and consumption.

4. How can looking at sustainability projects as "experiments" help achieve the goals of sustainable urban development?

Acknowledgements—RIM was supported by a David H Smith Conservation Fellowship. P Kareiva and RTT Forman provided helpful comments and encouragement on a draft of this manuscript. The Graduate School of Design at Harvard University, and C Steinitz and N Kirkwood in particular, provided space to work.

Article   Prepared by: Richard Eathorne, *Northern Michigan University*

The New Land Rush

Fears of violence and a hunger for profit are sparking a worldwide run on farmland.

TERRY J. ALLEN

Learning Outcomes

After reading this article, you will be able to:

- Explain why foreign investors are buying up vast tracts of farmland in developing countries.

- Discuss the consequences that this new land rush may have on the people of already impoverished nations.

- List the largest investors in the foreign cropland.

A 21st-century land rush is on. Driven by fear and lured by promises of high profits, foreign investors are scooping up vast tracts of farmland in some of the world's hungriest countries to grow crops for export.

As the climate changes and populations shift and grow, billions of people around the globe face shortages of land and water, rising food prices, and increasing hunger. Alarm over a future without affordable food and water is sparking unrest in a world already tinder-dried by repression and recession, corruption and mismanagement, boundary disputes and ancient feuds, ethnic tension and religious fundamentalism.

World leaders feel the heat. Calling food security concerns "extremely significant," a 2009 U.N. report noted, "The acquisition of land internationally is one possible strategic choice to address the challenge."

Fortunately for nervous rulers, the strategy of growing food abroad as shelter against the fires of revolution dovetails nicely with the goals of private and public capital. Governments drawing on sovereign wealth funds, and rich investors accessing state subsidies, have negotiated deals to acquire tens of millions of acres of farmland in Africa, South America, and South Asia. When they export the food to their home countries, the valuable water used to grow the crops will ride along as a free bonus.

The largest investors in foreign croplands hail from China, India, and South Korea, along with Saudi Arabia and other oil-rich Gulf states. What these countries have in common is that all were shaken financially or politically by the 2007–08 food

crisis. And all lack sufficient land or water to ensure that they can feed their populations in the coming years.

Available for Chump Change and unsecured promises, land around the world is changing hands at a rate unseen since the colonial era, when white men applied the ink of nationalism and greed to redraw maps of Africa, Asia, and the New World. The "new colonialism" is less like a crusade and more like a business transaction floated on a promise of "win-win."

The deal-makers include international agribusinesses, investment banks, hedge funds, and commodity traders, as well as pension funds, foundations, and individuals attracted by the lure of cheap land and high profits. Even universities, including Harvard and Vanderbilt, are getting into the act, according to an extensive report by the Oakland Institute, a progressive policy think tank.

Most of the land deals occur in the private sector, "though often with strong financial and other support from government, and significant levels of government-owned investments," according to the Food and Agriculture Organization. Conforming to this pattern and awash in oil income, the Saudi government "earmarked $5 billion to provide loans at preferential rates to Saudi companies to invest in countries with strong agricultural potential," reports the U.K.-based Institute of Science in Society, including large swaths of Indonesia and Thailand for rice, and possibly 6,000 acres for wheat in war-ravaged Sudan.

The investors are negotiating land transfers all the way from the top, with heads of state down to tribal chiefs and impoverished landowners. Water rights, tax breaks, and waivers on labor and environmental standards often sweeten the deals.

When they cannot buy land outright at prices ranging from cheap (a few dollars an acre) to stolen ("You get a bottle of Johnnie Walker, kneel down, clap three times, and make your offer of Johnnie Walker whiskey," in one transaction reported by the Oakland Institute), investors lease vast tracts for as long as 99 years and for as little as 40 cents per acre per year.

According to the U.N.'s International Fund for Agricultural Development, some 2 billion people in the developing world depend on 500 million smallholder farms for their livelihoods.

In Asia and sub-Saharan Africa, these farmers produce about 80 percent of the food that local people consume.

But with spectacular speed, patchworks of plots that used to support local populations through subsistence farming and grazing are being amalgamated into massive industrial plantations. In Awassa, Ethiopia, a "plastic and steel structure already stretches over 50 acres—the size of 20 soccer fields," writes John Vidal in South Africa's *Mail and Guardian.*

With a 99-year lease for 2,500 acres, the developer, Saudi Sheikh Mohammed al-Amoudi, has brought in Spanish engineers and Dutch water technology, and hired 1,000 women to pick, pack, and send 50 tons of food a day to the Middle East, writes Vidal.

The Years 2007 and 2008 marked a turning point for both environmental consciousness and food insecurity. Before then, agricultural land had expanded by less than 10 million acres a year. But with the pileup of evidence for global warming, no one but the ideologically blinkered could see extensive droughts and other weather-related catastrophes as flukes. Sharply diminished yields triggered exporting countries to ban or curb grain sales, pushed prices up, and helped trigger riots that shook dozens of countries. World Bank President Robert Zoellick warned in 2008 that "33 countries around the world face potential social unrest because of the acute hike in food and energy prices."

By 2009 deals were being struck for 111 million acres, with 75 percent in sub-Saharan Africa, according to a World Bank report. A year later, the bank upped the total to nearly 140 million acres.

These "land grabs," says Lester Brown, founder of the Worldwatch Institute and the Earth Policy Institute, encompass "an area that exceeds the croplands devoted to corn and wheat combined in the United States."

Then, as if out of nowhere, the Arab Spring struck in 2011. Long-standing un- and underemployment and repression were key triggers, but as the International Institute for Strategic Studies noted, a "proximate factor behind the unrest was a spike in global food crises, which in turn was due in part to the extreme weather throughout the globe over the past year."

In the seven months before Egypt's President Hosni Mubarak was driven from power in February, the trading price of wheat had more than doubled. In August 2010, faced with droughts and wildfires, Russia gave its own people first priority and restricted most grain exports, ensuring that prices would skyrocket. The choked supply line seriously affected Egypt, which imports more than half its food.

By early 2011 some 21 countries had imposed export control measures including limits and outright bans on the foreign sale of particular crops.

Saudi Arabia had A Ringside Seat as the Arab Spring spread across the region. The House of Saud understood that its security rests on its ability to buy the quiescence, if not the loyalty, of its citizens with affordable food and social welfare programs that make Sweden look like a Tea Party paradise.

The sheiks had been watching the writing in the sand since the 1970s, when, after the Arab oil-export embargo, they realized their vulnerability: Just as the West was dependent on them for oil, they were dependent on others for food. The prospect of being forced to bend the stiff royal knee to Western-imposed economic pressures inspired the Saudis to apply their oil technology to drilling deep for water. Using heavy irrigation, the country soon became self-sufficient in wheat. But unlike underground water supplies that are replenished by precipitation, fossil aquifers can rapidly be drained dry—and that is what is happening under the Arabian Peninsula.

Within a few decades, the prehistoric aquifer was almost exhausted, and by 2007, when food riots were roiling the region, the Saudi wheat harvest had dropped precipitously. The Saudi Ministry of Agriculture predicts that by 2016 the country will have to import 100 percent of the wheat it needs to feed its nearly 26 million people.

Saudi Arabia is one of 18 countries—which together contain half the world's people—where water for irrigation is draining aquifers. But the export of "virtual water" incorporated into growing crops promises not only ecological problems, but also political trouble downstream. Large-scale irrigation in Ethiopia and Sudan, for example, diverts water from the upper Nile River basin and cuts into Egypt's already limited water supply.

Despite water woes, Sudan welcomes investors. "It's the first country that gives us land without complicated procedures," Mohammed Rasheed al-Balawi, a former manager of the Saudi firm Hadco, told the *Financial Times.* "The area is big, the people are friendly, [and] they gave us the land almost free."

That characterization of terms is hotly disputed. Although both investors and host countries often refer to acquired land as underdeveloped or empty, the deals typically displace herders and small farmers, who are not consulted and, in any case, lack legal deeds. The World Bank estimates that between 2 and 10 percent of Africa's land is held under formal land tenure, and most of that is in urban areas.

As foreign investors pour in—from Arab princedoms, India, South Korea, China, and other nations—hundreds of thousands of Ethiopians are being relocated.

Ironically, key targets of foreign agro-investment include the world's hungriest countries: In Ethiopia, 13 million people receive international food aid and 41 percent are undernourished. The country's massive transfer of physical wealth to foreign corporations is overseen by Prime Minister Meles Zenawi. One of the parties he controls owns at least five state-affiliated companies and has major stakes in the agricultural products market. Zenawi's regime has granted control of 1.48 million acres to foreign entities, according to the *Mail and Guardian.*

Foreign Land Investors are banking on profits of up to 25 percent, buoyed by loose environmental and labor regulations common in desperately poor and corrupt countries. "Lack of transparency and of checks and balances in contract negotiations creates a breeding ground for corruption," the FAO says, adding with understatement, "and deals that do not maximize the public interest."

One of the public costs, lax environmental regulation, is a key perk for investors. If history is any guide, eventually—but not before great profits can be extracted—industrial monoculture agriculture will deplete soil and water; perpetual chemical inputs including fertilizers, pesticides, and herbicides will poison the environment; and pest and disease problems will strangle biodiversity.

But even when host governments impose contractual restrictions and protections, "there does not appear to be any significant enforcement of lease terms," according to the Oakland Institute report. "Government is charging us a rent," a foreign investor in Ethiopia told the institute. "What we choose to do on the land for our own commercial intent is our own business. There are . . . no constraints, no contracts, none of that."

With $332 Billion in Assets, the China Investment Corporation is one of the world's largest sovereign wealth funds. And like the Saudis', China's concerns about growing unrest and food insecurity are factors in its increasing investment in foreign farmland.

China's "embrace of [Africa] is strategic, planned, long-term, and still unfolding," writes Deborah Brautigam, an American University specialist in China-Africa relations. She argues that China is more concerned with economic expansion than with food security, which significant portions of its leadership believe is better ensured by adequate home production.

That may be difficult to achieve. While the United States has almost 3 acres of farmland per person, China has only .23. And 5,000 years of intensive farming has depleted China's soil, industrialization has poisoned much of its water, and development and urbanization have depleted rivers and land so that even as population and per capita consumption increase, the country has lost more than 20 million acres of arable land—just since the mid-1990s.

In addition to its interest in Africa, China is investing in diverse cropland in Australia and New Zealand and looking to Indonesia for biofuels and to South America for soy for livestock production to feed its increasingly affluent population's taste for meat and dairy. China's South American interests are so extensive that some Brazilians, while crediting Chinese investment for their booming economy, fear for their autonomy.

"They are moving in," Carlo Lovatelli, president of the Brazilian Association of Vegetable Oil Industries, told the *New York Times*, "looking for land and reliable partners. But what they would like to do is run the show alone."

"Some experts," the *Times* noted, "say the partnership has devolved into a classic neocolonial relationship in which China has the upper hand."

Many Foreign Land Investors say that they give back at least as much as they take. "We've really created something out of nothing in Africa," says Anthony Poorter, Africa director for EmVest, the African subsidiary of Emergent Asset Management. "There are no shady deals."

In areas with hungry people, inadequate roads, and other infrastructural deficiencies, foreign capital is sorely needed to develop more rational farming operations that can promote prosperity, food security, and jobs. And there is little doubt that monoculture industrial farming, genetically engineered seeds, and input from pesticides and chemical fertilizers can more quickly create higher yields than small-scale subsistence farming. Properly managed, supporters of expo-agriculture argue, investment dollars can bring educational opportunities, health care, and the possibility of safer, higher living standards to subsistence farmers and impoverished rural populations.

Some investors also believe they are serving humanity: "Unless food production is boosted 50 percent before 2050," says Poorter's boss, Emergent CEO Susan Payne, "we face serious shortages globally." Her company, which "went on record in 2007 to identify food security as the next energy security," invests in 14 countries in sub-Saharan Africa and is aiming for an annual return of 25 percent or more.

But just as international development aid schemes, such as USAID's, conform to the geopolitical strategies and economic goals of the dispensing country, private investment is shaped by an inner imperative: the need to turn a profit. Whatever the investors promise, or however decent they are as individuals, their bottom line is the bottom line.

"There is a real risk that the current scramble for land will transfer wealth from the poor and the marginalized to those who have access to capital and markets, with deeply regressive consequences," warns U.N. Special Rapporteur Olivier de Schutter.

Backlashes have already occurred. When word leaked that Madagascar planned to sell 3 million acres to the South Korean firm Daewoo Logistics, popular outrage quashed the deal and toppled Madagascar's government. In the Philippines, as food prices were spiking in 2007, outcries from Filipino farmers stopped China from buying 2.5 million acres on which to grow export crops.

It is clear that the geopolitics of food scarcity has undergone a major shift. Land is the new gold, and mining it for export food, extracting its water to incorporate into crops, and taking advantage of cheap labor and lax environmental laws are now, as Brown puts it, "integral parts of a global power struggle for food security."

When people are hungry enough, they are likely to choose the risk of revolution over the certainty of starvation. Governments that are unable to secure affordable food for their people are vulnerable to the kind of social unrest that has long been part of history's hunger not only for food, but also for justice.

Critical Thinking

1. Why are foreign investors buying up cropland in poor countries?

2. What could be some of the negative consequences of such a land rush?

3. Why is this being allowed?

Create Central

www.mhhe.com/createcentral

Internet References

Alliance for Global Sustainability (AGS)
www.global-sustainability.org

Geography and Socioeconomic Development
www.ksg.harvard.edu/cid/andes/Documents/Background%20Papers/
Geography&Socioeconomic%20Development.pdf

Penn Library: Resources by Subject
www.library.upenn.edu/cgi-bin/res/sr.cgi

U.S. Information Agency (USIA)
www.america.gov

TERRY J. ALLEN is a senior editor at *In These Times.*

Development at the Urban Fringe and Beyond: Impacts on Agriculture and Rural Land by Ralph E. Heimlich and William D. Anderson

139

Article

Development at the Urban Fringe and Beyond: Impacts on Agriculture and Rural Land

RALPH E. HEIMLICH AND WILLIAM D. ANDERSON

I. Overview

In the early 1970's, bipartisan legislation was introduced in Congress to establish a national land-use policy, but failed after extensive debate. In the decades that followed, urban area in the United States has more than doubled. Public concerns about ill-controlled growth once again have raised the issue of the Federal role in land-use policy.

Purpose of This Report

Although land-use issues have traditionally been the prerogative of State and local government, policymakers at the Federal level are increasingly urged to respond to concerns about development and growth, particularly with regard to their impacts on agriculture and rural land uses. While anecdotes are legion, and much has been written by commentators, advocates, and experts, there are surprisingly few places to find a comprehensive picture of land-use changes in urbanizing areas, relative to the rural landscape. This report responds to that need in two ways.

This overview provides a summary of our findings about the forces driving development, its character and impacts on agriculture and rural communities, the means available to channel and control growth, and the pros and cons of potential Federal roles.

The following chapters provide the details, presented in a documented, objective way that make the case for the arguments presented here. A consensus culled from the literature supports some of the points, while original analyses presented in this report have not been published elsewhere.

What Is Sprawl?

This report is about urban development at the edges of cities and in rural areas, sometimes called "urban sprawl." With no widely accepted definition of sprawl (U.S. GAO, 1999; Staley, 1999), attempts to define it range from the expansive to the prescriptive.

Most definitions have some common elements, including:

- Low-density development that is dispersed and uses a lot of land;
- Geographic separation of essential places such as work, homes, schools, and shopping; and
- Almost complete dependence on automobiles for travel.

Without an agreed definition, any growth in suburban areas may be accused of "sprawling."

Short of a return to a form of urban living not seen since before World War II, it is not clear how growth can be accommodated at suburban densities without incurring the worst features of "sprawl." Because "sprawl" is not easily defined, this report is couched in the more neutral terms "development" or "growth," without making implicit judgments about the quality or outcomes of that development or growth. See *Trends in Land Use: Two Kinds of Growth.*

How to Think about Development

Concerns about development around urban areas are not new, but have arisen periodically during most of the last century, and certainly since automobile ownership became widespread after World War II. Amid the environmental concerns during the 1970's, bipartisan legislation was introduced in Congress to establish a national land-use policy. Recognizing the primacy of State authority over land use, the legislation sought to provide Federal grants to States to strengthen their ability to plan for development and channel growth. After 5 years of debate, the legislation was passed in the Senate, but narrowly defeated in the House on June 11, 1974. What lessons have been learned about urban development and the Federal role in managing it in the 26 years since then?

There are two kinds of growth, but both affect the amount and productivity of agricultural land and create other problems—Our existing urban areas continue to grow into the countryside, and more isolated large-lot housing development is occurring, generally beyond the urban fringe.

At the urban fringe—The urban "fringe" is that part of metropolitan counties that is not settled densely enough to be called "urban." Low-density development (2 or fewer houses per acre) of new houses, roads, and commercial buildings causes urban areas to grow farther out into the countryside, and increases the density of settlement in formerly rural areas. The extent of urbanized areas and urban places, as defined by the Bureau of Census, more than doubled over the last 40 years from 25.5 million acres in 1960 to 55.9 million acres in 1990, and most likely reached about 65 million acres by 2000.

Beyond the urban fringe—Another kind of development often occurs farther out in the rural countryside, beyond the edge of existing urban areas and often in adjacent nonmetropolitan counties. Development of scattered single-family houses removes land from agricultural production and changes the nature of open space, but is not "urban." Large lots dominate this process, and growth in large-lot development has accelerated with business cycles since 1970. Nearly 80 percent of the acreage used for new housing construction in 1994–97—about 2 million acres—is outside urban areas. Almost all of this land (94 percent) is in lots of 1 acre or larger, with 57 percent on lots 10 acres or larger. About 16 percent was located in existing urban areas and 5 percent was on farms. See *Two Kinds of Growth.*

Growth in developed areas is increasing, but at rates only slightly higher than in the past—Urbanized areas and urban places increased at about the same 1 million acres per year between 1960 and 1990. Developed land, including residential and other development that is not dense enough to meet urban definitions, increased from 78.4 million acres in 1982 to 92.4 million acres in 1992, and was estimated to be about 107 million acres in 2000. The rate of increase in developed land grew from 1.4 million acres per year to about 1.8 million acres. See *Two Kinds of Growth.*

The processes of land-use change are well understood and flow predictably from population growth, household formation, and economic development—Changes in land use are the end result of many forces that drive millions of separate choices made by homeowners, farmers, businesses, and government. The ultimate drivers are population growth and household formation. Economic growth increases income and wealth, and preferences for housing and lifestyles, enabled by new transportation and communications technologies, spur new housing development and new land-use patterns. Metropolitan areas grow organically, following well-known stages of growth.

Almost alone among developed nations, the United States continues to add population from high fertility rates, high immigration, and longer life expectancy, increasing 1 percent per year, or another 150 million people by 2050. Average household size has dropped to 2.6 persons, creating about 1 million new households, the unit of demand for new housing, each year in the 1990's.

Increased income and wealth increased the number of new houses constructed each year by 1.5 million units, faster than the rate of household formation. Two-thirds of these houses are single-family dwellings. While average lot sizes have been dropping near cities as owners turn to townhouses and condominiums, a parallel growth in large-lot (greater than 1 acre) housing has occurred beyond the urban fringe.

Metropolitan expansion since 1950 has occurred because rural people moved off the farms, and residents of the densely populated central cities dispersed to surrounding suburbs. Urbanized areas (excluding towns of 2,500 or more) increased from 106 to 369 and expanded to five times their size. Population density in urbanized areas dropped by more than 50 percent, from 8.4 to 4 people per acre, over the last 50 years. Growth is spilling out of metropolitan areas, as population disperses to rural parts of metropolitan counties and previously rural nonmetropolitan counties.

Enabling this dispersion are investments in new infrastructure such as roads, sewers, and water supplies. New information and communication technologies, such as the Internet and cellular telephone networks, facilitate population in rural areas, and free employment to follow. New retail, office, warehouse, and other commercial development follows in the wake of new housing development, to serve the new population and to employ the relocated labor force. See *Driving Forces.*

There are benefits of low-density development that attract people—Living beyond the edge of the city is a lifestyle much sought after by the American people. While 55 percent of Americans living in medium to large cities preferred that location, 45 percent wanted to live in a rural or small town setting 30 or more miles from the city (Brown et al., 1997). Of those living in rural or small towns more than 30 miles from large cities, 35 percent wanted to live closer to the city. The urban fringe is thus under development pressure from both directions. The most obvious benefit is that growth in rural areas has allowed many people, including those who cannot afford city real estate, to buy single-family homes because land costs are cheaper on the fringe than in the core.

The automobile imposes private and social costs in exchange for the comfort, flexibility, low door-to-door travel time, freight-carrying capacity (for shopping trips), cheap long-distance travel, and aesthetic benefits of extensive, automobile-dependent development. Air quality improvements may also result from decentralizing population and employment, because emissions are dispersed over larger rural airsheds and are reduced by higher speeds. Automobile pollution is more strongly related to the number of trips than to the length of each trip, with a major part of auto pollution deriving from cold starts.

Not everyone wants to live the rural lifestyle. The "new urbanism" school of urban design is redesigning conventional suburban developments as small towns and finding a market (Chen, 2000; Duany et al., 2000). In 1992, 55 percent of those surveyed living in large cities (over 50,000) preferred that type of community (Brown et al., 1997). See *Demand for Low-Density Development.*

Development imposes direct costs on the communities experiencing it, as well as indirect costs in terms of the rural lands sacrificed to it—A number of studies show that less dense, unplanned development requires higher private and public capital and operating costs than more compact, denser planned development. Eighty-five studies gauging the cost of community services around the country have shown that residential development requires $1.24 in expenditures for public services for every dollar it generates in tax revenues, on average. By contrast, farmland or open space generates only 38 cents in costs for each dollar in taxes paid. See *Impacts on Taxpayers*.

Finally, development can disrupt existing social, community, environmental and ecological patterns, imposing a variety of costs on people, wildlife, water, air, and soil quality. Agricultural production has its own negative environmental impacts, but these are generally less severe than those from urban development. See *Impacts on Landscape, Open Space, and Sense of Community*.

However, does moving out into the "country" ultimately destroy all the good things that prompt that move? In the words of the National Governor's Association, "In the context of traditional growth patterns, the desire to live the 'American Dream' and purchase a single-family home on a large lot in a formerly open space can produce a negative outcome for society as a whole" (Hirschorn, pp. 55).

Continued demand for low-density development despite negative consequences for residents can be understood as a market failure—Consumers, businesses, and communities fail to anticipate the results of development because they often lack information on potential or approved development proposals for surrounding land. When communities fail to plan and zone, there is no institutional framework within which development can proceed, and little information to help housing buyers anticipate their future landscape setting.

Spillovers from development include the loss of rural amenities, open space, and environmental goods when previously existing farms and rural land uses are developed. Negative spillovers from increased housing consumption in developing areas can include traffic congestion, crowding, and destruction of visual amenities. If the landscape features that contribute to rural amenity were marketed in developments, housing prices would be higher.

Real estate markets are based on many small decisions which, when taken without an overall context, produce results that can neither be envisioned by nor anticipated by consumers and developers. Cumulative impacts from this myriad of decisions can be large, but are not reflected in market prices until disamenities become large. Inaccurate judgments about future landscapes are locked in because development is irreversible. See *An Economic Interpretation of the Demand for Low-Density Development*.

Urban growth and development is not a threat to national food and fiber production, but may reduce production of some high-value or specialty crops—Despite doubling since 1960, urban area still made up less than 3 percent of U.S. land area in 1990 (excluding Alaska). Developed area, including rural roads and transportation, made up less than 5 percent in 1992. Development affects local agricultural economies and can cause other environmental and resource problems in local areas, but the increase in urban area in the United States poses no threat to U.S. food and fiber production. Some crops in some areas are particularly vulnerable to development. For example,

61 percent of U.S. vegetable production is located in metropolitan areas, but vegetable production takes up less than 1 percent of U.S. cropland. See *Consequences for Farming*.

Agriculture can adapt to development, but does so by changing the products and services offered—Low-density, fragmented settlement patterns leave room for agriculture to continue. Farms in metropolitan areas are an increasingly important segment of U.S. agriculture. They make up 33 percent of all farms, 16 percent of cropland, and produce a third of the value of U.S. agricultural output. However, to adapt to rising land values and increasing contact with new residents, farmers may have to change their operations to emphasize higher value products, more intensive production, enterprises that fit better in an urbanizing environment, and a more urban marketing orientation.

Development can be profitable for farmers who can see and take advantage of opportunities in the new situation. Forces of urbanization allow a variety of farm types to coexist. Farms in metropolitan areas are generally smaller, but produce more per acre, have more diverse enterprises, and are more focused on high-value production than nonmetropolitan farms. Metropolitan agriculture is characterized by recreational farmers who follow both farm and non-farm pursuits; a smaller group of adaptive farmers who have accommodated their farm operation to the urban environment; and a residual group of traditional farms that are trying to survive in the face of urbanization. Both of the latter types are generally working farms. See *Consequences for Farming*.

Benefits of conserving rural land are difficult to estimate, and vary widely depending on the circumstances—Because there are no markets for some characteristics of land, such as scenic amenity, there are no observable prices apart from the land's value for development. Lacking prices, it is difficult to develop economic benefit measures for policymaking.

Rural lands in a working landscape provide economic benefits as resources for agricultural production, as sources of employment, and through property and income taxes. Working landscapes are defined as farm, ranch, and forest lands actively used in agricultural or forestry production. While agricultural production can create environmental problems of its own, properly managed farmlands provide nonmarket benefits from improving water and air quality, protecting natural bio-diversity, and preserving wetlands relative to development. They create aesthetically pleasing landscapes and can provide social and recreational opportunities. The rural landscape reflects and conserves rural culture and traditions, and maintains traditions of civic leadership and responsibility in voluntary rural institutions, such as fire companies and village boards. See *Impacts on Landscape, Open Space, and Sense of Community*.

Based on information and assumptions about the number of acres likely subject to development in the future, and on limited studies of residents' willingness to pay to conserve farmland and open space, we estimate that households would be willing to pay $1.4–$26.6 billion per year to conserve rural lands. In addition, another $0.7–$1.1 billion in sediment and water quality damages would be avoided if the land were prevented from being developed. Conserving land for agriculture helps preserve farming as a part of the rural economy, and is often seen as a bulwark against the worst effects of development. See *Benefits of Farmland and Open Space.*

Local governments generally do not develop adequate capacity to plan for and manage growth until it is too late to effectively channel development—Because urban growth processes are well understood, strategically directing development to the most favorable areas well in advance of urban pressures offers the greatest hope for controlling growth. Planning and zoning have generally been upheld by the courts as valid out. If planning is not in place as development begins to occur, property owners' expectations about higher land values can exacerbate property rights conflicts and complicate subsequent growth-control efforts. Local governments often fail to appreciate impending growth facing them, and generally lack capacity to develop adequate responses before growth overwhelms them.

Better planning and zoning is central to the ability to respond to growth. A U.S. General Accounting Office survey found that 75 percent of the communities that were concerned with "sprawl" were highly involved in planning for and managing growth (U.S. GAO, 2000, p. 99).

However many cities and counties may be falling short of what is needed to control and manage growth effectively. A recent survey of Alabama's mayors and county commissioners found that only a minority of the responding officials (18 percent of the mayors and 19 percent of the commissioners) believed they currently had the necessary staff and resources to plan and manage growth effectively. High-growth communities were only somewhat more likely to have the capacity to manage growth than were other communities.

Most of the smaller rural towns do not have a full-time planner. To meet their planning needs, these communities may be served by a circuit riding planner, or several towns and a county may combine their efforts to set up one planning office to serve their joint needs. Even at the county level, rural planners often must spend part of their time doing other duties. See *Local Responses to Growth.*

State governments can do more to deal with growth strategically—Our Constitution reserves control of land use to the States, which usually have delegated the responsibility to local governments. Increasingly, States are realizing that local governments cannot adequately address growth pressures that transcend local boundaries. Some States have adopted "smart growth" strategies that actively direct transportation, infrastructure, and other resources to channel growth into appropriate areas.

The term "smart growth" is a catch-all phrase used to describe a group of land-use planning techniques that influence the pattern and density of new development. In general, smart growth strategies represent a movement away from State-imposed requirements for local compliance with State planning goals. Because smart growth strategies tend to use financial incentives to encourage voluntary adoption, they are generally supported by a broad spectrum of interest groups. These strategies also garner support because they direct, rather than inhibit, growth and development. There's no 'one size fits all': the specific smart-growth strategies that have been adopted

vary by location but often share common elements. Smart-growth principles favor investing resources in center cities and older suburbs, supporting mass transit and pedestrian-friendly development, and encouraging mixed-use development while conserving open space, rural amenities, and environmentally sensitive resources (Hirschhorn 2000). These strategies also typically remove financial incentives provided by State funding to develop outside designated growth areas. In essence, smart growth encourages development in designated areas without prohibiting development outside them. See *Slow Growth, No Growth, and Smart Growth.*

Existing monetary incentives for conserving rural land are not as effective as they could be—Use-value assessment, enacted in every State, is one of the most widespread public policies aimed at conserving rural land. Under use-value assessment, the owner is taxed based on what the land could earn in agriculture, rather than the higher developed value. We estimated the cost of tax reductions under use-value assessment nationally at $1.1 billion per year.

However, most students of use-value assessment acknowledge that it is not effective at preventing development. Use-value assessment spreads resources over all qualifying rural land, providing a small incentive to conserve land to all landowners. The size of the tax reduction is insufficient to keep land with the highest development potential from conversion, while tax expenditures to less developable land produce little result. Redirecting tax expenditures on use-value assessment could increase the resources available for incentives to conserve the most developable land, but could make some land currently getting the tax subsidy more vulnerable to urbanization and would face stiff opposition from property owners currently enjoying the tax reduction. See *Monetary Incentives for Conserving Farm and Forest Land.*

The cost of effective incentives would be large, but if resources were redirected, almost one-third of the cropland with the greatest development potential could be protected—Purchasing the development rights to rural land effectively protects it from being developed. The landowner retains ownership and can continue to farm the land, but the deed restriction continues indefinitely. The implicit economic value of the easement is the difference between the unrestricted or market value of the parcel and its restricted or agricultural value.

Nineteen States have State-level PDR (purchase of development rights) programs using public funds to compensate landowners for the easements on otherwise private farm or forest land. In addition, at least 34 county programs in 11 States operate separate programs. The American Farmland Trust estimates that, nationwide, PDR programs have cumulatively protected 819,490 acres of farmland with an expenditure of $1.2 billion.

We estimate the cost to purchase development rights on cropland most likely subject to urban pressure over the next 30 to 50 years at $88–$130 billion. If tax expenditures currently devoted to use-value assessment were redirected to purchase of development rights, almost one-third of the cropland with greatest potential for development could be protected.

Targeting funds to land under less development pressure could protect the same amount of land at lower cost. For

Development at the Urban Fringe and Beyond: Impacts on Agriculture and Rural Land by Ralph E. Heimlich and William D. Anderson

143

example, development rights on the 25 million acres under medium urban pressure are estimated to cost $25 billion, less than one-third the cost of the 33 million acres under heaviest development pressure. Selecting land with lowest current development pressure would reduce costs to $18 billion.

Even if funds were available to purchase development rights, it may not be desirable to do so. The development pressure exerted on this land will not disappear if this cropland is protected. While some growth might be accommodated in existing urban areas, demand for other rural land would intensify, and growth could fragment even more as development moves out farther into the rural countryside. Purchasing development rights is also no guarantee that the land will be used for working agricultural enterprises. The perpetual deed restrictions could prevent future desirable adjustments in land-use patterns. See *Monetary Incentives for Conserving Farm and Forest Land.*

There are neither clear requirements for nor restrictions on Federal roles in managing growth—Historically, authority over land-use decisions has been reserved to the States, who have delegated these powers to local governments. However, the evolution of environmental policy shows an expanding Federal involvement in site-specific, local circumstances that recur across the Nation. The Federal Government has no constitutional mandate to take action on urban growth and development issues, but it can define an appropriate role for itself. See *Potential Federal Roles.*

Federal activity in the potential roles identified below is described and pros and cons of expanding each role are enumerated.

Potential Federal Roles

Helping Increase State and Local Planning Capacity—The Federal Government has had a long history of programs to improve the planning capabilities of State and local governments. Perhaps the most notable of these efforts was the HUD 701 planning grant program, established in 1954 (40 USC 461). As late as 1975, the HUD 701 program spent $100 million per year paying as much as two-thirds of the costs of an "ongoing comprehensive planning process" required of all grant recipients. However, the budget was cut to $75 million in 1976 and was gradually phased down until eliminated in the early 1980's.

Within the U.S. Department of Agriculture, the Rural Development Act of 1972 established the Section A-111 Rural Development Planning Grants, also funded into the 1980's. In 1996, the farm bill established new authority for the Rural Business Opportunity Grant program (RBOG), which received $3.5 million in FY2000 appropriations. RBOG provides money to nonprofits, public bodies, Indian tribes, and cooperatives for planning and technical assistance to assist economic development in rural areas. FY 2001 appropriations legislation increased the funding for RBOG to $8 million. Several other smaller USDA grant programs could potentially assist local communities with planning, but they are not specifically directed at planning to guide growth and development and are not integrated into a coordinated program.

Pros—Funding requirements for such programs would be relatively small, and could potentially leverage significant impacts. Impacts from limited funding for such programs could be increased by targeting them to the areas most likely affected by growth in the medium term. Limiting program activities to those most directly relevant to guiding new growth and development would also increase the impact of the program.

Cons—Failures in past programs were attributed to wide use of consultants who provided little service for the money spent, and who did little to add permanently to local government planning capacity. Emphasis on "paper plans" did little to actually direct growth. Targeting funds to areas immediately affected by development wasted resources on efforts that were already too late, while spreading funding widely included areas with little development pressure in reasonable time-frames.

Coordinating Local, Regional, and State Efforts—Urban growth processes often create multi-jurisdictional impacts. Federal coordination and integration have been exercised in other areas of environmental concern, such as water quality, water quantity, and air quality. In addition, the U.S. Office of Management and Budget Circular A-95 review process formerly guided Federal agencies for cooperation with State and local governments in the evaluation, review, and coordination of Federal assistance programs and projects. A-95 review is no longer mandated by the Federal Government, although the process is still voluntarily practiced by some States. USDA has had a long history of area-wide coordination, dating back to efforts like the Great Plains Agricultural Council, the Resource Conservation and Development Council (RC&D), the Small Watershed Program (PL-566), and various river basin planning processes. While these have generally been focused on agricultural, resource, or rural development concerns, their extension to urban development and growth control issues would be reasonable.

Pros—Past Federal funding for transportation, water, and sewer construction and other major infrastructure projects has been identified as a major driver in growth and development. Explicitly monitoring and reviewing potential impacts on urbanization from such investments could, at a minimum, defuse these accusations. Federal funding could serve as a rationale for efforts to coordinate State and local growth control activities, especially where these cross jurisdictional boundaries. Such efforts would cost very little, but would leverage existing expenditures.

Cons—Without convincing resolution to reduce or deny funding to State and local governments that do not cooperate, attempts at coordination could prove futile and frustrating. Congressional attempts to obtain additional funding for local constituents can be at odds with Executive branch notions of coordination and integration.

Coordinating Federal Development Activities and Growth Management Goals—Lines between areas needing development assistance and those suffering from problems of growth and development are geographic ones, and are often exceedingly fine, and shift over time. The Federal Government has had a long history of programs to foster development, and less experience at helping control it. The superficial dichotomy disappears when considered in the context of directing growth and development to appropriate places and under an appropriate timetable, which serves both sets of interests.

Pros—A wide array of rural development and economic development activities in the Departments of Agriculture and Commerce, abetted by less direct activities in the Departments of Housing and Urban Development, Transportation, and Defense, date at least to the War on Poverty and related efforts of the 1960's. The existing institutional structure of these programs could be redirected to growth control and management, but would require new visions by leadership. Some existing resources could be leveraged.

Cons—These programs have become entrenched and rather balkanized and may be difficult to integrate into an effort of sufficient weight to effectively deal with the problem. While pro- and anti-growth interests would hopefully recognize common ground in wellplanned and appropriate development, extremes on both sides may be difficult to persuade, and both sides may be suspicious of Federal help.

Funding Monetary Conservation Incentives—The Federal Government has often been enlisted as an ally with deep pockets, and analogous programs for soil and water conservation, wildlife habitat acquisition, and other land resource issues have existed since the 1930's. USDA's Farmland Protection Program was authorized in the 1996 Farm Act for up to $35 million in matching funds for State programs over 6 years. The initial funding was $33.5 million and it was spent to protect 127,000 acres in over 19 States. The goal of the program is to protect between 170,000 and 340,000 acres of farmland. An additional $10 million was appropriated in FY2000. Direct Federal acquisition of easements is included in USDA's Conservation Reserve Program and Wetland Reserve Program, as well as in several of the U.S. Fish and Wildlife Service's habitat programs.

Pros—Limited Federal funding for farmland protection easements could act as seed money for programs in States with no current program, or as a bonus for States doing a particularly effective job. Utilizing existing State programs may be cost-effective because it both avoids creating a new bureaucracy within the Federal Government and provides an incentive to States that have not yet developed a program to do so. By carefully specifying rules for matching State funding, such a program could avoid discouraging State effort, and could maximize the incentive for new programs.

Cons—As outlined above, the amount of land and resources subject to development is large and State programs are relatively small, posing questions about the effectiveness of a small Federal program and larger questions about the ultimate size needed to make an impact. While the marginal benefits of a small program at this point are likely to be greater than the costs, the wisdom of a larger program becomes problematic. Questions about the displacement of growth and the longrun fate of protected land become more significant as the amount of land protected increases.

Conserving Rural Amenities as Part of Greater Agricultural and Trade Policy Goals—Conserving the amenities provided by rural land is no longer a matter of merely domestic concern. Proposals to direct agri-environmental assistance are widespread in the European Union and other Organization for Economic Cooperation and Development (OECD) countries. Such efforts meet the "green box" requirements for acceptable agricultural policies under agricultural trade reforms in the Uruguay Round of the General Agreement on Tariffs and Trade (GATT). Some proponents of greater Federal involvement in rural land conservation believe that a larger share of Federal funding for agriculture could be directed toward land conservation through agri-environmental payments designed to preserve more of the multiple functions of agriculture in an urbanizing context. While not required by trade agreements to date, such proposals are allowed by them and may garner support from constituents in urbanizing areas, the urban fringe, and among agricultural communities.

Pros—Frameworks for agri-environmental payments have already been proposed in the form of the Conservation Security Act of 2000 (S.3260/H.R. 5511), introduced by Senator Harkin and Congressman Minge, and in the Clinton Administration's proposal for a Conservation Security Program in October 2000. While not explicitly addressing farmland protection, eligible land in urbanizing areas could be included. This kind of program helps align U.S. agricultural support programs with legitimate purposes recognized in trade liberalization agreements.

Cons—The farmland conservation issues in Europe and the United States are fundamentally different. While European efforts are largely aimed at keeping economically marginal farmland from abandonment, U.S. concerns are with preventing otherwise viable farms from being developed. The latter is a far more expensive proposition. Channeling large amounts of assistance to farms in urbanizing areas risks losses if incentives are not sufficiently large to prevent development, and may be pyhrric if protected farms cannot viably continue in operation, despite protection. On balance, preventing the environmental problems from losing farms in urbanizing areas may not yield benefits as large as correcting environmental problems from farming in more rural areas.

Organization of the Remainder of the Report

The remainder of the report provides a more in-depth, documented discussion of this overview. . . .

II. Trends in Land Use: Two Kinds of Growth

In the early 1970's, bipartisan legislation was introduced in Congress to establish a national land-use policy. The proposals, recognizing the primacy of State authority over land use, would have provided Federal grants to States to better manage growth and development. The bills were debated for 5 years and passed by the Senate, but died on a narrow vote in the House on June 11, 1974.

In the decades that followed, urban area in the United States has more than doubled. Some of this growth has been at low densities, with little planning, and has fragmented the rural land-scape, prompting communities, States, and the Federal Government to examine more closely unplanned development and its consequences, including the loss of productive farmland. Public concerns about the consequences of ill-controlled growth once again have raised the issue of the Federal role in land-use policy.

Anecdotes of uncontrolled growth across the Nation abound:

- From 1950 to 1990, St. Louis experienced a 355-percent growth in developed land even though population increased by just 35 percent (Missouri Coalition for the Environment).

- Between 1970 and 1990, Kansas City's population grew by 29 percent while developed land increased by 110 percent (Missouri Coalition for the Environment).

- Between 1990 and 1996, the Denver metropolitan region increased by 66 percent. If each county in the Denver metro area grew based on its current comprehensive plan, Denver's urbanized area would swell to 1,150 square miles, an area larger than California's major cities combined (Sierra Club, 1998).

- The Chicago metropolitan area now covers over 3,800 square miles. Over the last decade, the population of the area grew by only 4 percent, but land occupied by housing increased by 46 percent and commercial land uses by 74 percent (U.S. OTA, 1995).

- From 1950 to 1980, population in the Chesapeake Bay watershed increased by 50 percent, while land used for commercial and residential activity climbed 180 percent (EPA, 1993).

- Philadelphia's population increased 2.8 percent between 1970 and 1990, but its developed area increased by 32 percent (U.S. OTA, 1995).

While anecdotes are legion, and much has been written by commentators, advocates, and experts, there are surprisingly few places to find a comprehensive picture of land-use changes in urbanizing areas, relative to the rural landscape. This report responds to that need.

What Is Sprawl?

This report is about urban development at the edges of cities and in rural areas, often referred to as "urban sprawl." There is no widely accepted definition of sprawl (U.S. GAO, 1999; Staley, 1999). Definitions range from the expansive . . .

> **"When you cannot tell where the country ends and a community begins, that is sprawl. Small towns sprawl, suburbs sprawl, big cities sprawl, and metropolitan areas stretch into giant megalopolises—formless webs of urban development like Swiss cheeses with more holes than cheese."**
>
> —U.S. House, 1980

> **"Cities have become impossible to describe. Their centers are not as central as they used to be, their edges ambiguous, they have no beginnings and apparently no end. Neither words, numbers, nor pictures can adequately comprehend their complex forms and social structures. . . . It's almost as if Frank Lloyd Wright's 1932 tract against the metropolis, *The Disappearing City*, has been vindicated, and the diffusionary proposal of Broad-acre City has become the de facto ideology of urbanism."**
>
> —Ingersoll, 1992

to the prescriptive . . .

> **". . . a spreading, low-density, automobile dependent development pattern of housing, shopping centers, and business parks that wastes land needlessly."**
>
> —Pennsylvania 21st Century Environment Commission cited in Staley, 1999

Burchell et al. (1998) devote the first chapter of their report, "The Costs of Sprawl—Revisited," to defining the elusive term. Commonly cited are several features that are captured in urban economist John F. McDonald's characterization:

- Low-density development that is dispersed and uses a lot of land;

- Geographic separation of essential places such as work, homes, schools, and shopping; and

- Almost complete dependence on automobiles for travel.

Myers and Kitsuse (1997) point out that "the very lack of agreed definition about what constitutes density, sprawl or compactness prevents any authoritative measurement." Any growth in suburban areas may be accused of "sprawling." Planned developments at relatively high densities can be accused of accelerating sprawl. As Ewing (1997) points out,

> . . . sprawl is a matter of degree. The line between scattered development, a type of sprawl, and multi-centered development, a type of compact development by most people's reckoning, is a fine one.
>
> . . . Equally elusive is the line between leapfrog development and economically efficient 'discontinuous development', or between commercial strips and 'activity corridors'.

Ewing also suggests that his notion of compact development—which is multicentered, has moderate average densities, and is

Metropolitan, Urban, and Rural Geography

Statistics describing trends in land use are based on one or another geographic entities defined by the U.S. Bureau of the Census (see U.S. Census, Geographic Areas Reference Manual), the USDA National Resources Inventory (NRI), or the American Housing Survey (AHS).

Census of Population . . .

Metropolitan/Nonmetropolitan Area—A core area containing a large population nucleus, together with adjacent communities that have a high degree of economic and social integration with that core. Metro areas are defined in terms of entire counties (except in New England, where towns are used). Metropolitan areas contain a mix of land uses, ranging from deserts, forests, and farms, to suburban landscapes, and include the densest urban core. In 1990, there were 274 metropolitan areas, containing 198.2 million people (80 percent of the total U.S. population) and covering 20 percent of U.S. land area.

Urban/Rural—Census defines urban as comprising all territory, population, and housing units located in urbanized areas (UAs), defined in terms of census tracts, and in places of 2,500 or more inhabitants outside of UAs. In 1990, 187 million people (75 percent of the total) lived in 8,510 places of 2,500 or more covering 2.5 percent of U.S. land area.

Urbanized Areas (UAs) are continuously built-up areas with a population of 50,000 or more, comprised of one or more places—central place(s)—and the adjacent densely settled surrounding area consisting of other places and territory not in defined places.

Urban Places Outside of UAs are any incorporated place or Census-designated place (CDP) with at least 2,500 inhabitants.

Rural Places and Territory not classified as urban are classified as rural. For instance, a rural place is any incorporated place or CDP with fewer than 2,500 inhabitants that is located outside of a UA. A place is either entirely urban or entirely rural.

Urban Fringe consists of rural areas in metropolitan counties. The part of the urban fringe nearest to existing UAs and urban places is likely to grow the fastest and eventually be absorbed when densities rise to urban levels.

Places—Census defines a place as a concentration of population, with a name and local recognition, that is not part of any other place. A place either is legally incorporated under the laws of its respective State or a statistical equivalent that the Census Bureau treats as a Census-designated place (CDP). Not everyone resides in a place; in 1990, approximately 66 million people (26 percent) in the United States lived outside of any place, either in small settlements, in the open countryside, or in the densely settled fringe of large cities in areas that were built-up, but not identifiable as places. Most Census places (19,289 out of a total of 23,435 in 1990) are incorporated.

National Resources Inventory (NRI)

Developed land in the National Resources Inventory consists of urban and built-up areas and land devoted to rural transportation.

Urban and built-up areas consist of residential, industrial, commercial, and institutional land; construction and public administrative sites; railroad yards, cemeteries, airports, golf courses, sanitary landfills, sewage plants, water control structures, small parks, and transportation facilities within urban areas.

Large urban and built-up areas include developed tracts of 10 acres and more.

Small built-up areas include developed tracts of 0.25 to 10 acres, which do not meet the definition of urban area, but are completely surrounded by urban and built-up land.

Rural transportation land includes highways, roads, railroads and rights-of-way outside of urban and built-up areas.

American Housing Survey (AHS)

The American Housing Survey, conducted every 2 years by the Bureau of the Census represents all housing units for the entire Nation, including housing lots on farms. The AHS started the current series in 1980.

Residential area is land devoted to residential housing lots, both urban and rural, based on respondents' estimates of lot size for their house. Sample-based responses are expanded to area totals.

Comparison

Due to differences in data collection techniques and definitions, the NRI estimates of "large urban and built-up areas" are usually higher than the Census "urban area" estimates for nearly all States. The Census urban area series runs from 1950, while the NRI started providing a consistent series in 1982. Prior to the 1982 NRI, Census urban area was the only reliable national source of urban area data available.

The American Housing Survey residential area is the sum of acres in lots used for housing units. While the data have limitations and are not available by State, the series does allow compilation of two important estimates. First, an estimate of the residential component of urban land shows how much land is used for housing in urban areas versus land used for all other urban purposes, such as commercial and industrial sites, institutional uses, urban parks, and all other non-housing urban uses. Second and more important, an estimate is made of land used for residences in rural areas. Recently there appears to be a growing trend toward an increasing demand for more and larger housing lots outside of urban areas. The AHS residential area does not include non-residential areas shown in the Census and NRI, but does include a large area of rural residential land not found in either the Census or the NRI.

continuous except for permanent open spaces or vacant lands to be developed in the near future—is not all that different from Gordon and Richardson's (1997) definition of sprawl.

Short of a return to a form of urban living not seen since before World War II, it is not clear how growth can be accommodated at suburban densities without being accused of being "sprawl."

Some people oppose any change in established land uses and react just as negatively to well-planned, reasonably dense and compact development as others do to "sprawl." Because "sprawl" is so hard to define, we use it only when citing others and set it off in quotation marks. We couch our discussion in the more neutral terms "development" or "growth," without making implicit judgments about the quality or outcomes of that development or growth.

Two Kinds of Growth

Government officials, housing consumers, farmers, and other interest groups appear to be concerned about two kinds of growth. First is the continuing accretion of urban development at the fringes of existing urban areas in rural parts of metropolitan counties. A second kind of growth is the proliferation of more isolated large-lot housing development (1 acre or more) well beyond the urban fringe and into adjacent nonmetropolitan counties. Growth at the edge of existing developed areas gradually shades out into more and more fragmented developments, farther out in the countryside, so there is no clear geographic dividing line between the two kinds of growth. While related, these two forms of growth have qualitatively different causes and have different consequences, especially for agriculture and the environment.

Trends at the Urban Fringe

Even low-density development (2 or fewer houses per acre) of new houses, roads, and commercial buildings at the fringe of existing urban areas can cause greater traffic congestion, loss of open space, loss of agricultural land, and impacts on the natural environment.

The amount of land in urban and developed land uses is measured in different ways, all of which have specific denotations (see box "Metropolitan, Urban, and Rural Geography" . . .). The concept of "urbanized area," defined by the Bureau of Census, includes the densely settled areas within and adjacent to cities with 50,000 people or more, while "urbanized places" include populations of 2,500 people or more that are outside of urbanized areas. Urbanized areas alone increased from 15.9 million acres in 1960 to 39 million acres in 1990, increasing 2.5 times. Total Census urban area (urbanized areas and urban places) more than doubled over the last 40 years from 25.5 million acres in 1960 to 55.9 million acres in 1990. These two categories of urbanization likely reached about 65 million acres by 2000 (. . . Daugherty, 1992).

"Urban and built-up areas" counted in USDA's National Resources Inventory (NRI) include those measured by the Census Bureau, as well as developed areas as small as 10 acres outside urban areas, encompassing some large-lot

development. NRI urban and built-up area increased from 51.9 million acres in 1982 to 76.5 million acres in 1997, and likely rose to about 79 million acres by 2000 (Table 1 . . .). "Developed land" defined by NRI adds the area in rural roads and other transportation developments. By this definition, developed area increased from 73.2 million acres in 1982 to 98.3 million acres in 1997, and likely reached 107 million acres by 2000.

Census-defined urban area has grown by about a million acres per year since 1960, an increase of about 4 percent per year. The rate of increase dropped from 3.5 percent per year in the 1960's and 1970's to 1.8 percent per year in the 1980's. NRI urban and built-up area increased faster than Census urban area in the 1980's, rising 2.9 percent. Much of the increase in NRI urban and built-up area is in less dense, extensive large-lot development beyond the urban fringe and in nonmetropolitan counties. This kind of development will not meet the population density criteria for Census-defined urban area for many years.

Despite doubling since 1960, urban areas still made up less than 3 percent of U.S. land area (excluding Alaska) in 1990. . . . Developed areas, including rural roads and transportation, made up less than 5 percent in 1992. Both kinds of growth (on the metro fringe and large-lot development) take land irreversibly out of commercial agricultural production that might otherwise be available for use. Growth causes social and environmental problems in local areas, but the increase in urban area in the United States poses no threat to U.S. food and fiber production capacity (Vesterby et al., 1994; USDA, 2000).

Trends beyond the Urban Fringe

Another kind of development occurs beyond the existing urban fringe, often far out in the rural countryside of metropolitan counties or adjacent nonmetropolitan counties. Development of new housing on large parcels of land is growth with a different character than that occurring at the city's edge. Instead of relatively dense development of 4–6 houses per acre, exurban development consists of scattered single houses on large parcels (often 10 acres or more). Rural large-lot development is not a new phenomenon, although it may be getting more attention than in the past. Growth in the area used for housing rose steadily throughout the last century (. . . Peterson and Branagan, 2000).

Large-lot categories dominate this process, and growth in large-lot development has accelerated with periods of prosperity and recession since 1970. The largest lot size category (10–22 acres) accounted for 55 percent of the growth in housing area since 1994, and lots greater than 1 acre accounted for over 90 percent of land for new housing. About 5 percent of the acreage used by houses built between 1994 and 1997 is for existing farms, and 16 percent is in existing urban areas within Metropolitan Statistical Areas (MSAs) defined by the Bureau of the Census. Thus, nearly 80 percent of the acreage used for recently constructed housing—about 2 million acres—is land outside urban areas or in non-metropolitan areas. Almost all of this land (94 percent) is in lots of 1 acre or larger, with 57 percent on lots of 10 acres or larger.

The people who move into these new houses may be pioneers moving from cities that once seemed distant. They may be pioneers in another sense: Areas experiencing this kind of development may be just starting on a gradual process of infill and expansion that will gradually transform the once-rural countryside into suburban and urban settlements resembling the existing urban fringe.

Critical Thinking

1. What is "urban sprawl" and how does it "consume" land?

2. Why does sprawl happen and who is responsible for it?

3. What do some people see as the benefits of low-density housing developments?

4. What are some of the costs of rural development? Who should be responsible for those costs?

5. Is continued worth at the urban fringe and into rural land a sustainable form of development? Can it be? Explain/discuss.

From *Economic Research Service, U.S. Department of Agriculture. Agricultural Economic Report No. 803*, 2001. Copyright © 2001 by United States Department of Agriculture. Reprinted by permission.

Article   Prepared by: Richard Eathorne, *Northern Michigan University*

Backyard Battlefields: The Bloody Business of Fracking in Arkansas

J. Malcolm Garcia

Learning Outcomes

After reading this article, you will be able to:

- Assess the threats to human health that fracking poses.
- Describe the general engineering process and environmental consequences of fracking.

A year after the gas companies moved in, Dirk DeTurck began taking notes.

May 2009: Bulldozers started out back building roads and burning trees. House had smoke in it. Like camping indoors. Bought an air purifier.

May 17, 2009: Started drilling behind house. Noise 24/7. Ears ringing. Still ring. Loud in the house. Roads all torn up. [The gas companies] spread white gooey stuff for dust control. . . . Strong diesel smell in the house. Afraid to light a match.

I visited Dirk at his home on the outskirts of Greenbrier, Arkansas, just as a spring hot spell swept through the area. It had rained days before and the trees I passed on the drive over shimmered in the wet heat. Soon, though, the forests gave way to clear-cut areas honeycombed with concrete drill pads. Brown and green tanks rose from the pads, pipes snaked out from pumps.

Uncut forests and vacant hills resurged shortly before I arrived at the DeTurcks' stone house, but the wooded acres behind their property struggled to swallow several more pads. The sight was far from threatening to an eye already conditioned to industrial intrusions, but this is a relatively new eyesore in Greenbrier, and Dirk knew better.

He answered the door as if we were in the middle of a conversation started elsewhere. "Hydrogen sulfide hangs in the air like a layer of fog," he said. "It comes off the tanks. Smells like rotten eggs and decaying compost with a little chemical thrown in."

Dirk is a retired mechanic and maintenance man. He studied mechanical engineering in school. He served as a Machinist's Mate in the Navy. You name it, he can fix it. He knows how things work.

He and his wife, Eva, moved to Greenbrier from Elmira, New York, in 2004. Eva had grown up in Mountain View, Arkansas, and Dirk came to love the area after they vacationed there. The land was so primitive, and you couldn't beat the weather.

They chose a home in Greenbrier because it was small and rural, and, unlike Mountain View, it had a hospital. Their son had broken forty-three bones after a bad fall from a roof, and subsequent surgery on his aorta left him paralyzed.

The house they found had been built on farmland divided into lots. Dirk and Eva grew a vegetable garden in the backyard. Dirk hunted deer and dried the meat. They were frugal with water and recycled as much as they could. "That's what you're supposed to do," Dirk told me.

In 2004, Dirk had no idea what fracking was. He would learn the hard way.

Short for "hydraulic fracturing," fracking is the process by which gas companies access underground deposits of natural gas, called shales. Millions of gallons of "fracking fluid"— that's water and sand mixed with hundreds of chemicals—are pumped deep into the earth's crust, breaking up rock and freeing natural gas reserves.

Natural gas is being marketed as a clean, green alternative to foreign-oil dependency; this year, the International Energy Agency found that carbon-dioxide emissions in the U.S. fell by four hundred and fifty tons, the result of an increase in the use of natural gas instead of coal. But since the inception of widespread fracking in 1997, horror stories have slowly entered the national conscience: illnesses coinciding with contaminated wells, citizens who can light their tap water on fire, pet and livestock deaths, exploding houses.

"The industry says [frack fluid] goes down and comes back up through pipes and is fine," says Daniel Botkin, ecologist and Professor Emeritus at the University of California, Santa Barbara. "In fact, stuff comes out and contaminates surface water and soil. If they wanted to do this in any reliable way, they would pick a few places and frack as an experiment and study the outcomes. That's not what's happening. There's so much money to be made, fracking is done on a very large scale. It could affect a lot of people."

Much of Northern Arkansas, including Greenbrier, sits atop the Fayetteville Shale, one of the largest natural-gas reserves in the country. Oil and gas companies began developing the area in late 2004; today, approximately four thousand gas wells plumb the depths of the shale. The Sam M. Walton School of Business at the University of Arkansas estimates that the first five years of Fayetteville Shale exploration generated eleven thousand jobs and eighteen billion dollars in revenue.

Is fracking a boon to flailing economies or a disaster in progress?

> *September 2009: Rash started on waist, armpits. Spread to knees. I don't know what started it. Face and neck tingle like something crawling on it. Tongue bleeding for no reason.*

When construction equipment started rumbling by in 2008, Dirk and Eva thought someone was damming Mill Creek for water to supply a nearby town. Then they noticed the trucks inching down Blackjack Road—ten to twelve eighteen-wheelers a day.

"Are they bulldozing to build houses?" Dirk asked a neighbor.

"No," the man said. "They're drilling gas wells."

At night, the gas pads blazed as if someone had switched on stadium lights. The drilling sent vibrations through the house and the noise filled every room, making it impossible to talk. Black smoke ringed the tops of trees. The air carried sharp and stinging odors. Magnolias and blue spruce began dying; deer, turkeys, raccoons, and opossums disappeared. Dirk found tumorous squirrels whose tails had fallen off.

For the next year, Dirk and Eva kept their doors and windows closed. They no longer sat on their deck. Their four grandchildren were not allowed to play outside the house for more than two hours; if they were out longer, they got headaches. Despite the precaution, one of the boys developed a rash. The doctor chalked it up to an allergy, prescribed a steroid cream.

Eva, meanwhile, was unable to sleep. She felt jittery, jacked up. Then Dirk noticed his own rashes. His nose began bleeding. His tongue began bleeding.

> *January 1, 2011: Tap water turned light brown. Cleared up same day. Started getting pink rings in toilet bowls. What is in water?*

Whatever was in the water, the DeTurcks decided to quit drinking it. Eva also started taking motion-sickness pills to cope with the earthquakes, which had been rattling the area since 2009. In December of 2010, civic leaders scheduled a community meeting in which geologists explained how earthquakes worked, but failed to account for the severe uptick in tremors. The large congregation of concerned citizens turned sour, and the meeting was broken up by sheriffs.

At the request of the Arkansas Oil and Gas Commission, Haydar Al-Shukri, chair of Applied Sciences at the University

of Arkansas, Little Rock, had been monitoring an injection well in the Greenbrier area. Re-injection into the ground is one of several methods by which gas companies dispose of the fluid that makes its way back up to the surface after fracking. Al-Shukri's equipment was able to detect seismic activity within a twenty-five-mile radius that included three other injection wells. He found a strong correlation between the earthquakes and two of the wells.

"They were very close to the fault," Al-Shukri said. "Injection wells close to the fault can cause the fault to slip." In February 2011, the Greenbrier area experienced a quake that registered 4.7 on the Richter Scale—the state's worst in thirty-five years. A month later, when a moratorium was placed on the injection wells, the earthquakes all but stopped. In the six months prior to the shutdown, over twelve hundred earthquakes had been recorded.

About the same time the earthquakes began to subside, Dirk noticed numbers on the tanks of the trucks he saw coming and going from drill sites. He knew from work experience that the numbers were assigned by the United Nations Committee of Experts on the Transport of Dangerous Goods and are meant to alert emergency crews to adopt hazard-specific procedures in case of a wreck or spill. Dirk recorded all of the numbers he saw, along with notes like "Saw driving through a school zone."

Under an exemption pushed through Congress in 2005, the contents of frack fluid are considered proprietary; in other words, oil and gas companies are under no obligation to disclose which chemicals they use, so they don't. Independent efforts like Dirk's, however, suggest frack fluid often contains antifreeze, detergents, known human carcinogens, and neurotoxins.

Memphis lawyer Tim Holton wants courts to require independent monitoring of water supplies and public health in areas near fracking activities. He is representing a number of Arkansas families who claim fracking has damaged their health.

Holton tells me of a family he represents—two children who live with their grandparents. In August 2011, three natural gas wells were placed within two hundred and fifty feet of their home. Their suit alleges that, during the fracking process, large amounts of xylene, methylene chloride, and benzene were released and contaminated the air inside the home to toxic levels. Several procedures related to fracking can cause volatile organic compounds, or VOCs, to become airborne.

Long-term xylene exposure can cause harmful effects to the nervous system, liver, and kidneys. Prolonged exposure to methylene chloride can cause neurological damage. Benzene is a carcinogen.

"I was amazed by the extent of emissions wafting over the home. It looked like a refinery in Texas but it was one frack site," Holton says. "The health effects of this are in their infancy in Arkansas. The effect won't be seen for several years. You sit around breathing it in and you won't know right away what it's doing. You'll have no idea. Then you turn forty-five and you can't draw a breath."

The sign right outside of Guy, Arkansas, reads: Welcome to Guy. A small town with a big heart. It's about a ten-minute drive from Dirk's house. I spoke to the mayor there, Johnny Wilson, who thinks the dangers of fracking are exaggerated.

Mayor Wilson tells me the gas companies employ lots of people in Guy. Folks have been moving in from Louisiana, Oklahoma, Texas. Going on six years now. The population shot up to 708 when a few years back it was just 203. A fracking company employs Wilson's own son.

"They're just jealous," he says of citizens who criticize the gas companies. He chuckles. "They don't have mineral rights to sell. The naysayers don't get checks and that makes them mad."

Jackie McPherson, mayor of Heber Springs, Arkansas, is equally enthusiastic about the industry. He tells me natural gas saved his town from the recession. Sure, it staggered during the hardest times, but people were still going to jobs or getting royalty checks. They bought homes and new cars. Some had never bought new cars before. Since the drilling started, people have moved in from other states. Hotels filled with oil prospectors. Despite the recession, the tax base of Heber Springs is growing.

Mayor McPherson has lived in Heber Springs since 1964. He's president of the local water-skiing club. He owns two boats. No one, he says, wants to protect the environment like he does.

I ask Mayor Wilson for the names of people he knows who got work through the gas companies. I call each one, but they all refuse to talk to me when I identify myself as a reporter, save for one man. The man says he would still be "kicking the can down the road" if the gas companies hadn't given him a job. Before he speaks further or lets me use his name, he says he needs to ask his work supervisor for permission. He says he'll get right back to me. He never does.

Tracy Wilson and her husband, Keith, an Iraq War veteran, live in a white house with a broad front porch. Two llamas stand fenced in beyond their gravel drive. Keith is hosing out animal pens as I drive up, his shorts and shirt soaked. Tracy comes out of the house on crutches, shrugging blond hair off her shoulders.

Keith is a police officer. Tracy takes in exotic species people once owned as pets but can no longer manage. Llamas, bobcats, lynx, and deer are among the wildlife in their care. They speak to me on the condition that I not mention where they live, for fear someone might try to steal their animals.

The Wilsons grew up near Little Rock, but decided to leave the city for the country when Tracy started her wildlife sanctuary. The property they chose offered plenty of space; none of their neighbors lived on fewer than ten acres. Many of the families around them raised beef and dairy cows. After she and Keith moved in, Tracy planted close to a thousand pines to create even more privacy.

In 2005, the Wilsons heard rumors that oil companies would soon be drilling for gas in the Fayetteville Shale. They began receiving letters from those same companies, offering to buy their mineral rights for one hundred dollars an acre. The amount increased with each letter. Two hundred, two hundred and fifty. Tracy tossed them. Neither she nor Keith were interested. Tracy bought more pines, thinking the trees would create a buffer between their home and the wells.

The pines, however, were not enough to prevent landmen from stopping by the house. Petroleum landmen perform various services for oil and gas exploration companies. According to the American Association of Professional Landmen's website, these services include negotiating for the acquisition and divestiture of mineral rights.

The men who came by the Wilsons' house knew their business. Hair slicked back, fresh-pressed shirts. They told Tracy her mineral rights could be worth hundreds of thousands of dollars. They told her she would pay cash for new Cadillacs. She asked the landmen to show her something in writing, but they never did. Instead, they threatened to have the property condemned if Tracy and Keith didn't sell their mineral rights voluntarily.

Tracy thought he was bluffing and spoke to an attorney. The attorney told her that a gas company could appeal to the Arkansas Oil and Gas Commission. State laws can force a homeowner to turn over his or her mineral rights if everyone else in the area has already signed a lease. "Forced pooling" compels holdout landowners to join gas-leasing agreements with their neighbors. In Arkansas, drillers can extract minerals from an entire pool if leases have been negotiated for a certain percentage of the land.

The attorney advised the Wilsons to work out a lease wherein they sold their mineral rights for four hundred and fifty dollars an acre. They kept their property rights, however, so the gas companies could not drill within five hundred feet of their property. It was flimsy protection; if the gas company changed its mind and decided to drill on their property, it could have just taken them to court. The Wilsons didn't have the money to fight them.

In 2008, helicopters dropped fiber-optic cables and depth charges for seismic tests, Tracy recalls. A gas well was constructed within eighteen hundred feet of the Wilsons' home. When the drilling started, the Wilsons' house shook as if a train were running through it. Twenty-four hours a day, seven days a week.

In 2009, Tracy started getting dizzy. Her head ached. She broke out in rashes. She smelled something like plastic burning. At night, she would shine a flashlight and see particulates in the air. *I'm breathing that stuff in,* she thought.

That was the year Keith returned from his second deployment in Iraq. When he saw the gas wells near his house, he was reminded of the oil plants in Iraq, the noise of drill rigs. Soldiers, he told Tracy, were coming back with respiratory problems because of smoke coming off the oil wells and the trash pits on U.S. bases, where everything from body parts to plastics were burned. He smelled that same stench again, only this time in his backyard.

Keith didn't want to think about Iraq, but the tankers and water trucks reminded him of the vehicles he'd seen in Iraq's oil fields. In Iraq, if an eighteen-wheeler pulled up on him, it either backed off or got blown away.

Tracy had headaches for the entire month of August 2010. Skin lesions and blisters broke out on her back. Her lymph nodes swelled to golf-ball size, she says. Her doctor gave her antibiotics and topical creams, but nothing worked. Keith developed nosebleeds; he'd never had them before. His nose would start running and there would be blood.

A month before the big quake, Tracy blacked out and fell down the stairs. She tore a tendon and chipped a bone in her left ankle. The bone refused to heal. Her doctor didn't know why.

I break off our conversation for a moment and call Adam Law, a clinical assistant professor at Weill Cornell Medical College and practicing endocrinologist in New York. He is calling on gas companies to stop the use of hydraulic fracturing until its effects on people and the environment have been thoroughly studied. I tell him about the symptoms the Wilsons and DeTurcks experienced.

"As doctors, we're not really trained in environmental health," he says. "There's very little training with occupational exposure. When you see stuff like this for the first time, it's a little uncomfortable. You don't know who to send the patient to or what to prescribe. It's difficult to know what they've been exposed to. You can tell people how to reduce exposure—don't bathe or drink the water—but it's hard to say don't breathe."

Tracy and Keith had planned to retire on their land and never move again. In 2009, they spent seventy thousand dollars on improvements to the fourteen-year-old house; they added a sunroom, replaced the roof, put in new central air, painted inside and out. They had the house appraised when they finished in 2011. It was valued at seventy thousand dollars less than it had been in 2009. Back then, there wasn't as much traffic. There weren't gas wells nearby.

When the big quake struck, the Wilsons' roosters, dogs, and donkeys began barking and crowing and braying all at once. The ground shifted. A kind of growl passed through the house. The noise was like thunder, Keith says, but it lasted longer. They bought earthquake insurance for eight hundred dollars a year. It costs more than any royalty payment they have received from the gas company.

From the Wilsons' house, I drive west to Hartford, Arkansas, to meet Jack and Mary White. They live on a stretch of road flanked by tall grass and scrub brush. Cows poke their heads through warped fences and the cloudless sky wavers from an oppressive heat.

Jack is eighty-two years old. Mary uses a cane to help her walk. Jack helps her, crouching forward a little bit, a hand on her elbow. After lunch, Jack drives me to a graveyard called Sugar Loaf Cemetery. A creek runs not far from it. Water brought people here to Hartford, Jack says. Since the 1800s, the people have depended on water for their farms, crops, and cattle.

In 2005, when a landman knocked on Jack's door, he knew what was coming. Jack had been an oilman himself. After he was honorably discharged from the Air Force during the Korean War, his older brother got him a job working the oil fields in West Texas. He started as a roughneck, then became an oil-well servicer, a driller, and, later, a superintendent. He met Mary in Kermit, Texas, right after she finished high school. A mutual friend said, "Oh, there's Mary," and introduced them. Jack doesn't know how these things work out, but they do.

Jack worked oil in Egypt and Iran in the early '60s. He and Mary returned to the states in 1966 so their son could attend high school here. When they moved to Hartford, they planned to retire and produce organic food for their livelihood and sustenance. Jack wanted to put in hoop houses beside their house. In a hoop house, vegetables don't know it's winter, he says. You don't have insect problems. The vegetables taste sweeter, crisper. Hoop houses need a lot of water, so Jack drilled a well.

"I'm a farm boy at heart," he tells me. "Some of my people have lived in Arkansas and Oklahoma forever. There's no such thing as worn-out soil. There is neglect and abuse."

In 2006, the gas company drilled a well to extract water for fracking, Jack says. Their well was deeper than his and drew his water away. His water pump came up dry. Nowadays it occasionally kicks in, but doesn't pull enough water for hoop houses. "I have to pick and choose what lives and what dies," he says.

"When they drill a gas well," Jack continues, "they blow all the liquid and dust out of the hole. Sounds like a scream rushing out of the ground." The fracking noise started as a roar before it rose to the pitch of a siren. Days, weeks. Jack quit counting after a while. Twelve diesel compressors added to the racket. Jack and Mary got desperate for sleep and rented motel rooms. They came back to the house as much as they could, so that it wouldn't appear abandoned, but people knew they were gone. Someone raided their shed and stole Jack's tools.

One day, when the gas company was blowing out a well, Jack was on a neighbor's property helping him clear brush. When he got back to his house, he found Mary lying prostrate on the floor. According to Jack, she'd inhaled too much methane—a doctor told him ten minutes later might have been too late.

Jack says Mary has never been the same. He says oilmen used to have more respect, but he understands there's a lot of money to be made. He's angry at the state of Arkansas for failing to regulate, failing to protect. He wonders how many more of his neighbors will clear out before it's over. He's not leaving, he says, not at his age. After travelling to over sixty foreign countries, he still thinks Hartford is the best place on Earth.

Jack pauses for a moment. He squints through his glasses, runs a hand over a yarrow plant. "Ancient Greek warriors used it when they were hurt," he says. "Rub it on and it will keep fleas and chiggers off. Make tea out of it, too."

In the distance, the gas company's water well sounds like two buckets swinging against each other. Jack listens, releases the yarrow.

"We're supposed to have record heat this summer," he says. "Am I going to have any water at all?"

> *May 2012: Last two days, ears popping. Metal taste in mouth.*

These days, Dirk and Eva DeTurck sit in their living room and peer out closed windows at their vacant wood deck. They've noticed birds and squirrels returning, but still don't see any turkeys and not many deer. Their health improved somewhat after they installed an air purifier designed to remove VOCs, but Eva still developed little bumps on her chin. When the wind blows away from the house, Dirk notices his rashes begin to clear.

He and Eva recently put the house up for sale. An Arizona couple visited and offered to buy it. They had two boys, ten and twelve. "Do you know about the gas drilling here?" Dirk asked them. They said no. Dirk refused to sell. How would he sleep at night believing that those two boys were being poisoned?

Tracy Wilson still has trouble with her ankle. As of June 2012, she's been reliant on crutches for eighteen months. She says the gas companies come and go without contacting residents. She wakes up and *oopsy,* there's a new crane or rig.

One night in May, Tracy woke up feeling something wet on her back. Another open abscess. Clear fluid draining from it. Some of her cats have half-dollar-sized blisters that look like burns. "We got ourselves chemical hazard suits and emergency kits, complete with gas masks, to have on hand in case of a chemical spill or worse," she writes in an e-mail. "Who lives with emergency chemical hazard kits hanging on their coat rack in their home?"

Keith dreams of Iraq. In one dream, he walks across a battlefield picking up weapons amid the eerie orange glow of burning wells. For a long time, he didn't understand why he dreamed that dream night after night. Then he understood.

In Iraq, Keith passed an oil well on his left every time he went on patrol. When he returned to base, he would pass a well on his right. Now, when he leaves the house for work, he sees a gas well to his left. Returning home, he sees a well on his right.

Every day he sees Iraq.

When I leave the Wilsons' house, I make a wrong turn and get lost on a gravel road. I stop at a convenience store and ask for directions to Highway 65.

The man behind the counter tells me to go west. He says I'll see a lot of tanker trucks that haul water and chemicals to gas pads. Then a lot of white pickups, some with gas company names on the side, but not all. And then lots of dump trucks, the ones that run dirt and gravel to the pads.

Once you're on 65, he tells me, it'll take a while to get past the drilling. After that, the drive up is beautiful, especially with the trees this time of year. You won't see quite as many gas pads with the trees all leafed-out. You won't know they're there.

Support for this article was provided by the Nation Institute's Investigative Fund.

Critical Thinking

1. Explain the general engineering process of fracking.
2. What kinds of human health issues (in Arkansas) have been reported as the result of fracking?
3. If fracking is so dangerous to human health and the environment, why is it being allowed?

Create Central

www.mhhe.com/createcentral

Internet References

Alternative Energy Institute (AEI)
  www.altenergy.org
Energy Justice Network
  www.energyjustice.net/peak
Hydrolic Fracturing; U.S. Environmental Protection Agency
  www.epa.gov/hydraulicfracture
Natural Resources Defense Council
  http://nrdc.org

Gracia, J. Malcom. From *The Oxford American,* August 27, 2012. Online. Copyright © 2012 by Malcom J. Gracia. Reprinted by permission of the author.

Article   Prepared by: Richard Eathorne, *Northern Michigan University*

Fracking Ourselves to Death in Pennsylvania

Farming communities are being turned into huge, open-air laboratories by energy companies—with ordinary people serving as guinea pigs.

ELLEN CANTAROW

Learning Outcomes

After reading this article, you will be able to:

- Describe some of the potential health hazards associated with fracking.

- Outline the evidence presented regarding health issues in rural Pennsylvania and fracking operations there.

- Compare and contrast the evidence presented in this article with other similar articles.

More than seventy years ago, a chemical attack was launched against Washington State and Nevada. It poisoned people, animals, everything that grew, breathed air and drank water. The Marshall Islands were also struck. This formerly pristine Pacific atoll was branded "the most contaminated place in the world." As their cancers developed, the victims of atomic testing and nuclear weapons development got a name: downwinders. What marked their tragedy was the darkness in which they were kept about what was being done to them. Proof of harm fell to them, not to the US government agencies responsible.

Now, a new generation of downwinders is getting sick as an emerging industry pushes the next wonder technology—in this case, high-volume hydraulic fracturing. Whether they live in Texas, Colorado or Pennsylvania, their symptoms are the same: rashes, nosebleeds, severe headaches, difficulty breathing, joint pain, intestinal illnesses, memory loss and more. "In my opinion," says Yuri Gorby of Rensselaer Polytechnic Institute, "what we see unfolding is a serious health crisis, one that is just beginning."

The process of "fracking" starts by drilling a mile or more vertically, then outward laterally into 500-million-year-old shale formations, the remains of oceans that once flowed over parts of North America. Millions of gallons of chemical and sand-laced water are then propelled into the ground

at high pressures, fracturing the shale and forcing the methane it contains out. With the release of that gas come thousands of gallons of contaminated water. This "flowback" fluid contains the original fracking chemicals, plus heavy metals and radioactive material that also lay safely buried in the shale.

The industry that uses this technology calls its product "natural gas," but there's nothing natural about up-ending half a billion years of safe storage of methane and everything that surrounds it. It is, in fact, an act of ecological violence around which alien infrastructures—compressor stations that compact the gas for pipeline transport, ponds of contaminated flowback, flare stacks that burn off gas impurities, diesel trucks in quantity, thousands of miles of pipelines and more—have metastasized across rural America, pumping carcinogens and toxins into water, air and soil.

Sixty percent of Pennsylvania lies over a huge shale sprawl called the Marcellus, and that has been in the fracking industry's sights since 2008. The corporations that are exploiting the shale come to the state with lavish federal entitlements: exemptions from the Clean Air, Clean Water and Clean Drinking Water Acts, as well as the Superfund Act, which requires cleanup of hazardous substances. The industry doesn't have to call its trillions of gallons of annual waste "hazardous." Instead, it uses euphemisms like "residual waste." In addition, fracking companies are allowed to keep secret many of the chemicals they use.

Pennsylvania, in turn, adds its own privileges. A revolving door shuttles former legislators, governors and officials from the state's Department of Environmental Protection (DEP) into gas industry positions. The DEP itself is now the object of a lawsuit that charges the agency with producing deceptive lab reports, and then using them to dismiss homeowners' complaints that shale gas corporations have contaminated their water, making them sick. The people I interviewed have their own nickname for the DEP: "Don't Expect Protection."

The Downwinders

Randy Moyer is a pleasant-faced, bearded 49-year-old whose drawl reminds you that Portage, his hardscrabble hometown in southwestern Pennsylvania, is part of Appalachia. He worked eighteen years—until gasoline prices got too steep—driving his own rigs to haul waste in New York and New Jersey. Then what looked like a great opportunity presented itself: $25 an hour working for a hydraulic-fracturing subcontractor in northeastern Pennsylvania.

In addition to hauling fracking liquid, water and waste, Randy also did what's called, with no irony, "environmental." He climbed into large vats to squeegee out the remains of fracking fluid. He also cleaned the huge mats laid down around the wells to even the ground out for truck traffic. Those mats get saturated with "drilling mud," a viscous, chemical-laden fluid that eases the passage of the drills into the shale. What his employer never told him was that the drilling mud, as well as the wastewater from fracking, is not only highly toxic but radioactive.

In the wee hours of a very cold day in November 2011, he stood in a huge basin at a well site, washing 1,000 mats with high-pressure hoses, taking breaks every so often to warm his feet in his truck. "I took off my shoes and my feet were as red as a tomato," he told me. When the air from the heater hit them, he "nearly went through the roof."

Once at home, he scrubbed his feet, but the excruciating pain didn't abate. A "rash" that covered his feet soon spread up to his torso. A year and a half later, the skin inflammation still recurs. His upper lip repeatedly swells. A couple of times his tongue swelled so large that he had press it down with a spoon to be able to breathe. "I've been fried for over thirteen months with this stuff," he told me in late January. "I can just imagine what hell is like. It feels like I'm absolutely on fire."

Family and friends have taken Moyer to emergency rooms at least four times. He has consulted more than forty doctors. No one can say what caused the rashes, or his headaches, migraines, chest pain and irregular heartbeat, or the shooting pains down his back and legs, his blurred vision, vertigo, memory loss, the constant white noise in his ears and the breathing troubles that require him to stash inhalers throughout his small apartment.

In an earlier era, workers' illnesses fell into the realm of "industrial medicine." But these days, when it comes to the US fracking industry, the canaries aren't restricted to the coal mines. People like Randy seem to be the harbingers of what happens when a toxic environment is no longer buried miles beneath the earth. The gas fields that evidently poisoned him are located near thriving communities. "For just about every other industry I can imagine," says Anthony Ingraffea of Cornell University, coauthor of a landmark study that established fracking's colossal greenhouse-gas footprint, "from making paint, building a toaster, building an automobile, those traditional kinds of industry occur in a zoned industrial area, inside of buildings, separated from home and farm, separated from schools." By contrast, natural gas corporations, he says, "are imposing on us the requirement to locate our homes, hospitals and schools inside their industrial space."

The Death and Life of Little Rose

Little Rose was Angel Smith's favorite horse. When the vet shod her, Angel told me proudly, she obligingly lifted the next hoof as soon as the previous one was done. "Wanna eat, Rosie?" Angel would ask, and Rosie would nod her head. "Are you sure?" Angel would tease, and Rosie would raise one foreleg, clicking her teeth together. In Clearville, just south of Portage, Angel rode Little Rose in parades, carrying the family's American flag.

In 2002, a "landman" knocked on the door and asked Angel and her husband Wayne to lease the gas rights of their 115-acre farm to the San Francisco–based energy corporation PG&E (Pacific Gas & Electric.) At first, he was polite, but then he started bullying. "All your neighbors have signed. If you don't, we'll just suck the gas from under your land." Perhaps from weariness and a lack of information (almost no one outside the industry then knew anything about high-volume hydraulic fracturing), they agreed. Drilling began in 2002 on neighbors' land and in 2005 on the Smith's.

On January 30, 2007, Little Rose staggered, fell and couldn't get up. Her legs moved spasmodically. When Wayne and Angel dragged her to a sitting position, she'd just collapse again. "I called every vet in the phone book," says Angel. "They all said, 'Shoot her.'" The couple couldn't bear to do it. After two days, a neighbor shot her. "It was our choice," says Angel, her voice breaking. "She was my best friend."

Soon, the Smiths' cows began showing similar symptoms. Those that didn't die began aborting or giving birth to dead calves. All the chickens died, too. So did the barn cats. And so did three beloved dogs, none of them old, all previously healthy. A 2012 study by Michelle Bamberger and Cornell University pharmacology professor Robert Oswald indicates that, in the gas fields, these are typical symptoms in animals and often serve as early warning signs for their owners' subsequent illnesses.

The Smiths asked the DEP to test their water. The agency told them that it was safe to drink, but Angel Smith says that subsequent testing by Pennsylvania State University investigators revealed high levels of arsenic.

Meanwhile, the couple began suffering from headaches, nosebleeds, fatigue, throat and eye irritation and shortness of breath. Wayne's belly began swelling oddly, even though, says Angel, he isn't heavy. X-rays of his lungs showed scarring and calcium deposits. A blood analysis revealed cirrhosis of the liver. "Get him to stop drinking," said the doctor who drew Angel aside after the results came in. "Wayne doesn't drink," she replied. Neither does Angel, who at 42 now has liver disease.

By the time the animals began dying, five high-volume wells had been drilled on neighbors' land. Soon, water started bubbling up under their barn floor and an oily sheen and foam appeared on their pond. In 2008, a compressor station was built half a mile away. These facilities, which compress natural gas for pipeline transport, emit known carcinogens and toxins like benzene and toluene.

The Smiths say people they know elsewhere in Clearville have had similar health problems, as have their animals. For a while they thought their own animals' troubles were over, but just this past February several cows aborted. The couple would like to move away, but can't. No one will buy their land.

The Museum of Fracking

Unlike the Smiths, David and Linda Headley didn't lease their land. In 2005, when they bought their farm in Smithfield, they opted not to pay for the gas rights under their land. The shallow gas drilling their parents had known seemed part of a bygone era and the expense hardly seemed worth the bother.

With its hills and valleys, the creek running through their land and a spring that supplied them with water, the land seemed perfect for hiking, swimming and raising their son Grant. Adam was born after all the trouble started.

Just as the couple had completed the purchase, the bulldozers moved in. The previous owner had leased the gas rights without telling them. And so they found themselves, as they would later put it, mere "caretakers" on a corporate estate.

Today, the Headleys' property is a kind of museum of fracking. There are five wells, all with attendant tanks that separate liquids from the gas, and a brine tank where flowback is stored. Four of the wells are low-volume vertical ones, which use a fracking technology that predates today's high-volume method. A couple minutes' walk from the Headleys' front door stands a high-volume well. A pipeline was drilled under their creek.

"Accidents" have been a constant. When the well closest to the house was fracked, their spring, which had abounded in vegetation, crawfish and insects, went bad. The DEP told the Headleys, as it did the Smiths, that the water was still safe to drink. But, says David, "everything in the spring died and turned white." Adam had just been born. "No way was I exposing my kids to that." For two years he hauled water to the house from the homes of family and friends and then he had it connected to a city water line.

All the brine tanks have leaked toxic waste onto the Headley's land. Contaminated soil from around the high-volume tank has been alternately stored in dumpsters and in an open pit next to the well. The Headleys begged the DEP to have it removed. David says an agency representative told them the waste would have to be tested for radioactivity first. Eventually, some of it was hauled away; the rest was buried under the Headleys' land. The test for radioactivity is still pending, though David has his own Geiger counter which has measured high levels at the site of the well.

An independent environmental organization, Earthworks, included the Headleys among fifty-five households it surveyed in a recent study of health problems near gas facilities. Testing showed high levels of contaminants in the Headleys' air, including chloromethane, a neurotoxin, and trichloroethene, a known carcinogen.

Perhaps more telling is the simple fact that everyone in the family is sick. Seventeen-year-old Grant has rashes that, like Randy Moyer's, periodically appear on different parts of his body. Four-year-old Adam suffers from stomach cramps that make him scream. David says he and Linda have both had "terrible joint pain. It's weird stuff, your left elbow, your right hip, then you'll feel good for three days, and it'll be your back." At 42, with no previous family history of either arthritis or asthma, Linda has been diagnosed with both. Everyone has had nosebleeds—including the horses.

Five years into the Marcellus gas rush in this part of Pennsylvania, symptoms like Randy Moyer's, the Smiths' and the Headleys' are increasingly common. Children are experiencing problems the young almost never have, like joint pain and forgetfulness. Animal disorders and deaths are widespread. The Earthworks study suggests that living closer to gas-field infrastructure increases the severity of twenty-five common symptoms, including skin rashes, difficulty breathing and nausea.

Don't Expect Protection

DEP whistleblowers have disclosed that the agency purposely restricts its chemical testing so as to reduce evidence of harm to landowners. A resident in southwestern Pennsylvania's Washington County is suing the agency for failing fully to investigate the drilling-related air and water contamination that she says has made her sick. In connection with the lawsuit, Democratic state representative Jesse White has demanded that state and federal agencies investigate the DEP for "*alleged misconduct and fraud.*"

In the absence of any genuine state protection, independent scientists have been left to fill the gap. But as the industry careens forward, matching symptoms with potential causes is a constant catch-up effort. A 2011 study by Theo Colborn, founder of the Endocrine Disruption Exchange and recipient of the National Council for Science and Environment's Lifetime Achievement Award, identified 353 industry chemicals that could damage the skin, the brain, the respiratory, gastrointestinal, immune, cardiovascular and endocrine (hormone production) systems. Twenty-five percent of the chemicals found by the study could cause cancers.

David Brown is a veteran toxicologist and consultant for an independent environmental health organization, the Southwest Pennsylvania Environmental Health Project. According to him, there are four routes of exposure to gas-field chemicals: water, air, soil and food. In other words, virtually everything that surrounds us.

Exposure to water comes from drinking, but showering and bathing makes possible water exposure through the skin and inhaling water vapor. "Air exposure is even more complicated," says Brown. The impacts of contaminated air, for example, are greater during heavy activity. "Children running around," he says, "are more apt to be exposed than older people." What further complicates the emerging toxicology is that chemicals act not as single agents but synergistically. "The presence of one agent," says Brown, "can increase the toxicity of another by several-fold."

Brown deplores the government's failures to heed citizens' cries for help. "No one is asking, 'What happened to you? Are there other people who have been affected in your area?' I teach ethics. There's a level of moral responsibility that we should have nationally. We seem to have decided that we need energy so badly . . . that we have in almost a passive sense identified individuals and areas to sacrifice."

Circles of Trust

No one I interviewed in communities impacted by fracking in southwestern Pennsylvania drinks their water anymore. In fact, I came to think of a case of Poland Spring as a better house gift than any wine (and I wasn't alone in that). Breathing the air is in a different universe of risk. You can't bottle clean air, but you can donate air purifiers, as one interviewee, who prefers to be unnamed, has been doing.

Think of her as a creator of what a new Pennsylvania friend of mine calls "circles of trust." The energy industry splits communities and families into warring factions. Such hostilities are easy to find, but in the midst of catastrophe I also found mutual assistance and a resurgence of the human drive for connection.

Ron Gulla, a John Deere heavy equipment salesman, is driven by fury at the corporation that ruined his soil—his was the second farm in Pennsylvania to be fracked—but also by deep feeling for the land: "A farm is just like raising a child. You take care of it, you nurture it and you know when there are problems."

Gulla credits Barbara Arindell, founder of the country's first anti-fracking organization, Pennsylvania's Damascus Citizens for Sustainability, with teaching him about the dangers of the industry's efforts. Now, he is a central figure in an ever-widening network of people who are becoming their own documentarians. Everyone I interviewed brought out files of evidence to show me: photographs, videos, news reports and their own written records of events.

Moreover, in the midst of ongoing stress, many have become activists. Linda Headley and Ron Gulla, for instance, traveled with other Pennsylvanians to Albany this past February to warn New York State officials not to endorse fracking. "A lot of people have said, 'Why don't you just walk away from this?' " says Gulla. "[But] I was raised to think that if there was something wrong, you would bring it to people's attention.' "

"You have to believe things happen for a reason," says David Headley. "It's drawn so many people together we didn't know before. You have these meetings, and you're fighting [for] a common cause and you feel so close to the people you're working with. Including you guys, the reporters. It's made us like a big family. Really. You think you're all alone, and somebody pops up. God always sends angels."

Still, make no mistake: this is an alarming and growing public health emergency. "Short of relocating entire communities or banning fracking, ending airborne exposures cannot be done," David Brown said in a recent address in New York State. "Our only option in Washington County . . . has been to try to find ways for residents to reduce their exposures and warn them when the air is especially dangerous to breathe."

In the vacuum left by the state's failure to offer protection to those living in fracking zones, volunteers, experts like Brown, and fledgling organizations like the Southwest Pennsylvania Environmental Health Project have become the new protectors of citizens' health. Growing numbers of fracking victims, including Angel and Wayne Smith, are also suing gas corporations. "If I could go back to 2000, I'd show them the end of the road and say, 'Don't come back,' " Angel told me. "But we're in the situation now. Fight and go forward."

Critical Thinking

1. How does fracking contribute to human health problems?
2. Why is fracking acceptable if so much evidence suggests that it is harmful to both humans and the environment?
3. If the victims reported in this article were wealthy Americans, would the fracking issue be different?

Create Central

www.mhhe.com/createcentral

Internet References

Alternative Energy Institute (AEI)
www.altenergy.org
Energy Justice Network
www.energyjustice.net/peak
Hydrolic Fracturing; U.S. Environmental Protection Agency
www.epa.gov/hydraulicfracture
Natural Resources Defense Council
http://nrdc.org

ELLEN CANTAROW, musician and writer, reported from the West Bank and Israel during the 1980s for the *Village Voice*.

Article Prepared by: Richard Eathorne, *Northern Michigan University*

The Whole Fracking Enchilada

Violating the bedrock, the atmosphere, and everything in between.

SANDRA STEINGRABER

Learning Outcomes

After reading this article, you will be able to:

• Describe the process of fracking.

• Outline the reasons why fracking is currently considered the most important environmental issue.

I have come to believe that extracting natural gas from shale using the newish technique called hydrofracking is *the* environmental issue of our time. And I think you should, too.

Saying so represents two points of departure for me. One: I primarily study toxic chemicals, not energy issues. I have, heretofore, ceded that topic to others, such as Bill McKibben, with whom I share this column space in *Orion*.

Two: I'm on record averring that I never tell people what to do. If you are a mother who wants to lead the charge against vinyl shower curtains, then you should. If the most important thing to you is organic golf courses, then they are. So said I.

But high-volume slick water hydrofracturing of shale gas—fracking—is way bigger than PVC and synthetic fertilizer. In fact, it makes them both cheaply available. Fracking is linked to every part of the environmental crisis—from radiation exposure to habitat loss—and contravenes every principle of environmental thinking. It's the tornado on the horizon that is poised to wreck ongoing efforts to create green economies, local agriculture, investments in renewable energy, and the ability to ride your bike along country roads. It's worth setting down your fork, pen, cellular phone—whatever instrument you're holding—and looking out the window.

The environmental crisis can be viewed as a tree with two trunks. One trunk represents what we are doing to the planet through atmospheric accumulation of heat-trapping gasses. Follow this trunk along and you find droughts, floods, acidification of oceans, dissolving coral reefs, and species extinctions.

The other trunk represents what we are doing to ourselves and other animals through the chemical adulteration of the planet with inherently toxic synthetic pollutants. Follow this trunk along and you find asthma, infertility, cancer, and male fish in the Potomac River whose testicles have eggs inside them.

At the base of both these trunks is an economic dependency on fossil fuels, primarily coal (plant fossils) and petroleum (animal fossils). When we light them on fire, we threaten the global ecosystem. When we use them as feedstocks for making stuff, we create substances—pesticides, solvents, plastics—that can tinker with our subcellular machinery and the various signaling pathways that make it run.

Natural gas is the vaporous form of petroleum. It's the Dr. Jekyll and Mr. Hyde of fossil fuels: when burned, natural gas generates only half the greenhouse gases of coal, but when it escapes into the atmosphere as unburned methane, it's one of the most powerful greenhouse gases of them all—twenty times more powerful than carbon dioxide at trapping heat and with the stamina to persist nine to fifteen years. You can also make petrochemicals from it. Natural gas is the starting point for anhydrous ammonia (synthetic fertilizer) and PVC plastic (those shower curtains).

Until a few years ago, much of the natural gas trapped underground was considered unrecoverable because it is scattered throughout vast sheets of shale, like a fizz of bubbles in a petrified spill of champagne. But that all changed with the rollout of a drilling technique (pioneered by Halliburton) that bores horizontally through the bedrock, blasts it with explosives, and forces into the cracks, under enormous pressure, millions of gallons of water laced with a proprietary mix of poisonous chemicals that further fracture the rock. Up the borehole flows the gas. In 2000, only 1 percent of natural gas was shale gas. Ten years later, almost 20 percent is.

International investors began viewing shale gas as a paradigm-shifting innovation. Energy companies are now looking at shale plays in Poland and Turkey. Fracking is under way in Canada. But nowhere has the technology been as rapidly deployed as in the United States, where a gas rush is under way. Gas extraction now goes on in thirty-two states, with half a million new gas wells drilled in the last ten years alone. We are literally shattering the bedrock of our nation and pumping it full of carcinogens in order to bring methane out of the earth.

And nowhere in the U.S. is fracking proceeding more manically than Appalachia, which is underlain by the formation called the Marcellus Shale, otherwise referred to by the *Intelligent Investor Report* as "the Saudi Arabia of natural gas" and by the Toronto *Globe and Mail* as a "prolific monster" with the potential to "rearrange the continent's energy flow."

In the sense of "abnormal to the point of inspiring horror," *monster* is not an inappropriate term here. With every well drilled—and thirty-two thousand wells per year are planned—a couple million gallons of fresh water are transformed into toxic fracking fluid. Some of that fluid will remain underground. Some will come flying back out of the hole, bringing with it other monsters: benzene, brine, radioactivity, and heavy metals that, for the past 400 million years, had been safely locked up a mile below us, estranged from the surface world of living creatures. No one knows what to do with this lethal flowback—a million or more gallons of it for every wellhead. Too caustic for reuse as is, it sloshes around in open pits and sometimes is hauled away in fleets of trucks to be forced under pressure down a disposal well. And it is sometimes clandestinely dumped.

By 2012, 100 billion gallons per year of fresh water will be turned into toxic fracking fluid. The technology to transform it back to drinkable water does not exist. And, even if it did, where would we put all the noxious, radioactive substances we capture from it?

Here, then, are the environmental precepts violated by hydrofracking: 1) Environmental degradation of the commons should be factored into the price structure of the product (full-cost accounting), whose true carbon footprint—inclusive of all those diesel truck trips, blowouts, and methane leaks—requires calculation (life-cycle analysis). 2) Benefit of the doubt goes to public health, not the things that threaten it, especially in situations where catastrophic harm—aquifer contamination with carcinogens—is unremediable (the Precautionary Principle). 3) There is no away.

This year I've attended scientific conferences and community forums on fracking. I've heard a PhD geologist worry about the thousands of unmapped, abandoned wells scattered across New York from long-ago drilling operations. (What if pressurized fracking fluid, to be entombed in the shale beneath our aquifers, found an old borehole? Could it come squirting back up to the surface? Could it rise as vapor through hairline cracks?) I've heard a hazardous materials specialist describe to a crowd of people living in fracked communities how many parts per million of benzene will raise risks for leukemia and sperm abnormalities linked to birth deformities. I've heard a woman who lives by a fracking operation in Pennsylvania—whose pond bubbles with methane and whose kids have nosebleeds at night—ask how she could keep her children safe. She was asking me. And I had no answer. Thirty-seven percent of the land in the township where I live with my own kids is already leased to the frackers. There is no away.

Critical Thinking

1. Explain what the author means when she says that "fracking is linked to every part of the environmental crisis."

2. Why is fracking not prohibited in populated areas when so much evidence suggests that it is dangerous to human health?

Create Central

www.mhhe.com/createcentral

Internet References

Alternative Energy Institute (AEI)
 www.altenergy.org

Energy Justice Network
 www.energyjustice.net/peak

Hydrolic Fracturing; U.S. Environmental Protection Agency
 www.epa.gov/hydraulicfracture

Natural Resources Defense Council
 http://nrdc.org

Unit 4

UNIT

Prepared by: Richard Eathorne, *Northern Michigan University*

Earth Economics: Calculating Environmental Values

Fourth law of ecology: There's no such thing as a free lunch.

Barry Commoner, scientist, *The Closing Circle*, 1971

Earth economics—calculating environmental values—not only shapes the patterns of resource access and levels of consumption, it also plays a significant role in ascribing accountability for the inevitable environmental externalities (waste, pollutants, habitat loss, human health risks, and so on) that result from resource consumption. For example, the production and consumption of agricultural food products and fossil fuels, in addition to higher wealth, are believed to be some of the most important drivers of environmental stress.

Resource consumption is fundamentally an economic production function that requires environmental decision making at nearly every step of the transformation process of converting raw materials (Earth's resources) into finished consumable products. For example, seeds, soil, and water are transformed into food, and environmental decisions have to be made; oil, coal, and natural gas are transformed into energy, and decisions have to be made; ores are transformed into machines, and decisions have to be made; precipitation is transformed into plastic bottles of drinking water, and more environmental decisions have to be made. However, the "best" environmental (transformation and consumption) decisions are made with the most information regarding the costs and benefits (referred to as *full-cost accounting*) accruing to both people (shareholders) and the environment.

Full-cost accounting (FCA) is the process of collecting and presenting information to decision makers on the trade-offs inherent in resource transformation choices and can be especially important for government agencies that represent a variety of interests when deciding how to allocate public funds or natural resources. FCA can be a valuable tool for correctly pricing the things humans consume by including not only the production costs but the environmental costs as well. Ascribing the "real" price to the material and nonmaterial goods and services we consume can go a long way toward influencing sustainable consumption behaviors. However, the success of FCA will depend almost entirely on the structure of a society's or nation's economy.

Another way of attempting to meet the challenge of better accounting of valuing nature is to find more and more common ground between business and environmentalists. Business and industry have traditionally been viewed as source of environmental degradation. While on the other hand, environmental advocates have championed "restraint and responsibility" as the path to ensuring environmental health. However, advocates for working together believe that business and environmental groups can and should join forces to create sustainable relationships with the earth and ecosystems.

Article

Prepared by: Richard Eathorne, *Northern Michigan University*

Mark Tercek: Valuing Nature

How do you convince individuals, corporations, governments and others that nature's value stretches far beyond intrinsic beauty to include natural capital—the economic value of goods and services, such as clean air or flood mitigation, provided by the environment? As president and CEO of The Nature Conservancy, one of the world's largest conservation organizations, Mark Tercek is used to tackling this and other weighty questions on a daily basis. He recently sat down with *Ensia* to discuss his new book, putting a price on nature and expanding the conservation community.

TODD REUBOLD

Learning Outcomes

After reading this article, you will be able to:

- Explain why recognizing the value of natural capital can help businesses contribute to tackling environmental challenges.

- Discuss why ideas of conservation and sustainability must be valued by "nonenvironmentalists."

Why did you write *Nature's Fortune: How Business and Society Thrive by Investing in Nature*—and why now?

I wrote the book because I really believe in the arguments of the book. As environmentalists, we've got great environmental organizations we can all be proud of, but we have to somehow elevate our game. I don't claim natural capital is the best or the only strategy, but I think it is a damn good strategy. Why? Because it broadens support. You name the business or government, and I can find ways they depend on and should be investing in nature.

Do you think it's more effective right now to work with the business sector than government on difficult environmental issues?

Well, it's not more important. I never say that. Sometimes, because of my business background, people think I'm arguing that business can be the answer for everything. It cannot. More important than anything else is the role of government through its regulations. So we need strong, effective, smart government.

Government is a bigger investor in infrastructure than the private sector. Infrastructure is generally a shared common good. So even more important than the business case is the government case to invest in nature.

Do you see benefits to working with the business sector, though?

I think business is more nimble [than government]. And certainly for me, it's probably easier to persuade businesses to act fast now. At a time when government maybe is weaker— a little bit missing in action—having some evident and high-profile progress by business not only is progress in and of itself, but might provide good examples to motivate government.

What more do you think has to happen, especially in the private sector, when it comes to tackling environmental challenges?

Oh, a lot more. First of all, the number of companies that have genuine, CEO-led environmental efforts is not huge. It's growing and there are some really high profile great cases, but we need a lot more players.

A company I admire is Rio Tinto, and we [TNC] work with Rio Tinto in the U.K. You might say, "Rio Tinto, it's a mining company. Its environmental footprint is huge." That's right, but unless humankind radically, and I mean *radically*, changes its lifestyle, we need the products that come from these mines. And to Rio Tinto's credit, they want to leave the environment net better than when they showed up, and that's a bold commitment. So we're working with them in Mongolia, and their big project in the Gobi Desert, and I think they will live up to that commitment. The mine itself is huge, and has an environmental impact, but they're using our science to minimize and to more than offset that impact.

There are other players that have really good corporate social responsibility or corporate philanthropy efforts. I think those are very nice, admirable starts, but they are insufficient. They've got to go further.

When you talk to people about natural capital, I'm sure there are some who say, "You can't put a price on nature. It's priceless." What's your response?

I understand that. Nature *is* priceless, and most environmentalists, including me, love nature. And we care just as much about those precious ecosystems that don't provide these quantifiable services that deserve investment. We want to protect everything. In fact, part of The Nature Conservancy's strategic plan is to protect all habitats. The practical things [some of these habitats] do aren't as obvious.

Nevertheless, there are some shortcomings to that approach. If you talk about nature just in those terms, some people who are not environmentalists—and remember, the pool of people who are not environmentalists is much bigger—will think, "Oh, I see. Nature is like a luxury good. It's something that we should take care of after we've taken care of everything else."

And so, poorer countries, or richer countries at a time of economic challenge, think they can't afford to invest in the environment. I think that's wrong; that's why we have to elevate this argument. Because if you read my book or you believe in the environment you'll see that nature is the vital underpinning of economic progress.

I was surprised to hear you refer to yourself as an environmentalist because in certain circles that word has taken on a negative connotation. Do you ever hear that critique?

I do. I'm a proud environmentalist, and I'm also a proud pragmatist. And I love nature as much as anyone else. When I joined TNC some people seemed very surprised by my urban upbringing and the fact that I wasn't an accomplished fly fisherman, and things like that. Nature belongs to everybody. One very nice outcome of that for The Nature Conservancy, and I'm really proud of this, is we're now looking at opportunities to do TNC-type conservation projects in cities.

There's a passage toward the end of the book where you write, "The prominent perception that conservation is something that concerns only a narrow and elite segment of the population is potentially devastating." What's your strategy for expanding the conversation to include groups that aren't in the "environmental camp" now?

At The Nature Conservancy we take this challenge very seriously. We really are a science-driven organization, and so we always look at data. And my chief scientist, Peter Kareiva, [said] when I joined TNC, "There's troubling data now and on the horizon. Your kids spend less than one-third of the time outdoors than you did when you were a kid." Now that's a problem, because if you talked to TNC supporters or TNC employees, in a surprisingly frequent number of cases during

their childhood they had powerful outdoor experiences, often because their grandparents had a ranch or a farm or something. Well, let's face it, the world's changing. It's an ever more urban world and kids are indoors. We have to deal with that.

We have a program called LEAF [Leaders in Environmental Action for the Future], where we take inner-city kids from tough circumstances and put them in one of our projects during the summer. We now have more than 500 graduates from that program, and more than one-third have gone on to major in the sciences. Now they're rolling out of college and going into environmental fields. We think that's exciting.

What's the biggest challenge you face running one of the world's largest conservation organizations?

The biggest challenge is we are overwhelmed with worthy opportunities. If we take them all on—and it's really hard not to—we spread ourselves too thin and don't get things done. So we've got to force ourselves to set priorities and stick to them.

What motivates you personally to keep going?

I want to protect nature because it's the right thing to do. I want to protect nature because I want to look my kids in the eye and say I did everything I could to give them a natural world as good as the one I enjoyed. I also want to protect nature for the practical reasons I talk about in the book. And I want to rebuild bipartisan support for nature. I want to do all that as an environmentalist. I want to make it safe and attractive and popular to be an environmentalist.

Critical Thinking

1. Why does Tercek believe it's effective to work with the business sector when trying to resolve environmental issues?
2. Why is it important to put a price on nature?
3. Do you think poor, starving people in impoverished counties would agree with this article? Discuss.

Create Central

www.mhhe.com/createcentral

Internet References

Earth Renewal
www.earthrenewal.org/global_economics.htm
Going Green
www.goinggreen.com
IISDnet
www.iisd.org
The Green Guide
http://environment.nationalgeographic.com/environment/green-guide

Reubold, Todd. From *Ensia.Com*, May 23, 2013. Online. Copyright © 2013 by Todd Reubold. Reprinted by permission of the author.

Article   Prepared by: Richard Eathorne, *Northern Michigan University*

What Is a Tree Worth?

JILL JONNES

Learning Outcomes

After reading this article, you will be able to:

- Explain the ecosystem services that trees provide.

- Describe the ways in which trees play a crucial role in the health of urban areas.

- Outline the scientific evidence available to support the valuable ecological and economic benefits that trees provide to cities.

O n April 8, 1905, President Theodore Roosevelt, attired in a dark suit and top hat, could be found in Fort Worth, Texas, where youngsters looked on from a nearby window as he shoveled soil over the roots of a sapling. It was Arbor Day, which schools across the nation had recently begun commemorating, and the ever vigorous president was demonstrating his hands-on love of trees. For Roosevelt, Arbor Day was no publicity stunt. In an address to America's schoolchildren a couple of years later, he celebrated "the importance of trees to us as a Nation, of what they yield in adornment, comfort, and useful products." He saw trees as vital to the country's well-being: "A people without children would face a hopeless future; a country without trees is almost as hopeless."

For centuries, tree lovers mighty and humble have planted and nurtured trees—elms, oaks, ginkgoes, magnolias, apples, and spruces (to name but a handful of America's 600-some species). "I never before knew the full value of trees," wrote Thomas Jefferson in 1793. "Under them I breakfast, dine, write, read, and receive my company. What would I not give that the trees planted nearest the house at Monticello were full grown." But trees were often taken for granted in a new nation that seemed to have a limitless supply.

Then along came Julius Sterling Morton, a nature lover who moved to Nebraska in the 1850s, briefly edited the state's first newspaper, and soon entered politics. He conceived of an annual day of tree planting, inaugurating a tradition that was rapidly adopted around the country and then the world. (Today, Arbor Day is observed nationwide on the last Friday in April, though individual states mark it on other days.) In 1874, when Nebraska proclaimed Arbor Day an official holiday, *The Nebraska City News* rhapsodized about trees: "The birds will

sing to you from their branches, and their thick foliage will protect you from the dust [and] heat."

But tree lovers quickly learn that many practical-minded Americans—especially politicians—see little value in trees, except perhaps as board timber. Roosevelt was an exception. An ardent birder and conservationist, he reveled in his power to create or enlarge 150 national forests, mainly by presidential fiat. In 1905, he appointed his partner in boxing and bushwhacking, forester Gifford Pinchot, to run the newly created U.S. Forest Service and ensure the wise conservation and use of these public lands.

Roosevelt's national forests were the grand gesture, but they were supplemented by the more modest efforts of a number of arborists who saw a need for trees in the nation's cities and towns. The Progressive Era witnessed a great burst of urban tree planting, with Chicago's municipal forester declaring in 1911 that "trees planted in front of every home in the city cost but a mere trifle, and the benefits derived therefrom are inestimable." In the years after World War II, city forestry departments planted new trees and maintained maturing ones, while the U.S. Forest Service became known for Smokey Bear and efforts to fight forest fires that raged out west during the dry season.

By the 1970s, most Americans lived in cities and suburbs, and the tree lovers among them watched sadly as graceful old elms, big oaks, and verdant small woodlands disappeared, victims of Dutch elm disease, development, and shrinking municipal budgets. This urban deforestation was one more blow to declining cities. City streets stripped of trees lost much of their character and beauty. "Elm trees were part of my life," one Chicago woman ruefully told a forester in the 1980s. She cherished the deep shade and cathedral-like canopy of these majestic giants. "As each one died in my neighborhood . . . the place began to look old, worn, and crowded." Soon thereafter, she moved to another neighborhood that still had trees.

Chicago mayor Richard Daley Jr., a self-proclaimed treehugger born on Arbor Day, was equally heart sore. Upon taking office in 1989, he vowed to plant a half-million trees as part of his effort to revive his decaying Rust Belt city. "What's really important? . . . A tree, a child, flowers," the mayor said in a *Chicago Wilderness Magazine* interview. "Taking care of nature is part of life. If you don't take care of your tree and don't take care of your child, they won't thrive." Knowing that his city's air was among the most polluted in the nation, he asked, "Don't trees clean the air?"

Lumberjacks had long known how to calculate the board feet value of a single lodgepole pine or a vast forest, farmers the price of fruit-tree crops. And yet, in the late 20th century, city trees collectively created an urban forest about which we knew almost nothing. The truth was that no one could provide an answer to Daley's question that was grounded in science.

In fact, no one had concrete answers to a host of fundamental questions. What was the character of an American urban forest? How many poplars, ashes, or lindens were there? How old were they and what size? How healthy? How did trees interact with the ecosystem? Did they really affect air quality? Anyone whose family home was shaded by large oaks or maples knew the delicious cool of those trees on a hot summer day, but how much did they reduce the need for air conditioning?

When thunderstorms lashed down, how many gallons of rainwater did the leaves of a Norway maple absorb and keep out of the stressed sewerage system? And what effect did tree-lined streets and tree-rich landscaping have on commerce? Or crime? Or human well-being? Finally, how could you quantify the benefits so as to persuade city officials that trees were valuable green infrastructure and not mere ornamentation—or, worse yet, a leafy liability?

Daley hired a young arborist named Edith Makra to be his "Tree Lady." She was to get lots of trees planted, but the mayor still wanted to know if more trees meant cleaner air. To get an answer, he prevailed on a fellow tree lover in Congress, 20-term representative Sidney R. Yates (D-Ill.), to earmark some serious federal research dollars. Makra was soon on the phone to the man she believed could answer the mayor's question, and many others about city trees: Rowan Rowntree, a 55-year-old visionary U.S. Forest Service scientist and the grandson of the famous California wildflower botanist and author Lester Rowntree.

"I told him the mayor would be getting us $900,000 and could he help us," Makra recalls. The timing was perfect. While studying urban forests in Oakland, Tucson, and Menlo Park, New Jersey, Rowntree and his colleagues had figured out how to establish a science of urban trees, but they lacked critical funding, staff, and data. Now, not only was Makra offering significant financing, but Rowntree had trained two young scientists, Gregory McPherson and David Nowak, who were ideally suited to work on the ambitious project.

McPherson had grown up in a small, elm-shaded town in southern Michigan, then discovered a love for the American West while studying in Utah for a master's degree in landscape architecture. Design was not his strong point, but marshaling data was. He became Rowan's doctoral student at the College of Environmental Science and Forestry at the State University of New York (SUNY), Syracuse, before taking a tenured position at the University of Arizona in Tucson. That's where he was when Rowntree lured him to Chicago.

Rowntree had met Nowak in the early 1980s when the younger man was a SUNY undergraduate, and was so impressed that he suggested Nowak do a master's in urban forestry with him. In 1987, when Rowntree returned home to Berkeley to help run a U.S. Forest Service research project there, Nowak

came out with him to work on his Ph.D. at the University of California. Chicago would be Nowak's first post-doctoral job.

In 1994, after three years of work that encompassed Chicago as well as surrounding Cook and Du Page counties, Rowntree and his protégés issued their study, the "Chicago Urban Forest Climate Project." They could at last report the size of the Chicago metro area's urban forest: It consisted of roughly 51 million trees, two-thirds of which were in "good or excellent condition." The report was replete with charts and graphs and included detailed information about commercial and residential distribution, tree canopy density, and other attributes of Chicago's woodlands. In Chicago, street trees made up only a tenth of the urban forest, but they provided a quarter of the tree canopy—what a bird flying overhead would see of the leafy tree crowns and foliage that provide shade and cover. And the canopy shaded only 11 percent of the city, less than half of the proportion city officials believed was ideal.

So how *did* all these trees benefit the city? Certainly the trees of Chicago had long sweetened the air and sheltered homes and streets from hot summers and freezing winters, but now here were actual data to show it. "In 1991, trees in Chicago removed an estimated 17 tons of carbon monoxide, 93 tons of sulfur dioxide, 98 tons of nitrogen dioxide, 210 tons of ozone, and 234 tons of particulate matter," Rowntree and his colleagues said in the conclusion to their report. In neighborhoods where trees were large and lush, they could improve air quality by as much as 15 percent during the hottest hours of midday. More trees and bigger trees meant cleaner air.

Trees in the Chicago metro area sequestered about 155,000 tons of carbon a year. This sounded like a large amount, but, the report noted, that annual intake equaled the amount of carbon emitted by transportation vehicles in the Chicago area in just one week. However, over time the urban forest could sequester as much as eight times more carbon if the city planted greater numbers of large, long-lived species such as oaks or London planes and actively nurtured existing trees to full maturity. A big tree that lives for decades or even a century or two can sequester a thousand times more carbon than, say, a crab apple with a life span of 10 or 20 years.

Everyone "knew" that trees cooled down buildings. McPherson measured the *actual* energy savings from Chicago's trees. The shade from a large street tree growing to the west of a typical brick residence, he found, could reduce annual air-conditioning energy use by two to seven percent. By planting more trees to cool down built-up city neighborhoods whose higher temperatures made them urban "heat islands," and promoting utility-sponsored residential tree plantings, the city government could further curtail energy use.

All of this information about an urban forest, never fully documented before, meant that Rowntree and his colleagues could calculate that forest's monetary value. The benefits that each tree planted among Chicago's streets, yards, and businesses provided over its life span came to $402—more than twice its cost.

Oddly, Daley, who was remaking Chicago as a glamorous green city, never embraced the implications of the report. He pushed tree planting, but not in the scaled-up, strategic way

Rowntree and his team had hoped for. In the byzantine world of Chicago politics, no one ever discovered exactly why. Still, Daley's patronage had made possible groundbreaking tree science.

The Chicago study introduced a radically new way to think about city trees, even for those who had been thinking about urban forests for years. Ray Tretheway, longtime head of the Sacramento Tree Foundation, a nonprofit tree-planting organization, vividly remembers hearing McPherson speak at an urban forestry conference in 1991. "He just blew me away," Tretheway recalls. "These tree benefits, I'd never heard of this before." After meeting with McPherson and Rowntree, Tretheway persuaded the U.S. Forest Service to open a new research station in Davis, not far from Sacramento. With the Chicago study concluded, McPherson headed to California to become head of the station's Center for Urban Forest Research. The University of California, Davis, provided a source of graduate students to carry out the research.

Tretheway acquired a wealth of studies and new data from McPherson and other tree scientists, who in the late 1990s worked up a detailed portrait of Sacramento's five million trees and their numerous benefits. McPherson's graduate student Qingfu Xiao did pioneering research on the impact of trees on stormwater dispersal—an expensive problem for the many cities faced with federal mandates to upgrade their sewerage and water systems—by measuring how much rainfall trees of various species and sizes intercepted.

When McPherson had come west, he found under way in Sacramento a real-life study of how trees save energy. In 1989, the Sacramento Municipal Utility District had been forced by outraged voters to close its dysfunctional Rancho Seco nuclear plant. To reduce its peak load, the electric utility's new, tree-loving CEO, S. David Freeman, had partnered with Tretheway's foundation to plant half a million young trees for free in the yards of residential customers over the course of a decade.

By 1993, more than 111,000 trees had been planted, and the utility wanted to assess whether they were starting to reduce energy use. It gathered information from 326 homes on tree mortality, location, species, and size, as well as all the relevant specs on each house. McPherson's number crunching revealed that a tree planted to the west of a house saved about three times more energy ($120 versus $39) in a year than the same kind of tree planted to the south. The shade program underwent "a paradigm shift," according to economist Misha Sarkovich, whom the utility had assigned to monitor the program's impact. Today Sarkovich runs the program, and he evaluates performance not by how many trees are planted but according to the "present value benefit" of each tree, expressed in a dollar amount.

About half of the nearly 500,000 trees the utility has planted in the last 20 years are still alive, and their overhanging boughs have done much to improve customers' quality of life. Some of that improvement can be measured. The trees' shade collectively saves the utility from having to supply $1.2 million worth of electricity annually. Running the shade program costs the utility $1.5 million a year. As more trees are planted and the new canopy becomes lusher, the energy savings will continue

to grow. When and if it can begin selling carbon credits, the utility will start to make a profit on its shade tree program.

In the post-Chicago years, McPherson and Nowak developed their science and models, engaging in ever more ambitious studies. McPherson began systematically studying a reference city in each of 16 climate zones to expand his database. As this new research became known, city foresters and nonprofit arbor groups increasingly drew on it to advocate for trees.

In 2006, McPherson and his colleagues were adding Queens as a reference city when the New York Parks Department asked them to value *all* of New York City's 592,000 street trees. With the advances made over the preceding dozen years, McPherson could deliver a far more sophisticated report than he had for Chicago. Energy savings: New York City's trees annually saved roughly $28 million, or $47.63 per tree. Air pollution: Each street tree removed an average of 1.73 pounds of air pollutants per year (a benefit of $9.02 per tree), for a total of more than $5 million. The report also calculated that street trees reduced stormwater runoff by nearly 900 million gallons each year, saving the city $35.6 million it would have had to spend to improve its stormwater systems. The average street tree intercepted 1,432 gallons, a service worth $61, a figure large enough to impress cost-conscious city managers.

McPherson and his colleagues were also able to tally various benefits associated with aesthetics, increased property values and economic activity, reduced human stress, and improved public health, which were estimated at $52.5 million, or $90 a tree. These drew on straight-up economic studies of real estate prices as well as social science research, which showed, for example, that hospital patients who could see a tree out the window of their room were discharged a day earlier than those without such a view. Other studies showed that shopping destinations with trees had more customers than those that didn't, and leafy public-housing projects experienced less violence than barren ones.

All these data led to the finding that each year New York City's street trees delivered $122 million in benefits, or about $209 a tree. As New York City's parks and forestry officials well knew, they received $8 million a year to plant and tend street trees, and spent another $6.3 million to pay personnel. The net benefit they were getting for all these trees was an impressive $100 million.

For the first time, urban forestry science had a dramatic effect on public policy: In 2008, Mayor Michael Bloomberg quadrupled the city's forestry budget, from $8 million to $31 million (down last year to $27 million), when he launched Million Trees NYC, a partnership with entertainer Bette Midler's nonprofit New York Restoration Project. McPherson was thrilled to see science elevate urban forestry above the level of "a kumbaya idea." The million trees (350,000 are in the ground so far) planted by 2018 will transform the Big Apple, and those lush, tree-lined streets and shaded parks may well become Bloomberg's most visible legacy.

In Los Angeles, meanwhile, another tree-hugging mayor, Antonio Villaraigosa, had already launched his own Million Trees initiative back in 2006. McPherson and his team, who had worked with the city's schools a few years earlier to determine how trees could cool and shade school property, were called in again. Their mission for Million Trees LA was to gauge the size of the existing canopy, figure out if there was room for another million trees in the 500-square-mile city, and, if there was, determine the best places to plant them.

City officials directed McPherson to create a map showing the canopy cover in each of the 15 councilmanic districts. While Los Angeles's overall tree canopy covered a respectable 21 percent of the city, the map revealed that the districts with the fewest trees were also the poorest. "When we went around with this map," notes one official, "people who didn't care about trees started to care. Council members in east and south L.A. wanted to know why they didn't have the same level of trees as wealthier neighborhoods."

In the wake of the report, the emphasis of Million Trees LA shifted. "We all knew there were places with fewer trees, but with the map you can really *see* it," says executive director Lisa Sarno. "It's become a matter of social and environmental justice." In poor residential neighborhoods where tree-planting efforts have been stepped up, the demand is for lemon, lime, and orange trees, which produce fruit that is expensive to buy at grocery stores. At long last, this radical new way of thinking about city trees had begun to influence politicians, planners, and city managers.

Once they had the science, urban forestry champions became frustrated by the puzzle of how to disseminate what they had learned. David Nowak, who has long worked out of the U.S. Forest Service's Northeastern Research Station in Syracuse, New York, had begun collaborating with the Davey Tree Expert Company, a nationwide tree care company, to create free computer software that could help others to replicate his work on the structure and benefits of urban forests. At the University of California, Davis, graduate student Scott Maco was creating similar software for McPherson just for urban street trees, the major concern of most foresters wanting to impress city hall with trees' benefits.

In early 2003, Mark Buscaino, the new head of urban forestry at the U.S. Forest Service, proposed pulling together Nowak and McPherson's work into a free software suite—christened i-Tree—aimed at city foresters, landscape architects, urban planners, and nonprofit tree groups. Gregory Ina, general manager of the Davey Institute at the Davey Tree Expert Company, loved the idea and brought Maco on board in 2005 to run the effort. (Of course, in the long run, more trees will be good for Davey Tree's business.) In tandem with the U.S. Forest Service and other partners, Maco and Davey Tree have worked to make the i-Tree software more sophisticated and easier to customize, and they provide customer support to the municipalities, scholars, foresters, consultants, and nonprofit and citizen groups that use it.

Davey estimates that last year 2,000 i-Tree projects were under way, mostly in the United States. A software package called i-Tree Hydro, which models stormwater hydrology, will be released this winter. One spin-off, developed in partnership with the Washington, D.C., nonprofit organization Casey Trees, is the Tree Benefit Calculator, which tells homeowners the value of their trees. It recently informed me that my 25-year-old backyard pin oak last year provided the following benefits:

It intercepted and absorbed 7,669 gallons of rainwater ($75.92), raised my property value ($75.67), saved 229 kilowatts of electricity ($17.36), and improved air quality and stored carbon ($17.58). Of course, my family also enjoys the pin oak's beauty, the squirrels frolicking about its branches and feasting on acorns, and the many cardinals and other birds it attracts. It buffers us from a nearby busy street, abates noise, and once held a rope swing for my daughter.

Most of us take trees for granted, but when we do think of them, generally we appreciate how they beautify and soften our world and connect us to nature. (We also sometimes curse them for clogging our gutters with fallen leaves or damaging our property when they fall down.) Trees are the largest and longest-lived structures on our planet. At the White House, one bedroom is still shaded by a magnolia planted by President Andrew Jackson in memory of his wife. But such benefits don't always have traction with public planners and politicians. Money does much of the talking. "The monetizing is a necessary evil," Nowak says. "We know trees have great value, but they're intrinsically underrated. You have to talk the language of people who make decisions."

As we humans wrestle with how to repair the damage we have wrought on nature, and how to slow climate change, urban trees offer an obvious low-tech solution. Every city, McPherson says, should have a "maximally functional" canopy. "We should shoot for a performance standard, like how many megawatt hours of air conditioning we can save, or how many pounds of nitrogen dioxide we can absorb, reducing ozone and smog." Trees can play a role in cooling cities while making them more beautiful, healthier, and friendlier to humans. And at a time when everyone seems to want to go "green," urban forestry science offers meaningful ways to think about how to do that. Business sage Warren Buffett, who knows something about the value of thinking long term, has said, "Someone's sitting in the shade today because someone planted a tree a long time ago."

It is easy to imagine that Theodore Roosevelt, who believed that trees added "immeasurably to the wholesome beauty of life," would have been delighted but not surprised to learn of the many practical roles played by the very trees most familiar to Americans—those that surround them in their daily life in cities and suburbs. While science and technology are transforming and expanding the way we think about trees, Rowntree, now a scientist emeritus with the U.S. Forest Service, estimates, "We are only 50 percent of the way to knowing what trees really do for us." What we *have* learned only proves the old proverb truer than ever: "The best time to plant a tree was 20 years ago, the next best time is today."

Critical Thinking

1. Describe the brief history of our nation's changing perception of trees.

2. How did the "Chicago Urban Forest Climate Project" contribute to better understanding the benefits that trees provide in urban areas?

3. Provide examples of the monetary values ascribed to trees in cities.

Create Central

www.mhhe.com/createcentral

Internet References

Earth Renewal
www.earthrenewal.org/global_economics.htm

Going Green
www.goinggreen.com

IISDnet
www.iisd.org

The Green Guide
http://environment.nationalgeographic.com/environment/green-guide

---

JILL JONNES is a historian and author of *Eiffel's Tower* (2009), *Conquering Gotham* (2007), and *Empires of Light* (2003).

Article

The Efficiency Dilemma

If our machines use less energy, will we just use them more?

DAVID OWEN

In April, the federal government adopted standards for automobiles requiring manufacturers to improve the average fuel economy of their new-car fleets thirty percent by 2016. The *Times,* in an editorial titled "Everybody Wins," said the change would produce "a trifecta of benefits." Those benefits were enumerated last year by Steven Chu, the Secretary of Energy: a reduction in total oil consumption of 1.8 billion barrels; the elimination of nine hundred and fifty million metric tons of greenhouse-gas emissions; and savings, for the average American driver, of three thousand dollars.

Chu, who shared the Nobel Prize in Physics in 1997, has been an evangelist for energy efficiency, and not just for vehicles. I spoke with him in July, shortly after he had conducted an international conference called the Clean Energy Ministerial, at which efficiency was among the main topics. "I feel very passionate about this," he told me. "We in the Department of Energy are trying to get the information out that efficiency really does save money and doesn't necessarily mean that you're going to have to make deep sacrifices."

Energy efficiency has been called "the fifth fuel" (after coal, petroleum, nuclear power, and renewables); it is seen as a cost-free tool for accelerating the transition to a green-energy economy. In 2007, the United Nations Foundation said that efficiency improvements constituted "the largest, the most evenly geographically distributed, and least expensive energy resource." Last year, the management-consulting firm McKinsey & Company concluded that a national efficiency program could eliminate "up to 1.1 gigatons of greenhouse gases annually." The environmentalist Amory Lovins, whose thinking has influenced Chu's, has referred to the replacement of incandescent light bulbs with compact fluorescents as "not a free lunch, but a lunch you're paid to eat," since a fluorescent bulb will usually save enough electricity to more than offset its higher purchase price. Tantalizingly, much of the technology required to increase efficiency is well understood. The World Economic Forum, in a report called "Towards a More Energy Efficient World," observed that "the average refrigerator sold in the United States today uses three-quarters less energy than the 1975 average, even though it is 20 percent larger and costs 60 percent less"—an improvement that Chu cited in his conversation with me.

But the issue may be less straightforward than it seems. The thirty-five-year period during which new refrigerators have plunged in electricity use is also a period during which the global market for refrigeration has burgeoned and the world's total energy consumption and carbon output, including the parts directly attributable to keeping things cold, have climbed. Similarly, the first fuel-economy regulations for U.S. cars—which were enacted in 1975, in response to the Arab oil embargo—were followed not by a steady decline in total U.S. motor-fuel consumption but by a long-term rise, as well as by increases in horsepower, curb weight, vehicle miles travelled (up a hundred percent since 1980), and car ownership (America has about fifty million more registered vehicles than licensed drivers). A growing group of economists and others have argued that such correlations aren't coincidental. Instead, they have said, efforts to improve energy efficiency can more than negate any environmental gains—an idea that was first proposed a hundred and fifty years ago, and which came to be known as the Jevons paradox.

Great Britain in the middle of the nineteenth century was the world's leading military, industrial, and mercantile power. In 1865, a twenty-nine-year-old Englishman named William Stanley Jevons published a book, "The Coal Question," in which he argued that the bonanza couldn't last. Britain's affluence, he wrote, depended on its endowment of coal, which the country was rapidly depleting. He added that such an outcome could not be delayed through increased "economy" in the use of coal—what we refer to today as energy efficiency. He concluded, in italics, *"It is wholly a confusion of ideas to suppose that the economical use of fuel is equivalent to a diminished consumption. The very contrary is the truth."*

He offered the example of the British iron industry. If some technological advance made it possible for a blast furnace to produce iron with less coal, he wrote, then profits would rise, new investment in iron production would be attracted, and the price of iron would fall, thereby stimulating additional demand. Eventually, he concluded, "the greater number of furnaces will more than make up for the diminished consumption of each." Other examples of this effect abound. In a paper published in 1998, the Yale economist William D. Nordhaus estimated the cost of lighting throughout human history. An ancient Babylonian, he calculated, needed to work more than forty-one hours to acquire enough lamp oil to provide a thousand lumen-hours of light—the equivalent of a seventy-five-watt incandescent bulb burning for about an hour. Thirty-five hundred years later, a contemporary of Thomas Jefferson's could buy the same amount of illumination, in the form of tallow candles, by working for about five hours and twenty minutes. By 1992, an average American, with access to compact fluorescents, could do the same in less than half a second. Increasing the energy efficiency of illumination is nothing new; improved lighting has been "a lunch you're paid to eat" ever since humans upgraded from cave fires (fifty-eight hours of labor for our early Stone Age ancestors). Yet our efficiency gains haven't reduced the energy we expend on illumination or shrunk our energy consumption over all. On the contrary, we now generate light so extravagantly that darkness itself is spoken of as an endangered natural resource.

Jevons was born in Liverpool in 1835. He spent two years at University College, in London, then went to Australia, where he had been offered a job as an assayer at a new mint, in Sydney. He left after five years, completed his education in England, became a part-time college instructor, and published a well-received book on gold markets. "The Coal Question" made him a minor celebrity; it was admired by John Stuart Mill and William Gladstone, and it inspired the government to investigate his findings. In 1871, he published "The Theory of Political Economy," a book that's still considered one of the founding texts of mathematical economics. He drowned a decade later, at the age of forty-six, while swimming in the English Channel. In 1905, John Maynard Keynes, who was then twenty-two and a graduate student at Cambridge University, wrote to Lytton Strachey that he had discovered a "thrilling" book: Jevons's "Investigations in Currency and Finance." Keynes wrote of Jevons, "I am convinced that he was one of *the* minds of the century."

Jevons might be little discussed today, except by historians of economics, if it weren't for the scholarship of another English economist, Len Brookes. During the nineteen-seventies oil crisis, Brookes argued that devising ways to produce goods with less oil—an obvious response to higher prices—would merely accommodate the new prices, causing energy consumption to be higher than it would have been if no effort to increase efficiency had been made; only later did he discover that Jevons had anticipated him by more than a century. I spoke with Brookes recently. He told me, "Jevons is very simple. When we talk about increasing energy efficiency, what we're really talking about is increasing the productivity of energy. And, if you increase the productivity of anything, you have the effect of reducing its implicit price, because you get more return for the same money—which means the demand goes up."

Nowadays, this effect is usually referred to as "rebound"—or, in cases where increased consumption more than cancels out any energy savings, as "backfire." In a 1992 paper, Harry D. Saunders, an American researcher, provided a concise statement of the basic idea: "With fixed real energy price, energy efficiency gains will increase energy consumption above where it would be without these gains."

In 2000, the journal *Energy Policy* devoted an entire issue to rebound. It was edited by Lee Schipper, who is now a senior research engineer at Stanford University's Precourt Energy Efficiency Center. In an editorial, Schipper wrote that the question was not whether rebound exists but, rather, "how much the effect appears, how rapidly, in which sectors, and in what manifestations." The majority of the *Energy Policy* contributors concluded that there wasn't a lot to worry about. Schipper, in his editorial, wrote that the articles, taken together, suggested that "rebounds are significant but do not threaten to rob society of most of the benefits of energy efficiency improvements."

I spoke with Schipper recently, and he told me that the Jevons paradox has limited applicability today. "The key to understanding Jevons," he said, "is that processes, products, and activities where energy is a very high part of the cost—in this country, a few metals, a few chemicals, air travel—are the only ones whose variable cost is very sensitive to energy. That's it." Jevons wasn't wrong about nineteenth-century British iron smelting, he said; but the young and rapidly growing industrial world that Jevons lived in no longer exists.

Most economists and efficiency experts have come to similar conclusions. For example, some of them say that when you increase the fuel efficiency of cars you lose no more than about ten percent of the fuel savings to increased use. And if you look at the whole economy, Schipper said, rebound effects are comparably trivial. "People like Brookes would say—they don't quite know how to say it, but they seem to want to say the extra growth is more than the saved energy, so it's like a backfire. The problem is, that's never been observed on a national level."

But troublesome questions have lingered, and the existence of large-scale rebound effects is not so easy to dismiss. In 2004, a committee of the House of Lords invited a number of experts to help it grapple with a conundrum: the United Kingdom, like a number of other countries, had spent heavily to increase energy efficiency in an attempt to reduce its greenhouse emissions. Yet energy consumption and carbon output in Britain—as in the rest of the world—had continued to rise. Why?

M ost economic analyses of rebound focus narrowly on particular uses or categories of uses: if people buy a more efficient clothes dryer, say, what will happen to the energy they use as they dry clothes? (At least one such study has concluded that, for appliances in general, rebound is nonexistent.) Brookes dismisses such "bottom-up" studies, because they ignore or understate the real consumption effects, in economies as a whole.

A good way to see this is to think about refrigerators, the very appliances that the World Economic Forum and Steven Chu cited as efficiency role models for reductions in energy use. The first refrigerator I remember is the one my parents owned when I was little. They acquired it when they bought their first house, in 1954, a year before I was born. It had a tiny, uninsulated freezer compartment, which seldom contained much more than a few aluminum ice trays and a burrow-like mantle of frost. (Frost-free freezers stay frost-free by periodically heating their cooling elements—a trick that wasn't widely in use yet.) In the sixties, my parents bought a much improved model—which presumably was more efficient, since the door closed tight, by means of a rubberized magnetic seal rather than a mechanical latch. But our power consumption didn't fall, because the old refrigerator didn't go out of service; it moved into our basement, where it remained plugged in for a further twenty-five years—mostly as a warehouse for beverages and leftovers—and where it was soon joined by a stand-alone freezer. Also, in the eighties, my father added an icemaker to his bar, to supplement the one in the kitchen fridge.

This escalation of cooling capacity has occurred all over suburban America. The recently remodelled kitchen of a friend of mine contains an enormous side-by-side refrigerator, an enormous side-by-side freezer, and a drawer-like under-counter mini-fridge for beverages. And the trend has not been confined to households. As the ability to efficiently and inexpensively chill things has grown, so have opportunities to buy chilled things—a potent positive-feedback loop. Gas stations now often have almost as much refrigerated shelf space as the grocery stores of my early childhood; even mediocre hotel rooms usually come with their own small fridge (which, typically, either is empty or—if it's a minibar—contains mainly things that don't need to be kept cold), in addition to an icemaker and a refrigerated vending machine down the hall.

The steadily declining cost of refrigeration has made eating much more interesting. It has also made almost all elements of food production more cost-effective and energy-efficient: milk lasts longer if you don't have to keep it in a pail in your well. But there are environmental downsides, beyond the obvious one that most of the electricity that powers the world's refrigerators is generated by burning fossil fuels. James McWilliams, who is the author of the recent book "Just Food," told me, "Refrigeration and packaging convey to the consumer a sense that what we buy will last longer than it does. Thus, we buy enough stuff to fill our capacious Sub-Zeros and, before we know it, a third of it is past its due date and we toss it." (The item that New Yorkers most often throw away unused, according to the anthropologist-in-residence at the city's Department of Sanitation, is vegetables.) Jonathan Bloom, who runs the Website wastedfood.com and is the author of the new book "American Wasteland," told me that, since the mid-nineteen-seventies, per-capita food waste in the United States has increased by half, so that we now throw away forty percent of all the edible food we produce. And when we throw away food we don't just throw away nutrients; we also throw away the energy we used in keeping it cold as we lost interest in it, as well as the energy that went into growing, harvesting, processing, and transporting it, along with its proportional share of our staggering national consumption of fertilizer, pesticides, irrigation water, packaging, and landfill capacity. According to a 2009 study, more than a quarter of U.S. freshwater use goes into producing food that is later discarded.

Efficiency improvements push down costs at every level—from the mining of raw materials to the fabrication and transportation of finished goods to the frequency and intensity of actual use—and reduced costs stimulate increased consumption. (Coincidentally or not, the growth of American

refrigerator volume has been roughly paralleled by the growth of American body-mass index.) Efficiency-related increases in one category, furthermore, spill into others. Refrigerators are the fraternal twins of air-conditioners, which use the same energy-hungry compressor technology to force heat to do something that nature doesn't want it to. When I was a child, cold air was a far greater luxury than cold groceries. My parents' first house—like eighty-eight percent of all American homes in 1960—didn't have air-conditioning when they bought it, although they broke down and got a window unit during a heat wave, when my mom was pregnant with me. Their second house had central air-conditioning, but running it seemed so expensive to my father that, for years, he could seldom be persuaded to turn it on, even at the height of a Kansas City summer, when the air was so humid that it felt like a swimmable liquid. Then he replaced our ancient Carrier unit with a modern one, which consumed less electricity, and our house, like most American houses, evolved rapidly from being essentially un-air-conditioned to being air-conditioned all summer long.

Modern air-conditioners, like modern refrigerators, are vastly more energy efficient than their mid-twentieth-century predecessors—in both cases, partly because of tighter standards established by the Department of Energy. But that efficiency has driven down their cost of operation, and manufacturing efficiencies and market growth have driven down the cost of production, to such an extent that the ownership percentage of 1960 has now flipped: by 2005, according to the Energy Information Administration, eighty-four percent of all U.S. homes had air-conditioning, and most of it was central. Stan Cox, who is the author of the recent book "Losing Our Cool," told me that, between 1993 and 2005, "the energy efficiency of residential air-conditioning equipment improved twenty-eight percent, but energy consumption for A.C. by the average air-conditioned household rose thirty-seven percent." One consequence, Cox observes, is that, in the United States, we now use roughly as much electricity to cool buildings as we did for all purposes in 1955.

As "Losing Our Cool" clearly shows, similar rebound effects permeate the economy. The same technological gains that have propelled the growth of U.S. residential and commercial cooling have helped turn automobile air-conditioners, which barely existed in the nineteen-fifties, into standard equipment on even the least luxurious vehicles. (According to the National Renewable Energy Laboratory, running a mid-sized car's air-conditioning increases fuel consumption by more than twenty percent.) And access to cooled air is self-reinforcing: to someone who works in an air-conditioned office, an un-air-conditioned house quickly becomes intolerable, and vice versa. A resident of Las Vegas once described cars to me as "devices for transporting air-conditioning between buildings."

In less than half a century, increased efficiency and declining prices have helped to push access to air-conditioning almost all the way to the bottom of the U.S. income scale—and now those same forces are accelerating its spread all over the world. According to Cox, between 1997 and 2007 the use of air-conditioners tripled in China (where a third of the world's units are now manufactured, and where many air-conditioner purchases have been subsidized by the government). In India, air-conditioning is projected to increase almost tenfold between 2005 and 2020; according to a 2009 study, it accounted for forty percent of the electricity consumed in metropolitan Mumbai.

All such increases in energy-consuming activity can be considered manifestations of the Jevons paradox. Teasing out the precise contribution of a particular efficiency improvement isn't just difficult, however; it may be impossible, because the endlessly ramifying network of interconnections is too complex to yield readily to empirical, mathematics-based analysis. Most modern studies of energy rebound are "bottom-up" by necessity: it's only at the micro end of the economics spectrum that the number of mathematical variables can be kept manageable. But looking for rebound only in individual consumer goods, or in closely cropped economic snapshots, is as futile and misleading as trying to analyze the global climate with a single thermometer.

Schipper told me, "In the end, the impact of rebound is small, in my view, for one very key reason: energy is a small share of the economy. If sixty percent of our economy were paying for energy, then anything that moved it down by ten percent would liberate a huge amount of resources. Instead, it's between six and eight percent for primary energy, depending on exactly what country you're in." ("Primary energy" is the energy in oil, coal, wind, and other natural resources before it's been converted into electricity or into refined or synthetic fuels.) Schipper believes that cheap energy is an environmental problem, but he also believes that, because we can extract vastly more economic benefit from a ton of coal than nineteenth-century Britons did, efficiency gains now have much less power to stimulate consumption. This concept is closely related to one called "decoupling," which suggests that the growing efficiency of machines has weakened the link between energy use and economic activity, and also to the idea of "decarbonization," which holds that, for similar reasons, every dollar we spend represents a shrinking quantity of greenhouse gas.

These sound like environmentally valuable trends—yet they seem to imply that the world's energy and carbon challenges are gradually solving themselves, since decoupling and decarbonization, like increases in efficiency, are nothing new. One problem with decoupling, as the concept is often applied, is that it doesn't account for energy use and carbon emissions that have not been eliminated but merely exported out of the region under study (say, from California to a factory in China). And there's a more fundamental problem, described by the Danish researcher Jørgen S. Nørgård, who has called energy decoupling "largely a statistical delusion." To say that energy's economic role is shrinking is a little like saying, "I have sixteen great-great-grandparents, eight great-grandparents, four grandparents, and two parents—the world's population must be imploding." Energy production may account for only a small percentage of our economy, but its falling share of G.D.P. has made it more important, not less, since every kilowatt we generate supports an ever larger proportion of our well-being. The logic misstep is apparent if you imagine eliminating primary energy from the world. If you do that, you don't end up losing "between six and eight percent" of current economic activity, as

Schipper's formulation might suggest; you lose almost everything we think of as modern life.

Blake Alcott, an ecological economist, has made a similar case in support of the existence of large-scale Jevons effects. Recently, he told me, "If it is true that greater efficiency in using a resource means less consumption of it—as efficiency environmentalists say—then less efficiency would logically mean more consumption. But this yields a reductio ad absurdum: engines and smelters in James Watt's time, around 1800, were far less efficient than today's, but is it really imaginable that, had technology been frozen at that efficiency level, a greater population would now be using vastly more fossil fuel than we in fact do?" Contrary to the argument made by "decouplers," we aren't gradually reducing our dependence on energy; rather, we are finding ever more ingenious ways to leverage B.T.U.s. Between 1984 and 2005, American electricity production grew by about sixty-six percent—and it did so despite steady, economy-wide gains in energy efficiency. The increase was partly the result of population growth; but per-capita energy consumption rose, too, and it did so even though energy use per dollar of G.D.P. fell by roughly half. Besides, population growth itself can be a Jevons effect: the more efficient we become, the more people we can sustain; the more people we sustain, the more energy we consume.

The Model T was manufactured between 1908 and 1927. According to the Ford Motor Company, its fuel economy ranged between thirteen and twenty-one miles per gallon. There are vehicles on the road today that do worse than that; have we really made so little progress in more than a hundred years? But focussing on miles per gallon is the wrong way to assess the environmental impact of cars. Far more revealing is to consider the productivity of driving. Today, in contrast to the early nineteen-hundreds, any American with a license can cheaply travel almost anywhere, in almost any weather, in extraordinary comfort; can drive for thousands of miles with no maintenance other than refuelling; can easily find gas, food, lodging, and just about anything else within a short distance of almost any road; and can order and eat meals without undoing a seat belt or turning off the ceiling-mounted DVD player.

A modern driver, in other words, gets vastly more benefit from a gallon of gasoline—makes far more economical use of fuel—than any Model T owner ever did. Yet motorists' energy consumption has grown by mind-boggling amounts, and, as the productivity of driving has increased and the cost of getting around has fallen, the global market for cars has surged. (Two of the biggest road-building efforts in the history of the world are currently under way in India and China.) And developing small, inexpensive vehicles that get a hundred miles to the gallon would only exacerbate that trend. The problem with efficiency gains is that we inevitably reinvest them in additional consumption. Paving roads reduces rolling friction, thereby boosting miles per gallon, but it also makes distant destinations seem closer, thereby enabling people to live in sprawling, energy-gobbling subdivisions far from where they work and shop.

Chu has said that drivers who buy more efficient cars can expect to save thousands of dollars in fuel costs; but, unless those drivers shred the money and add it to a compost heap, the environment is unlikely to come out ahead, as those dollars will inevitably be spent on goods or activities that involve fuel consumption—say, on increased access to the Internet, which is one of the fastest-growing energy drains in the world. (Cox writes that, by 2014, the U.S. computer network alone will each year require an amount of energy equivalent to the total electricity consumption of Australia.) The problem is exactly what Jevons said it was: the economical use of fuel is not equivalent to a diminished consumption. Schipper told me that economy-wide Jevons effects have "never been observed," but you can find them almost anywhere you look: they are the history of civilization.

Jevons died too soon to see the modern uses of oil and natural gas, and he obviously knew nothing of nuclear power. But he did explain why "alternative" energy sources, such as wind, hydropower, and biofuels (in his day, mainly firewood and whale oil), could not compete with coal: coal had replaced them, on account of its vastly greater portability, utility, and productivity. Early British steam engines were sometimes used to pump water to turn water wheels; we do the equivalent when we burn coal to make our toothbrushes move back and forth.

Decreasing reliance on fossil fuels is a pressing global need. The question is whether improving efficiency, rather than reducing total consumption, can possibly bring about the desired result. Steven Chu told me that one of the appealing features of the efficiency discussions at the Clean Energy Ministerial was that they were never contentious. "It was the opposite," he said. "No one was debating about who's responsible, and there was no finger-pointing or trying to lay blame." This seems encouraging in one way but dismaying in another. Given the known level of global disagreement about energy and climate matters, shouldn't there have been *some* angry table-banging? Advocating efficiency involves virtually no political risk—unlike measures that do call for sacrifice, such as capping emissions or putting a price on carbon or increasing energy taxes or investing heavily in utility-scale renewable-energy facilities or confronting the deeply divisive issue of global energy equity. Improving efficiency is easy to endorse: we've been doing it, globally, for centuries. It's how we created the problems we're now trying to solve.

Efficiency proponents often express incredulity at the idea that squeezing more consumption from less fuel could somehow carry an environmental cost. Amory Lovins once wrote that, if Jevons's argument is correct, "we should mandate inefficient equipment to save energy." As Lovins intended, this seems laughably illogical—but is it? If the only motor vehicle available today were a 1920 Model T, how many miles do you think you'd drive each year, and how far do you think you'd live from where you work? No one's going to "mandate inefficient equipment," but, unless we're willing to do the equivalent—say, by mandating costlier energy—increased efficiency, as Jevons predicted, can only make our predicament worse.

At the end of "The Coal Question," Jevons concluded that Britain faced a choice between "brief greatness and longer continued mediocrity." His preference was for mediocrity, by which he meant something like "sustainability." Our world is different from his, but most of the central arguments of his book still apply. Steve Sorrell, who is a senior fellow at Sussex University and a co-editor of a recent comprehensive book on rebound, called "Energy Efficiency and Sustainable Consumption," told me, "I think the point may be that Jevons has yet to be disproved. It is rather hard to demonstrate the validity of his proposition, but certainly the historical evidence to date is wholly consistent with what he was arguing." That might be something to think about as we climb into our plug-in hybrids and continue our journey, with ever-increasing efficiency, down the road paved with good intentions.

Critical Thinking

1. Describe the "efficiency dilemma."

2. Outline the facts and data used to support the idea of "Jevons' Paradox."

3. Do you see a connection between increasing energy efficiency and continued overconsumption? Is so, describe what you see.

4. How might increasing energy efficiency and the material goods and services it creates actually hinder our quest for environmental sustainability?

Article

Economic Report into Biodiversity Crisis Reveals Price of Consuming the Planet

Species losses around the world could really cost us the Earth with food shortages, floods and expensive clean up costs.

JULIETTE JOWIT

In every corner of the globe the evidence of the global biodiversity crisis is now impossible to ignore.

In the UK, a third of high priority species and two-thirds of habitats are declining, according to government figures that emerged today on the UK's Biodiversity Action Plan. Since 1994 despite the extra attention provided by the plan, 5% of the species it covered are thought to have gone extinct.

Around the world the picture is as bad or worse: the International Union for the Conservation of Nature believes one in five mammals, one in three amphibians and one in seven birds are extinct or globally threatened, and other species groups still being assessed are showing similar patterns.

Simon Stuart, a senior IUCN scientist, has warned that for the first time since the dinosaurs humans are driving plants and animals to extinction faster than new species can evolve.

For decades, nature lovers have watched the fens being drained, or noticed the decline of cuckoos in spring and butterflies in summer. But until recently these changes have been overshadowed by growing fears about the impact of climate change.

However, as the impact of these species losses around the world have mounted—riots over food shortages, costly floods and landslides, expensive bills for cleaning polluted water, and many more disasters—attention has finally started to turn to the impact of human beings literally consuming the planet's natural resources.

So it was in 2007, just months after the British government made global waves with the biggest ever report on the economics of climate change by Lord Stern, that world governments met in Potsdam, in Germany, and asked the leading economist and senior banker Pavan Sukhdev to do the same for the natural world.

The study—called The Economics of Ecosystems and Biodiversity (TEEB) shows that on average one-third of Earth's habitats have been damaged by humans—with, for example, 85% of seas and oceans and more than 70% of Mediterranean shrubland affected. It also warns that in spite of growing awareness of the danger of natural destruction it will "still continue on a large scale".

Following an interim report last year, the study group will publish its final findings this summer, in advance of the global Convention On Biological Diversity conference in Japan in October, marking 2010 as the International Year of Biodiversity.

Based on a host of academic and expert studies, the TEEB report is expected to say that the ratio of costs of conserving ecosystems or biodiversity to the benefits of doing so range from 10:1 to 100:1. "Our studies found ranges of 1:10, 1:25, 1:60," said Sukhdev. "The point is they are all big ratios: I'd do business on those ratios . . . I'm fine with 1:10."

One report estimated the cost of building and maintaining a more comprehensive network of global protected areas—increasing it from the current 12.5%–14% to 15% of all land and from 1% to 30% of the seas—would be $45bn a year, while the benefits of preserving the species richness within these zones would be worth $4–5tn a year. Another unpublished report for the UN by UK-based consultants Trucost claimed the combined cost of damage to the environment by the world's 3,000 biggest companies was $2.2tn in 2008.

Echoing Lord Stern's famous description of climate change as "the greatest and widest-ranging market failure ever", Sukhdev—who supports action on climate change as well—said the destruction of the natural world was "a landscape of market failures", because the services of nature were nearly always provided for free, and so not valued until they were gone.

"The earth and its thin surface is our only home, and there's a lot that comes to us from biodiversity and ecosystems: we get food, fuel, fibre; we get the ability to have clean air and fresh water; we get a stable micro-climate where we live; if we wander into forests and wildernesses we get enjoyment, we get recreation, we get spiritual sustenance; all kinds of things—which in many cases are received free, and I think that's perhaps the nub of the problem," said Sukhdev who was [visiting] the UK as a guest of science research and education charity, the Earthwatch Institute.

"We fail to recognise the extent to which we are dependent on natural ecosystems, and not just for goods and services, but also for the stability of the environment in which we survive—there's an element of resilience that's been built into our lives, the ability of our environment to withstand the shocks to which we expose it . . . the more we lose, the less resilience there is to these shocks, and therefore we increase the risk to society and risk to life and livelihoods and the economy," he added. Sukhdev is a senior banker at Deutsche Bank, adviser to the UN Environment Programme. He also owns a rainforest restoration and eco-tourism project in Australia and an organic farm in south India.

The final reports, in five sections covering the economic methods and advice to policy makers, administrators, businesses and citizens, will make a series of recommendations for how to use economic values for different parts of nature, such as particular forests, wetlands, ocean habitats like coral reefs or individual species (one example given is paying farmers to tolerate geese wintering in Scotland), into ways to protect them.

One of the most immediate changes could be reform of direct and indirect subsidies, such as tax exemptions, which encourage over-production even when there is clear destruction of the long-term ability of the environment to provide what is needed, and below-cost pricing which leads to wasteful use and poor understanding of the value of the products. "Particularly worrying" are about $300bn of subsidies to agriculture and fishing; subsidies of $500bn for energy, $238–$306bn for transport and $67bn for water companies are also singled out.

Although the report is likely to argue some subsidies should be reformed rather than axed, an example of the huge potential impact was given by Sukhdev [during] a meeting in New York this week. [Sukhdev indicated] that to stop the global collapse of fish stocks, more than 20 million people employed in the industry may need to be taken out of service and retrained over the next 40 years.

Other suggested reforms include stricter limits on extraction and pollution; other environmental regulations such as restrictions on fishing net sizes or more damaging agricultural practices; higher penalties for breaking the limits, reform of taxes to encourage better practices; better public procurement; public funds for restoring damaged ecosystems such as reedbeds or heathlands; forcing companies that want to develop an area of land to restore or conserve another piece of land to "offset" the damage; and paying communities for the use of goods and services from nature—such as the proposed Redd international forestry protection scheme. Money raised by some policies could pay for others, says the report.

Sukhdev's team also wants companies and countries to adopt new accounting systems so alongside their financial accounts of income, spending, profits and capital, they also publish figures showing their combined impact on environmental or natural capital, and also social capital, such improvements in workers' skills or national education levels.

"We're in a society where more is better, where we tend to reward more production and more consumption . . . GDP tends to get associated with progress, and that's not necessarily the case."

Critical Thinking

1. Summarize briefly the current state of our biodiversity crisis.

2. What are some of the primary drivers responsible for biodiversity loss?

3. While this is only a summary report, are the changes and policies advocated regarding the "price of consuming the earth" aimed at the consumption behavior of individuals, or at the consumption of the environment by groups of humans?

4. With reference to question 3, what are the pros and cons of the two different approaches (individual consumption behaviors and consumption of the environment by human groups) to dealing with the biodiversity issue?

Unit 5

UNIT

Prepared by: Richard Eathorne, *Northern Michigan University*

Sustainability and Planetary Consumption: Can We Have Our Green Eggs and Ham, and Eat It Too?

Where there is great doubt, there will be great awakening; small doubt, small awakening; no doubt, no awakening.

Zen Master Dōgen, circa 1230 A.D.

How can we continue to consume the earth—which we must—without destroying it and ourselves in the process? Currently, the answer and guiding light to our species survival has been the mantra of *sustainability*. And, it would seem that all members of the human race would intuitively agree that it makes sense to work toward building a sustainable relationship with our planet. However, when we put the two words together—*sustainable consumption*—coming to a global consensus as to what that actually means, not to mention a consensus on how we implement it and encourage (enforce) it, humanities intuitive faculties get a little muddled.

To begin, some critics feel that the term "sustainability" has become so widely used that it may be in danger of becoming meaningless. Others criticize the term for being applied to all manner of nonsustainable consumption behaviors in the hopes of "greening" them. Can a "green" factory making "green" Barbie dolls really be referred to as sustainable? Is the continuing production and consumption of material artifacts of status and self-centered pleasure sustainable? Can the amount of truly unessential material stuff that we produce through the transformation of Earth's natural resources and purchase on Black Friday really be a sustainable way to measure the nation's economic health and wealth?

Still other critics say the definition of sustainability is so vague that it is open to any and all interpretations. *Sustainability: development that meets the needs of the present without compromising the ability of future generations to meet their own needs.* Words like development, meet, needs, compromise, ability, and future generations will mean different things to different income groups, religious groups, ethnic groups, agricultural or urban economies, geographical regions, and nations.

On the other hand, some commentators believe that examining our resource consumption behaviors rather than engaging in more discourse about sustainability will bear more fruit for understanding. They argue that we are steeped in excessive materialism and that this obsession is threatening the earth and global stability. Yet, others see new social technologies and environmental imperatives moving us to a new realm of consumerism. But one point is agreed upon and it is that the formulation and implementation of policies for the greening of lifestyles and consumption policies will not be an easy task. Ultimately, most critical observers engaged in trying to find a resolution to the consumption–sustainability conundrum believe that humanity's overconsumption of the earth's natural resources must be understood at the individual level and validated at the global level.

Certainly, changes in social technologies, cultural values, and worldviews can change our current destructive consumption patterns. The first steps to these changes, however, must begin in the affluent societies. Many environmental scientists believe that "cornucopian" ideas of sustainability are simply wrong and that we cannot go forward thinking our natural resources are inexhaustible. The wealthy in particular cannot continue to pursue the high levels of material consumption that characterizes the rich. Nor can they continue as a role model for developing nations and economies. Critics argue that the wealthy have a distorted kind of mysticism that believes we can consume the earth at our current rates and avoid the consequences of this appetite.

The good news, however, is that sustainable consumption issues are more prominent than ever on public and political agendas. New approaches are being put forward to help facilitate the task of formulating polices for the greening of lifestyles and consumptions patterns. Other approaches are examining closely the overconsumption issues at the individual consumer level and trying to identify what overconsumption is at many levels and offer approaches that can be used to reduce the problem.

Ultimately, we find that in the non-socioeconomic-geopolitical world of biology and ecology, the term sustainability is really more of a *result* of a functioning life system than a *way to achieve* a functioning life system. In other words, living systems (cells, organisms, Earth), have the ability to regulate internal conditions, usually by a system of feedback controls, so as to stabilize health and functioning, regardless of the outside changing conditions. This is known as *homeostasis.* Thus, it is through homeostasis that an organism *achieves life sustainability.*

Is it possible for the human race to behave as a unified organism and employ this biological principle of homeostasis as the *modus operandi* to maintain the constancy of our *external* environment and thus achieve our *sustainable relationship* with Earth?

The answer to this question will lay ultimately within the social, cultural, and economic profiles of our future human populations. The population growth and composition trends of the near future will have significant political and economic consequences for everyone and all nations. However, the impacts of these trends will vary between places and peoples and will result in variable environmental consequences. Policymakers will have to reconsider a world that has traditionally been viewed as a mutually exclusive three-world economies paradigm and look upon a new paradigm based on interconnections; a need for geopolitical symbiotic relationships.

Article

The New Population Bomb: The Four Megatrends That Will Change the World

Jack A. Goldstone

Forty-two years ago, the biologist Paul Ehrlich warned in The Population Bomb that mass starvation would strike in the 1970s and 1980s, with the world's population growth outpacing the production of food and other critical resources. Thanks to innovations and efforts such as the "green revolution" in farming and the widespread adoption of family planning, Ehrlich's worst fears did not come to pass. In fact, since the 1970s, global economic output has increased and fertility has fallen dramatically, especially in developing countries.

The United Nations Population Division now projects that global population growth will nearly halt by 2050. By that date, the world's population will have stabilized at 9.15 billion people, according to the "medium growth" variant of the UN's authoritative population database World Population Prospects: The 2008 Revision. (Today's global population is 6.83 billion.) Barring a cataclysmic climate crisis or a complete failure to recover from the current economic malaise, global economic output is expected to increase by two to three percent per year, meaning that global income will increase far more than population over the next four decades.

But twenty-first-century international security will depend less on how many people inhabit the world than on how the global population is composed and distributed: where populations are declining and where they are growing, which countries are relatively older and which are more youthful, and how demographics will influence population movements across regions.

These elements are not well recognized or widely understood. A recent article in *The Economist*, for example, cheered the decline in global fertility without noting other vital demographic developments. Indeed, the same UN data cited by *The Economist* reveal four historic shifts that will fundamentally alter the world's population over the next four decades: the relative demographic weight of the world's developed countries will drop by nearly 25 percent, shifting economic power to the developing nations; the developed countries' labor forces will substantially age and decline, constraining economic growth in the developed world and raising the demand for immigrant workers; most of the world's expected population growth will increasingly be concentrated in today's poorest, youngest, and most heavily Muslim countries, which have a dangerous lack of quality education, capital, and employment opportunities;

and, for the first time in history, most of the world's population will become urbanized, with the largest urban centers being in the world's poorest countries, where policing, sanitation, and health care are often scarce. Taken together, these trends will pose challenges every bit as alarming as those noted by Ehrlich. Coping with them will require nothing less than a major reconsideration of the world's basic global governance structures.

Europe's Reversal of Fortunes

At the beginning of the eighteenth century, approximately 20 percent of the world's inhabitants lived in Europe (including Russia). Then, with the Industrial Revolution, Europe's population boomed, and streams of European emigrants set off for the Americas. By the eve of World War I, Europe's population had more than quadrupled. In 1913, Europe had more people than China, and the proportion of the world's population living in Europe and the former European colonies of North America had risen to over 33 percent. But this trend reversed after World War I, as basic health care and sanitation began to spread to poorer countries. In Asia, Africa, and Latin America, people began to live longer, and birthrates remained high or fell only slowly. By 2003, the combined populations of Europe, the United States, and Canada accounted for just 17 percent of the global population. In 2050, this figure is expected to be just 12 percent—far less than it was in 1700. (These projections, moreover, might even understate the reality because they reflect the "medium growth" projection of the UN forecasts, which assumes that the fertility rates of developing countries will decline while those of developed countries will increase. In fact, many developed countries show no evidence of increasing fertility rates.) The West's relative decline is even more dramatic if one also considers changes in income. The Industrial Revolution made Europeans not only more numerous than they had been but also considerably richer per capita than others worldwide. According to the economic historian Angus Maddison, Europe, the United States, and Canada together produced about 32 percent of the world's GDP at the beginning of the nineteenth century. By 1950, that proportion had increased to a remarkable 68 percent of the world's total output (adjusted to reflect purchasing power parity).

This trend, too, is headed for a sharp reversal. The proportion of global GDP produced by Europe, the United States, and Canada fell from 68 percent in 1950 to 47 percent in 2003 and will decline even more steeply in the future. If the growth rate of per capita income (again, adjusted for purchasing power parity) between 2003 and 2050 remains as it was between 1973 and 2003—averaging 1.68 percent annually in Europe, the United States, and Canada and 2.47 percent annually in the rest of the world—then the combined GDP of Europe, the United States, and Canada will roughly double by 2050, whereas the GDP of the rest of the world will grow by a factor of five. The portion of global GDP produced by Europe, the United States, and Canada in 2050 will then be less than 30 percent—smaller than it was in 1820.

These figures also imply that an overwhelming proportion of the world's GDP growth between 2003 and 2050—nearly 80 percent—will occur outside of Europe, the United States, and Canada. By the middle of this century, the global middle class—those capable of purchasing durable consumer products, such as cars, appliances, and electronics—will increasingly be found in what is now considered the developing world. The World Bank has predicted that by 2030 the number of middle-class people in the developing world will be 1.2 billion—a rise of 200 percent since 2005. This means that the developing world's middle class alone will be larger than the total populations of Europe, Japan, and the United States combined. From now on, therefore, the main driver of global economic expansion will be the economic growth of newly industrialized countries, such as Brazil, China, India, Indonesia, Mexico, and Turkey.

Aging Pains

Part of the reason developed countries will be less economically dynamic in the coming decades is that their populations will become substantially older. The European countries, Canada, the United States, Japan, South Korea, and even China are aging at unprecedented rates. Today, the proportion of people aged 60 or older in China and South Korea is 12–15 percent. It is 15–22 percent in the European Union, Canada, and the United States and 30 percent in Japan. With baby boomers aging and life expectancy increasing, these numbers will increase dramatically. In 2050, approximately 30 percent of Americans, Canadians, Chinese, and Europeans will be over 60, as will more than 40 percent of Japanese and South Koreans.

Over the next decades, therefore, these countries will have increasingly large proportions of retirees and increasingly small proportions of workers. As workers born during the baby boom of 1945–65 are retiring, they are not being replaced by a new cohort of citizens of prime working age (15–59 years old).

Industrialized countries are experiencing a drop in their working-age populations that is even more severe than the overall slowdown in their population growth. South Korea represents the most extreme example. Even as its total population is projected to decline by almost 9 percent by 2050 (from 48.3 million to 44.1 million), the population of working-age South Koreans is expected to drop by 36 percent (from 32.9 million to 21.1 million), and the number of South Koreans aged 60 and older will increase by almost 150 percent (from 7.3 million to 18 million). By 2050, in other words, the entire working-age population will barely exceed the 60-and-older population. Although South Korea's case is extreme, it represents an increasingly common fate for developed countries. Europe is expected to lose 24 percent of its prime working-age population (about 120 million workers) by 2050, and its 60-and-older population is expected to increase by 47 percent. In the United States, where higher fertility and more immigration are expected than in Europe, the working-age population will grow by 15 percent over the next four decades—a steep decline from its growth of 62 percent between 1950 and 2010. And by 2050, the United States' 60-and-older population is expected to double.

All this will have a dramatic impact on economic growth, health care, and military strength in the developed world. The forces that fueled economic growth in industrialized countries during the second half of the twentieth century—increased productivity due to better education, the movement of women into the labor force, and innovations in technology—will all likely weaken in the coming decades. College enrollment boomed after World War II, a trend that is not likely to recur in the twenty-first century; the extensive movement of women into the labor force also was a one-time social change; and the technological change of the time resulted from innovators who created new products and leading-edge consumers who were willing to try them out—two groups that are thinning out as the industrialized world's population ages.

Overall economic growth will also be hampered by a decline in the number of new consumers and new households. When developed countries' labor forces were growing by 0.5–1.0 percent per year, as they did until 2005, even annual increases in real output per worker of just 1.7 percent meant that annual economic growth totaled 2.2–2.7 percent per year. But with the labor forces of many developed countries (such as Germany, Hungary, Japan, Russia, and the Baltic states) now shrinking by 0.2 percent per year and those of other countries (including Austria, the Czech Republic, Denmark, Greece, and Italy) growing by less than 0.2 percent per year, the same 1.7 percent increase in real output per worker yields only 1.5–1.9 percent annual overall growth. Moreover, developed countries will be lucky to keep productivity growth at even that level; in many developed countries, productivity is more likely to decline as the population ages.

A further strain on industrialized economies will be rising medical costs: as populations age, they will demand more health care for longer periods of time. Public pension schemes for aging populations are already being reformed in various industrialized countries—often prompting heated debate. In theory, at least, pensions might be kept solvent by increasing the retirement age, raising taxes modestly, and phasing out benefits for the wealthy. Regardless, the number of 80- and 90-year-olds—who are unlikely to work and highly likely to require nursing-home and other expensive care—will rise dramatically. And even if 60- and 70-year-olds remain active and employed, they will require procedures and medications—hip replacements, kidney transplants, blood-pressure treatments—to sustain their health in old age.

All this means that just as aging developed countries will have proportionally fewer workers, innovators, and consumerist young households, a large portion of those countries' remaining economic growth will have to be diverted to pay for the medical bills and pensions of their growing elderly populations. Basic services, meanwhile, will be increasingly costly because fewer young workers will be available for strenuous and labor-intensive jobs. Unfortunately, policymakers seldom reckon with these potentially disruptive effects of otherwise welcome developments, such as higher life expectancy.

Youth and Islam in the Developing World

Even as the industrialized countries of Europe, North America, and Northeast Asia will experience unprecedented aging this century, fast-growing countries in Africa, Latin America, the Middle East, and Southeast Asia will have exceptionally youthful populations. Today, roughly nine out of ten children under the age of 15 live in developing countries. And these are the countries that will continue to have the world's highest birthrates. Indeed, over 70 percent of the world's population growth between now and 2050 will occur in 24 countries, all of which are classified by the World Bank as low income or lower-middle income, with an average per capita income of under $3,855 in 2008.

Many developing countries have few ways of providing employment to their young, fast-growing populations. Would-be laborers, therefore, will be increasingly attracted to the labor markets of the aging developed countries of Europe, North America, and Northeast Asia. Youthful immigrants from nearby regions with high unemployment—Central America, North Africa, and Southeast Asia, for example—will be drawn to those vital entry-level and manual-labor jobs that sustain advanced economies: janitors, nursing-home aides, bus drivers, plumbers, security guards, farm workers, and the like. Current levels of immigration from developing to developed countries are paltry compared to those that the forces of supply and demand might soon create across the world.

These forces will act strongly on the Muslim world, where many economically weak countries will continue to experience dramatic population growth in the decades ahead. In 1950, Bangladesh, Egypt, Indonesia, Nigeria, Pakistan, and Turkey had a combined population of 242 million. By 2009, those six countries were the world's most populous Muslim-majority countries and had a combined population of 886 million. Their populations are continuing to grow and indeed are expected to increase by 475 million between now and 2050—during which time, by comparison, the six most populous developed countries are projected to gain only 44 million inhabitants. Worldwide, of the 48 fastest-growing countries today—those with annual population growth of two percent or more—28 are majority Muslim or have Muslim minorities of 33 percent or more.

It is therefore imperative to improve relations between Muslim and Western societies. This will be difficult given that many Muslims live in poor communities vulnerable to radical appeals and many see the West as antagonistic and militaristic.

In the 2009 Pew Global Attitudes Project survey, for example, whereas 69 percent of those Indonesians and Nigerians surveyed reported viewing the United States favorably, just 18 percent of those polled in Egypt, Jordan, Pakistan, and Turkey (all U.S. allies) did. And in 2006, when the Pew survey last asked detailed questions about Muslim-Western relations, more than half of the respondents in Muslim countries characterized those relations as bad and blamed the West for this state of affairs.

But improving relations is all the more important because of the growing demographic weight of poor Muslim countries and the attendant increase in Muslim immigration, especially to Europe from North Africa and the Middle East. (To be sure, forecasts that Muslims will soon dominate Europe are outlandish: Muslims compose just three to ten percent of the population in the major European countries today, and this proportion will at most double by midcentury.) Strategists worldwide must consider that the world's young are becoming concentrated in those countries least prepared to educate and employ them, including some Muslim states. Any resulting poverty, social tension, or ideological radicalization could have disruptive effects in many corners of the world. But this need not be the case; the healthy immigration of workers to the developed world and the movement of capital to the developing world, among other things, could lead to better results.

Urban Sprawl

Exacerbating twenty-first-century risks will be the fact that the world is urbanizing to an unprecedented degree. The year 2010 will likely be the first time in history that a majority of the world's people live in cities rather than in the countryside. Whereas less than 30 percent of the world's population was urban in 1950, according to UN projections, more than 70 percent will be by 2050.

Lower-income countries in Asia and Africa are urbanizing especially rapidly, as agriculture becomes less labor intensive and as employment opportunities shift to the industrial and service sectors. Already, most of the world's urban agglomerations—Mumbai (population 20.1 million), Mexico City (19.5 million), New Delhi (17 million), Shanghai (15.8 million), Calcutta (15.6 million), Karachi (13.1 million), Cairo (12.5 million), Manila (11.7 million), Lagos (10.6 million), Jakarta (9.7 million)—are found in low-income countries. Many of these countries have multiple cities with over one million residents each: Pakistan has eight, Mexico 12, and China more than 100. The UN projects that the urbanized proportion of sub-Saharan Africa will nearly double between 2005 and 2050, from 35 percent (300 million people) to over 67 percent (1 billion). China, which is roughly 40 percent urbanized today, is expected to be 73 percent urbanized by 2050; India, which is less than 30 percent urbanized today, is expected to be 55 percent urbanized by 2050. Overall, the world's urban population is expected to grow by 3 billion people by 2050.

This urbanization may prove destabilizing. Developing countries that urbanize in the twenty-first century will have far lower per capita incomes than did many industrial countries when they first urbanized. The United States, for example, did not reach 65 percent urbanization until 1950, when per capita income was nearly $13,000 (in 2005 dollars). By contrast, Nigeria, Pakistan, and the Philippines, which are approaching similar levels of urbanization, currently have per capita incomes of just $1,800–$4,000 (in 2005 dollars).

According to the research of Richard Cincotta and other political demographers, countries with younger populations are especially prone to civil unrest and are less able to create or sustain democratic institutions. And the more heavily urbanized, the more such countries are likely to experience Dickensian poverty and anarchic violence. In good times, a thriving economy might keep urban residents employed and governments flush with sufficient resources to meet their needs. More often, however, sprawling and impoverished cities are vulnerable to crime lords, gangs, and petty rebellions. Thus, the rapid urbanization of the developing world in the decades ahead might bring, in exaggerated form, problems similar to those that urbanization brought to nineteenth-century Europe. Back then, cyclical employment, inadequate policing, and limited sanitation and education often spawned widespread labor strife, periodic violence, and sometimes—as in the 1820s, the 1830s, and 1848—even revolutions.

International terrorism might also originate in fast-urbanizing developing countries (even more than it already does). With their neighborhood networks, access to the Internet and digital communications technology, and concentration of valuable targets, sprawling cities offer excellent opportunities for recruiting, maintaining, and hiding terrorist networks.

Defusing the Bomb

Averting this century's potential dangers will require sweeping measures. Three major global efforts defused the population bomb of Ehrlich's day: a commitment by governments and nongovernmental organizations to control reproduction rates; agricultural advances, such as the green revolution and the spread of new technology; and a vast increase in international trade, which globalized markets and thus allowed developing countries to export foodstuffs in exchange for seeds, fertilizers, and machinery, which in turn helped them boost production. But today's population bomb is the product less of absolute growth in the world's population than of changes in its age and distribution. Policymakers must therefore adapt today's global governance institutions to the new realities of the aging of the industrialized world, the concentration of the world's economic and population growth in developing countries, and the increase in international immigration.

During the Cold War, Western strategists divided the world into a "First World," of democratic industrialized countries; a "Second World," of communist industrialized countries; and a "Third World," of developing countries. These strategists focused chiefly on deterring or managing conflict between the First and the Second Worlds and on launching proxy wars and diplomatic initiatives to attract Third World countries into the First World's camp. Since the end of the Cold War, strategists have largely abandoned this three-group division and have tended to believe either that the United States, as the sole superpower, would maintain a Pax Americana or that the world would become multipolar, with the United States, Europe, and China playing major roles.

Unfortunately, because they ignore current global demographic trends, these views will be obsolete within a few decades. A better approach would be to consider a different three-world order, with a new First World of the aging industrialized nations of North America, Europe, and Asia's Pacific Rim (including Japan, Singapore, South Korea, and Taiwan, as well as China after 2030, by which point the one-child policy will have produced significant aging); a Second World comprising fast-growing and economically dynamic countries with a healthy mix of young and old inhabitants (such as Brazil, Iran, Mexico, Thailand, Turkey, and Vietnam, as well as China until 2030); and a Third World of fast-growing, very young, and increasingly urbanized countries with poorer economies and often weak governments. To cope with the instability that will likely arise from the new Third World's urbanization, economic strife, lawlessness, and potential terrorist activity, the aging industrialized nations of the new First World must build effective alliances with the growing powers of the new Second World and together reach out to Third World nations. Second World powers will be pivotal in the twenty-first century not just because they will drive economic growth and consume technologies and other products engineered in the First World; they will also be central to international security and cooperation. The realities of religion, culture, and geographic proximity mean that any peaceful and productive engagement by the First World of Third World countries will have to include the open cooperation of Second World countries.

Strategists, therefore, must fundamentally reconsider the structure of various current global institutions. The G-8, for example, will likely become obsolete as a body for making global economic policy. The G-20 is already becoming increasingly important, and this is less a short-term consequence of the ongoing global financial crisis than the beginning of the necessary recognition that Brazil, China, India, Indonesia, Mexico, Turkey, and others are becoming global economic powers. International institutions will not retain their legitimacy if they exclude the world's fastest-growing and most economically dynamic countries. It is essential, therefore, despite European concerns about the potential effects on immigration, to take steps such as admitting Turkey into the European Union. This would add youth and economic dynamism to the EU—and would prove that Muslims are welcome to join Europeans as equals in shaping a free and prosperous future. On the other hand, excluding Turkey from the EU could lead to hostility not only on the part of Turkish citizens, who are expected to number 100 million by 2050, but also on the part of Muslim populations worldwide.

NATO must also adapt. The alliance today is composed almost entirely of countries with aging, shrinking populations and relatively slow-growing economies. It is oriented toward the Northern Hemisphere and holds on to a Cold War structure that cannot adequately respond to contemporary threats. The young and increasingly populous countries of Africa, the Middle East, Central Asia, and South Asia could mobilize insurgents much more easily than NATO could mobilize the troops it would need if it were called on to stabilize those countries. Long-standing

NATO members should, therefore—although it would require atypical creativity and flexibility—consider the logistical and demographic advantages of inviting into the alliance countries such as Brazil and Morocco, rather than countries such as Albania. That this seems far-fetched does not minimize the imperative that First World countries begin including large and strategic Second and Third World powers in formal international alliances.

The case of Afghanistan—a country whose population is growing fast and where NATO is currently engaged—illustrates the importance of building effective global institutions. Today, there are 28 million Afghans; by 2025, there will be 45 million; and by 2050, there will be close to 75 million. As nearly 20 million additional Afghans are born over the next 15 years, NATO will have an opportunity to help Afghanistan become reasonably stable, self-governing, and prosperous. If NATO's efforts fail and the Afghans judge that NATO intervention harmed their interests, tens of millions of young Afghans will become more hostile to the West. But if they come to think that NATO's involvement benefited their society, the West will have tens of millions of new friends. The example might then motivate the approximately one billion other young Muslims growing up in low-income countries over the next four decades to look more kindly on relations between their countries and the countries of the industrialized West.

Creative Reforms at Home

The aging industrialized countries can also take various steps at home to promote stability in light of the coming demographic trends. First, they should encourage families to have more children. France and Sweden have had success providing child care, generous leave time, and financial allowances to families with young children. Yet there is no consensus among policymakers—and certainly not among demographers—about what policies best encourage fertility.

More important than unproven tactics for increasing family size is immigration. Correctly managed, population movement can benefit developed and developing countries alike. Given the dangers of young, underemployed, and unstable populations in developing countries, immigration to developed countries can provide economic opportunities for the ambitious and serve as a safety valve for all. Countries that embrace immigrants, such as the United States, gain economically by having willing laborers and greater entrepreneurial spirit. And countries with high levels of emigration (but not so much that they experience so-called brain drains) also benefit because emigrants often send remittances home or return to their native countries with valuable education and work experience.

One somewhat daring approach to immigration would be to encourage a reverse flow of older immigrants from developed to developing countries. If older residents of developed countries took their retirements along the southern coast of the Mediterranean or in Latin America or Africa, it would greatly reduce the strain on their home countries' public entitlement systems. The developing countries involved, meanwhile, would benefit because caring for the elderly and providing retirement and leisure services is highly labor intensive. Relocating a portion of these activities to developing countries would provide employment and valuable training to the young, growing populations of the Second and Third Worlds.

This would require developing residential and medical facilities of First World quality in Second and Third World countries. Yet even this difficult task would be preferable to the status quo, by which low wages and poor facilities lead to a steady drain of medical and nursing talent from developing to developed countries. Many residents of developed countries who desire cheaper medical procedures already practice medical tourism today, with India, Singapore, and Thailand being the most common destinations. (For example, the international consulting firm Deloitte estimated that 750,000 Americans traveled abroad for care in 2008.)

Never since 1800 has a majority of the world's economic growth occurred outside of Europe, the United States, and Canada. Never have so many people in those regions been over 60 years old. And never have low-income countries' populations been so young and so urbanized. But such will be the world's demography in the twenty-first century. The strategic and economic policies of the twentieth century are obsolete, and it is time to find new ones.

Reference

Goldstone, Jack A. "The new population bomb: the four megatrends that will change the world." *Foreign Affairs* 89.1 (2010): 31. *General OneFile*. Web. 23 Jan. 2010. http://0-find.galegroup.com.www .consuls.org/gps/start.do?proId=IPS& userGroupName=a30wc.

Critical Thinking

1. What does the author contend will be the characteristics of future population growth?
2. The article argues that future population trends will have significant political and economic consequences. What do you see as the "environmental consequences"?
3. How might these environmental consequences vary for different populations around the world?
4. What impacts might these trends have on achieving the ideals of sustainability?

Article

Theses on Sustainability

A Primer

ERIC ZENCEY

[1]

THE TERM HAS BECOME so widely used that it is in danger of meaning nothing. It has been applied to all manner of activities in an effort to give those activities the gloss of moral imperative, the cachet of environmental enlightenment. "Sustainable" has been used variously to mean "politically feasible," "economically feasible," "not part of a pyramid or bubble," "socially enlightened," "consistent with neoconservative small-government dogma," "consistent with liberal principles of justice and fairness," "morally desirable," and, at its most diffuse, "sensibly far-sighted."

[2]

NATURE WILL DECIDE what is sustainable; it always has and always will. The reflexive invocation of the term as cover for all manner of human acts and wants shows that sustainability has gained wide acceptance as a longed-for, if imperfectly understood, state of being.

[3]

AN ACT, PROCESS, OR STATE of affairs can be said to be economically sustainable, ecologically sustainable, or socially sustainable. To these three some would add a fourth: culturally sustainable.

[4]

NATURE IS MALLEABLE and has enormous resilience, a resilience that gives healthy ecosystems a dynamic equilibrium. But the resiliency of nature has limits and to transgress them is to act unsustainably. Thus, the most diffuse usage, "sensibly far-sighted," is the usage that contains and properly reflects the strict ecological definition of the term: a thing is ecologically sustainable if it doesn't destroy the environmental preconditions for its own existence.

[5]

ECONOMIC SUSTAINABILITY describes the point at which a less-developed economy no longer needs infusions of capital or aid in order to generate wealth. This definition is misleading: for many of those who use it (including traditional economists and many economic aid agencies), "economic sustainability" means "sustainable within the general industrial program of using fossil fuels to generate wealth and produce economic growth," a program that is, of course, not sustainable.

[6]

SOCIAL SUSTAINABILITY describes a state in which a society does not contain any dynamics or forces that would pull it apart. Such a society has sufficient cohesion to overcome the animosities that arise from (for instance) differences of race, gender, wealth, ethnicity, political or religious belief; or from differential access to such boons as education, opportunity, or the nonpartisan administration of justice. Social sustainability can be achieved by strengthening social cohesion (war is a favorite device), through indoctrination in an ideology that bridges the disparities that strain that cohesion, or through diminishing the disparities themselves. (Or all three.)

[7]

CULTURAL SUSTAINABILITY asks that we preserve the opportunity for nonmarket or other nonindustrial cultures to maintain themselves and to pass their culture undiminished to their offspring.

[8]

HUMAN CIVILIZATION has been built on the exploitation of the stored solar energy found in four distinct carbon pools: soil, wood, coal, petroleum. The latter two pools represent antique, stored solar energy, and their stock is finite. Since agriculture and forestry exploit current solar income, civilizations built on the first two pools—soil and wood—had the opportunity to be sustainable. Many were not.

[9]

THE 1987 UN BRUNDTLAND REPORT offered one widely accepted definition of what sustainability means: "meet[ing] the needs of the present without compromising the ability of future generations to meet their own needs." This definition contains within it two key concepts. One is the presumption of a distinction between needs and wants, a distinction that comes into sharp relief when we compare the consumption patterns of people in rich and in poor nations: rich nations satisfy many of their members' wants—indeed, billions of dollars are spent to stimulate those wants—even as poor nations struggle to satisfy human needs. Two: we face what Brundtland called "limitations imposed by the state of technology and social organization on the environment's ability to meet present and future needs."

[10]

THAT A DISTINCTION can usefully be drawn between wants and needs seems obvious. Mainstream economics, however, refuses to countenance such a distinction. (Marxist economics does, which, from the viewpoint of an ecologically enlightened economics, is one of the few ways in which it is distinguishable from its neoclassical alternative.) The work of Wilfred Pareto was crucial to this refusal. His contribution to economic theory marks a turning point in the evolution (some would say devolution) of nineteenth-century political economy into the highly mathematized discipline of economics as we know it today. Pareto's novel idea: because satisfactions and pleasures are subjective—because no one among us can say with certainty, "I like ice cream more than you do"—there is no rational way to compare the degree of pleasure that different people will gain by satisfying desires. All we can do is assert that if an economic arrangement satisfies *more* human wants, it is objectively better than an arrangement that satisfies *fewer* human wants. This seems commonsensical until we unpack that caveat "all we can do." An economic arrangement achieves Pareto Optimality if, within it, no one can be made better off (in his own estimation) without making someone else worse off (in her own estimation). Economic science, in its desire to be grounded on rational, objective principles, thus concludes that were we to take a dollar from a billionaire and give it to a starving man to buy food, we can't know for certain that we have improved the sum total of human satisfaction in the world. For all we know, the billionaire might derive as much pleasure from the expenditure of his billionth dollar as would a starving man spending a dollar on food. All we can do—all!—is promote the growth of income; and if we care about that starving man, we must work to produce two dollars' worth of goods where before there was only one, so that both the billionaire and the starving man can satisfy their wants.

[11]

THUS WAS neoclassical economic theory, putatively value-free and scientific, made structurally dependent on a commitment to infinite economic growth, a value-laden, unscientific, demonstrably unsustainable commitment if ever there was one.

[12]

THE BRUNDTLAND assertion that we face "limitations imposed by the state of technology and social organization on the environment's ability to meet present and future needs" can be read as both acknowledging ecological limits to human activity and as sidestepping the major issue that those ecological limits have brought to the fore. Can humans, through technological development, solve any problem brought on by resource scarcity and the limited capacity of ecosystems to absorb our acts and works? When all is said and done, can we enlarge the economy's ecological footprint forever in order to create wealth? Gradually, we are coming to recognize that the answer is no.

[13]

AN ECONOMY CAN BE MODELED as an open thermodynamic system, one that exchanges matter and energy across its border (that mostly conceptual, sometimes physical line that separates culture from its home in nature). An economy sucks up valuable low-entropy matter and energy from its environment, uses these to produce products and services, and emits degraded matter and energy back into the environment in the form of a high-entropy wake. (Waste heat. Waste matter. Dissipated and degraded matter: yesterday's newspaper, last year's running shoes, last decade's dilapidated automobile.) An economy has ecological impact on both the uptake and emission side. The laws of thermodynamics dictate that this be so. "You can't make something from nothing; nor can you make nothing from something," the law of conservation of matter and energy tells us. With enough energy we could recycle all the matter that enters our economy—even the molecules that wear off the coins in your pocket. But energy is scarce: "You can't recycle energy," says the law of entropy. Or, in a colloquial analogy: Accounts must balance and bills must be paid. To operate our economic machine we pay an energy bill; we must ever take in energy anew.

[14]

ESTABLISHING an ecologically sustainable economy requires that humans accept a limit on the amount of scarce low entropy that we take up from the planet (which will also, necessarily, limit the amount of degraded matter and energy that we emit). An effective approach would be to use market mechanisms, such as would occur if we had an economy-wide tax on low-entropy uptake (the extraction of coal and oil, the cutting of lumber). The tax rate could be set to ensure that use doesn't exceed a limit—the CO_2 absorption capacity of the planet, the regenerative ability of forests. Producers and consumers would have freedom under the cap brought about by the tax. With such a tax, the tax on workers' income could be abandoned. (As the slogan says, we should "tax bads, not goods." Work is good. Uptake of scarce resources is bad.)

[15]

FOR DECADES environmentalism has been primarily a moral vision, with principles susceptible to being reduced to fundamentalist absolutes. Pollution is wrong; it is profanation. *We have no right,* environmentalism has said, to cause species extinction, to destroy habitat, to expand the dominion of culture across the face of nature. True enough, and so granted. But even Dick Cheney agreed that environmentalism is essentially, merely, a moral vision. ("Conservation," he said, on his way to giving oil companies everything they wanted, "may be a personal virtue, but it is not a sufficient basis for a sound, comprehensive energy policy.") The time has long since passed for the achievement of sustainability to be left to simple moral admonition, to finger-wagging in its various forms. It's time to use the power of the market—the power of self-interest, regulated and channeled by wise policy—to do good. Environmentalism must become an economic vision.

[16]

ACCEPTING A LIMIT on the economy's uptake of matter and energy from the planet does not mean that we have to accept that history is over, that civilization will stagnate, or that we cannot make continual improvements to the human condition. A no-growth economy is not a no-development economy; there would still be invention, innovation, even fads and fashions. An economy operating within ecological limits will be in dynamic equilibrium (like nature, its model): just as ecosystems evolve, so would the economy. Quality of life (as it is measured by the Index of Sustainable Economic Welfare, an ecologically minded replacement for GDP) would still improve. If a sustainable economy dedicated to development rather than growth were achieved through market mechanisms, consumers would still reign supreme over economic decision making, free to pursue satisfactions—and fads and fashions—as they choose.

[17]

OUR CHALLENGE is to create something unprecedented in human history: an ecologically sustainable civilization that offers a high standard of living widely shared among its citizens, a civilization that does not maintain itself through more-or-less hidden subsidies from antique solar income, or from the unsustainable exploitation of ecosystems and peoples held in slavery or penury, domestically or in remote regions of the globe. The world has never known such a civilization. Most hunting-and-gathering tribes achieved a sustainable balance with their environments, living off current solar income in many of its forms rather than on the draw-down of irreplaceable stocks, but we can't say that any of them achieved a high standard of material well-being. Medieval western Europe lived in balance with its soil community, achieving a form of sustainable agriculture that lasted until the invention of coal- and steam-propelled agriculture a few centuries ago, but few of us would trade the comforts and freedoms we enjoy today for life as a serf on a baronial estate, or even for the pre-electricity, pre-petroleum life of a mid-nineteenth-century farmer.

[18]

NO, THERE IS NO PRECEDENT for what we are struggling to create. We have to make it up ourselves.

Critical Thinking

1. What other issues regarding sustainability can you extrapolate from Thesis 9 that we will have to address in the near future?

2. Why might the idea of "sustainable economy" (Thesis 5) be misleading?

3. Make a list of what you think are "wants" and "needs" (10 each). After that, imagine you make less than $2 a day and live in sub-Saharan Africa. Compare and contrast the lists.

4. What does the author mean that "a no-growth economy is not a no-development economy"?

5. Describe how you incorporate the biology principle of "homeostasis" into the socioeconomic idea of sustainability.

Article

Collaborative Consumption: Shifting the Consumer Mindset

Collaborative consumption is organized sharing, bartering, lending, trading, renting, gifting and swapping through online and real-world communities. "What's Mine Is Yours: The Rise of Collaborative Consumption" explores this invigorating shift from an unfettered zeal for individual getting and spending toward a rediscovery of collective good.

RACHEL BOTSMAN AND ROO ROGERS

There is something sad about all this stuff we work so hard to buy, can't live with, but inevitably can't bear to part with. In the same way that we focus on where to bury our waste, not where the waste came from, we also spend inordinate amounts of energy and money storing excess stuff rather than asking the hard truths of why we have so much in the first place. The comedian George Carlin riffed on this in his classic stand-up routine about stuff: "The whole meaning of life has become trying to find a place to put your stuff. . . . Have you ever noticed how other people's shit is shit and your stuff is stuff?" The controversial David Fincher movie *Fight Club* struck a painful chord with viewers who have ever experienced that addictive feeling of always wanting more, regardless of how much they have. Most people remember two lines from the movies: "The first rule of Fight Club—you do not talk about Fight Club" and "The things you own end up owning you."

Tyler and Jack, the two main characters in the movie, seem to represent the stark choice that modern consumerism offers, best summarized by esteemed German social psychologist Erich Fromm as "To Have or to Be." Jack (Ed Norton), is a stereotypical 30-year-old insomniac yuppie who keeps trying to fill his emotional voids and feel "complete" with the things he acquires. "I flip through catalogues and wonder what kind of dining set defines me as a person." But no matter what Jack buys, he's never satisfied. That's before he meets Tyler (Brad Pitt), who, throughout the movie, takes anticonsumerist jabs such as, "You are not the clothes you wear. You are not the contents of your wallet. . . . You are not your grande latte. You are not the car you drive. You are not your fucking khakis. You're the all-singing, all-dancing crap of the world." Tyler shows Jack that acquiring more and more stuff is a meaningless pursuit devoid of purpose and fulfillment. "Goddamn it. . . . Advertising has us chasing cars and clothes, working jobs we hate so we can buy shit we don't need." The main theme of *Fight Club* runs counter to much of what consumer advertising preys on—we won't find happiness or the meaning of our lives in the shopping mall or in the click of a mouse.

Research has proved that people who can afford to buy and hold on to more material goods are not necessarily more satisfied with their lives. Indeed, the reverse is often true. Economist Richard Layard has researched the relationship between growth, hyper-consumerism and happiness. His findings are illustrated by a graph on which one line represents a soaring increase of income and personal consumption per capita since 1950 (it has more than doubled) and the other line, marking Americans and Britons that describe themselves as "very happy" in an annual Gallup survey, remains flat. In fact, the number of people reporting to be "very happy" peaked in 1957 just as the conspicuous cycle of "work and spend," and a revolution of rising materialistic expectations, began. Happiness became an elusive moving target. Nothing was ever enough.

Telling societal indicators paint a vivid picture of this decrease in well-being. Since 1960 the divorce rate has doubled in the United States; teen suicide rates have tripled; violent crime has quadrupled; the prison population has quintupled; and the percentage of babies born to unmarried parents has sextupled. Not exactly indicators of a satisfied consumer society. And it is only getting worse, as indicated by the massive increase in depression, anxiety, insomnia, heart disease, and obesity since the 1980s. As political scientist Robert Lane comments in *The Loss of Happiness in Market Democracies*, "The appetite of our present materialism depends upon stirring up our wants—but not satisfying them." Economists describe this emotional phenomenon as the "hedonic treadmill." We work hard to acquire more stuff but feel unfulfilled because there is always something better, bigger, and faster than in the present. The distance between what we have and what we want, the "margins of discontent," widens as the number of things we own increases. In other words, the more we have, the more we want.

We are taught to dream and desire new things from an early age, when asked frequently "What do you want for Christmas?" or "What do you want for your birthday?" Susan Fournier and Michael Guiry, former associate marketing professors at Harvard Business School, conducted a study called Consumption Dreaming Activity. They asked participants, "What things would you like to own or do someday?" Contrary to the researchers' expectations, the lists varied little regardless of sex, income, education or standard or living. Generally speaking, lists were full of desires for material possessions; almost half the sample (44 percent) mentioned new cars; more than one in four (29 percent) listed luxury items such as yachts, antiques, jewelry, and designer clothes; and 16 percent just asked for the money—enough to buy anything they could possibly want. Where the study gets most interesting is not just the type of items respondents wrote down but the level of detail and elaboration they included; 42 percent of all things listed were described vividly. One participant wrote down not just wanting a car but "an emerald green Jaguar."

As the professors noted, "This level of detail and elaboration could reflect that consumers have 'perfect things' in mind when they formulate wish lists." Here we see the amount of time and headspace most of us give to future purchases. Not only do the things we own fill up our closets and our lives, but they also fill our minds.

Changing the Consumer Mindset

The ideological debate between those who believe in self-interest as the purest way to maximize production and those who believe that it operates as an affront to the collective good and equality has dominated our political, economic and philosophical discourse for centuries. But while we've debated, the world has continued undistracted down a path of self-destructive growth. It is through the fog of anxiety that Collaborative Consumption has emerged with a simple consumer proposition. It meets all the same consumer needs as the old model of mass consumption but helps address some of our most worrying economic and environmental issues. While it is complex to audit and project the entire environmental impact of Collaborative Consumption, it reduces the number of new products and raw materials consumed and it creates a different consumer mindset.

When Jonathon Porritt was chairman of the Ecology Party in the U.K. from 1978 to 1984, he and his colleagues struggled with what became known as the Great Washing Machine Debate. Porritt, a leading environmental-thought leader in the U.K., serves as an adviser to many entities, from Marks & Spencer to Prince Charles to the sustainability think tank Forum for the Future. In the 1980s, when he was still active in the Ecology Party, which would later be renamed the Green Party, he was faced with the problem of what to do with the deterioration of one of the first mainstream product service systems: the laundromat. At the time, masses of people were going to shopping centers to purchase personal home washing machines, either for the first time, for upgrade or for replacement, resulting in what Porritt calls a "staggering increase in the number of personally owned machines." Between 1964 and 1992, the percentage of homes in the U.K. alone with washing machines rose from 53 percent to 88 percent. At the same time, 50 percent of all launderettes closed. Given that the average home washing machine was only used four to five times a week and consumed more than 21.7 percent of our personal water usage, and that each year around 2 million used washing machines were being discarded, Porritt and his colleagues were concerned. The move away from collective services and toward a self-service society had serious environmental implications.

The Ecology Party considered two choices: Lobby for some form of governmental taxation and incentives, or undertake a strong messaging program to change the consumer mindset back toward using laundromats. Neither option was attractive. Government was slow and infatuated with economic growth over sustainable causes. And a strong messaging campaign would only alienate the consumer. "By being over-prescriptive you become your own worst enemy and force people into even more defensive and negative behavior," Porritt said.

The Great Washing Machine Debate was just one example of a larger struggle taking place in the environmental movement. How do you address the public and inspire sustainable behavior without being negative or dogmatic? According to Porritt, this issue is still huge in the environmental movement today, which recognizes the inefficacy of trying to guilt people into a more sustainable choice but nonetheless struggles to find an alternative.

Fast-forward 20 years, and there is a different answer to the Great Washing Machine Debate and the conflict between enticing self-interest and ensuring social good. It exists at 122 Folsom St. in San Francisco. Brainwash is a laundromat founded in 1999 by Jeffrey Zalles. Zalles admits that his primary concern isn't being green. What he's done is figured out how to make Laundromats cool again. Brainwash woos customers with additional offerings of a café, happy hours, live music, stand-up comedy nights, pinball machines, free Wi-Fi, and even a place to do your homework. The space is bright and modern, with indoor and outdoor seating, cool music playing, funky artwork on the walls and helpful, friendly staff—a little different from the dark and dingy experience associated with most laundromats.

A big part of Brainwash's success is based on a simple insight: Customers need something to do while waiting for their laundry to finish, and it needs to be better than what they would do at home. That's why the sense of community that Zalles has built through cultural events and Meetups is so smart and critical. "Everyone who comes here could afford to get their own home washing machine . . . but where is the fun in that!" says Zalles. Indeed, the demand for Brainwash is so overwhelming that he is looking to open more franchises this year.

The idea behind Brainwash is simple, but the behavioral impact is significant. And by doing so it achieves seemingly opposing outcomes: clean clothes, fun, friends, affordability and environmental responsibility. Instead of forcing consumers to sacrifice personal convenience and comfort for doing the right thing, Jeff makes the right thing more attractive. By diversifying the motivations and putting the emphasis on consumer experience over a prescriptive sense of obligation, Brainwash achieves Porritt's goal with barely a whimper of activist politics. Brainwash hardly identifies itself with its purpose. Does it exist to provide a cheap alternative to get your clothes washed? Is it a cool café and culture club where you can hobnob and hang out? Or is a powerful green statement? The answer, of course, is all of the above.

The key difference in Brainwash's approach to the Great Washing Machine Debate is that instead of trying to change consumers, the system itself has changed to accommodate needs and wants in a more sustainable and appealing way, with little burden on the individual. In this respect, Collaborative Consumption actually enables an entitled, self-interested consumer who is so well-served he doesn't even realize he is doing something different or "good." By taking an indirect, open-ended approach, Collaborative Consumption enables consumers to break down the stereotypes of collectivism or environmentalism and simply do what works the best for them. It is so intuitive to our basic needs that consumers often fall into it by accident. One could argue that it doesn't matter whether the system leads to a change in mindset as long as it converts our consumption into positive outcomes: fewer products, more efficient usage, less material consumed, reduced waste and more social capital.

We've seen certain consistent and specific motivations for participating in Collaborative Consumption: cost savings, coming together, convenience, and being more socially conscious and sustainable. The fact that it attracts new consumers based on traditional self-interested motivation, including money, value and time, and that it converts this into positive social and environmental outcomes, should not distract from its overall impact on consumer behavior.

When someone enters Collaborative Consumption through one particular door—a clothing exchange, a car-sharing scheme or a [laundromat]—they become more receptive to other kinds of collective or community-based solutions. Over time, these experiences create a deep shift in consumer mindset. Consumption is no longer an asymmetrical activity of endless acquisition but a dynamic push and pull of giving and collaborating in order to get what you want. Along the way, the acts of collaboration and giving become an end in itself. Collaborative Consumption shows consumers that their material wants and needs do not need to be in conflict with the responsibilities of a connected citizen. The idea of happiness being epitomized by the lone shopper surrounded by stuff becomes absurd, and happiness becomes a much broader, more iterative process.

Critical Thinking

1. What is "collaborative consumption"?
2. How is/isn't the idea compatible with the ideas of sustainability?
3. Do you think the idea of collaborative consumption would work better in "developing countries" with a growing middle class than nations with small, powerful, wealthy elites?

Article

Consuming Passions

Everything That Can Be Done to Bring the Age of Heroic Consumption to Its Close Should Be Done

JEREMY SEABROOK

The age of heroic consumption is surely drawing to a close. The inspiration of those whose principal virtue is the money that permits them to lay claim to a disproportionate share of the earth's resources is being by-passed in a world where a population of 9 billion must be accommodated by 2050.

The price tag on the possessions of the wealthy—their £10m mansions, £5m yachts, extravagant couture and priceless jewels, their private jets and lives apart from the great majority of humankind—are rapidly losing their power to enchant the rest of us. In an age when scientists, humanitarians and moral leaders are exhorting human beings to look to our impact upon the earth—and not solely in relation to the carbon footprint—it has become obsolete to gaze with breathless admiration upon individuals dedicated to the proposition that a whole world should be dying of consumption, and not just the 1.6m who perish from tuberculosis each year.

The greatest threat to global stability comes not from the poor but from the rich. This startling proposition runs directly into another received idea, which is that the risk of disorder is a result of excessive materialism. What we suffer from is not a surfeit of materialism, but a deficiency of it; for if we truly valued the material basis upon which all human systems depend, we would exhibit a far greater reverence for the physical world we inhabit. If materialism means respect for the elements that sustain life, then we are gravely wanting in it. What is sometimes referred to as "materialism" is actually something else: perhaps a distorted kind of mysticism which believes we can use up the earth and still avoid the consequences of our omnivorous appetites.

This is why the gross consumers of the age will be scorned as the pitiable destroyers of the sustenance, not only of the poor of today, but of everyone's tomorrow. It is natural for people to want to do the best for their children, but this is generally interpreted as leaving them a private monetary inheritance; but if the other side of this legacy is a befouled world, the enjoyment of today's privilege may become the curse of the future. In any case, there is a great deal of humbug in pious concern expressed for our children's children, since this rarely prevents those who give voice to such tender sentiments from living as though there were no tomorrow. "Live the dream" has become the cliche of the hour; although it requires no great wisdom to understand that dreams realised soon turn to ashes.

Everything that can be done to bring the age of heroic consumption to its close should be done. This means the promotion of a different understanding of wealth. The myriad aspects of a truly rich and fulfilled life should be rescued from the tyranny of money. Perhaps we have not entirely forgotten that the most joyful and exhilarating of human occupations derive from self-reliance, self-provisioning, not only in the basic goods that sustain life, but also in satisfactions that arise from the cost-free resourcefulness of ourselves and others.

This is why the A-listers, the celebs, the fat cats, the big spenders, the conspicuous consumers do not represent a "lifestyle" to be emulated at all costs, but serve as warning of the spectre of depletion and exhaustion awaiting us within a short space of time. When Thorstein Veblen wrote his Theory of the Leisure Class at the end of the 19th century, he saw "conspicuous waste and show" as a replacement for "earlier and more primitive displays of physical prowess". Even his caustic insights could not anticipate the degree to which the ornamental inutility of the very rich would lead them to become pioneers of planetary demolition.

Of course, downgrading the exploits of the major culprits in ransacking the earth is easier said than done. Cultures are not, as journalists and politicians sometimes suggest, to be discarded or "changed" at will. But sooner or later, a reduction in the abuse of the elements of life will be forced upon the world. If it proves impossible to take preventive action in this regard, we shall soon enough be overtaken by events—oil wars, water wars, even more brutal conflicts over land than we have already seen, food wars, social disruption, rioting and breakdown, such as the World Bank has already detected in some 37 countries in the last two years, will be the form in which the relentless plunder of the planet will resolve itself.

Just as the age of heroic labour—the Stakhanovite idea of selfless dedication to the building of Communism—perished, so heroic consumption—that equally selfless dedication to sustaining capitalism—has also had its day. Stakhanovites were so called after a coal miner in the Soviet Union in 1935 who exceeded his work quota by 14 times the fixed level, producing 102 tons of coal in six hours. This became a kind of "spontaneous" official policy in the construction of socialism.

How laughably old-fashioned this now sounds. And how swiftly things that appear immutable can change. It should be our ambition to ensure that the work of predatory individuals upon the fruits of the earth comes to appear as archaic and futile as the sacrifice of human energies in the Soviet Union to release the resources which, according to Marx, "slumbered in the lap of social labour".

Heroic consumption, unlike heroic labour, requires no official sponsorship. The incentive to get rich is so deeply embedded in capitalism, that it has been seen as an expression of human nature itself. The first task in achieving a decent security for all people on earth is to affirm the distinction between human nature and the nature of capitalism.

Human beings want, above all, to survive. The moral and social elevation of the wealthy and their profligacy suggests that they are prepared to sacrifice even this hitherto imperishable goal for the sake of transforming the beauty and value of the world into a wasteland. Enslavement to a reductive, diminished version of what it means to lead a rich life is still bondage; and when it must be protected by razor wire, guns, security guards and impregnable barriers, these become the very symbols of that unfreedom.

Critical Thinking

1. "What we suffer from is not a surfeit of materialism, but a deficiency of it." Explain what that statement means and how it supports the ideals of sustainability.

2. "Everything that can be done to bring the age of heroic consumption to its close should be done." Please explain what that means. If you were a multimillionaire, what would you think about that statement?

3. What arguments would the wealthiest people of the world's wealthiest nations and the cornucopians say about the validity of the statement in Question 2?

HBR.ORG

Harvard Business Review

APRIL 2012
REPRINT R1204B

THE BIG IDEA

Saving The Planet: A Tale of Two Strategies

Thomas Malthus advised restraint; Robert Solow promotes innovation. Let's pursue both to solve the environmental crisis. *by Roger Martin and Alison Kemper*

The Big Idea

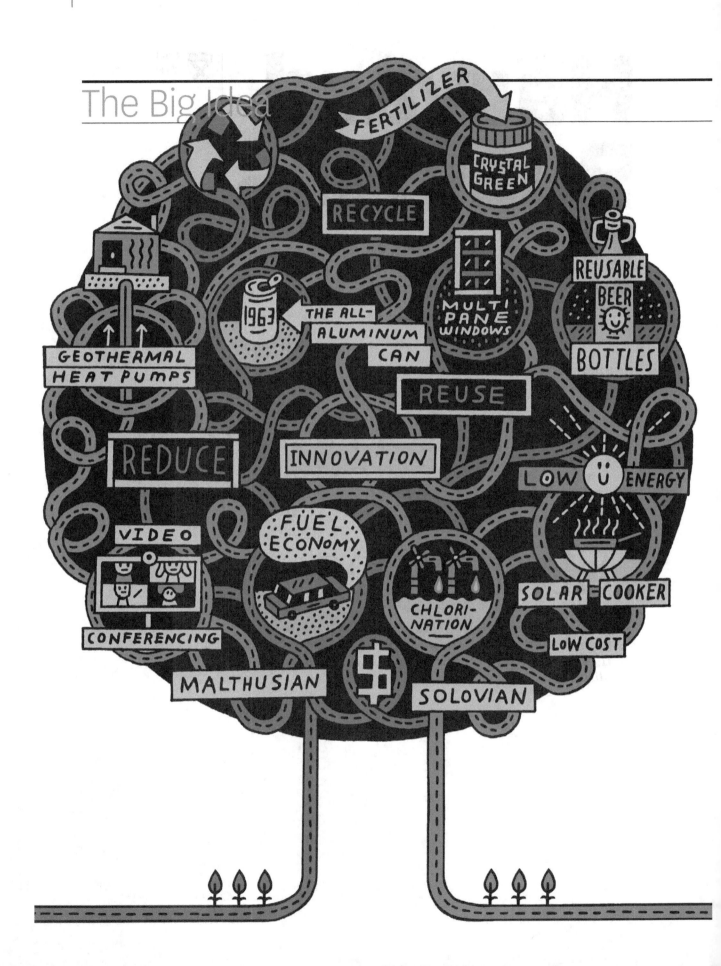

FOR ARTICLE REPRINTS CALL 800-988-0886 OR 617-783-7500, OR VISIT **HBR.ORG**

Saving The Planet: A Tale Of Two Strategies

Thomas Malthus advised restraint; Robert Solow promotes innovation. Let's pursue both to solve the environmental crisis.
by Roger Martin and Alison Kemper

ILLUSTRATION: SERGE SEIDLITZ

Businesses clearly have a major role to play in any strategy for saving the planet. They are the engines of the developed economies that devour a disproportionate share of the world's nonrenewable resources and produce a disproportionate share of its emissions. They also generate innovations that reduce resource use and lessen pollution. As both a cause of and a solution to environmental degradation, they are inevitably at the center of sustainability debates.

But how, exactly, can businesses contribute? According to one line of reasoning, rescuing the environment involves restraint and responsibility: Consumers and companies must do more with the resources they consume, recycle and process their waste more efficiently, and curb their appetite for consumption. In short, resources are finite and need to be carefully husbanded—an argument that appeals directly to the traditional virtue of moderation. This worldview achieved perhaps its clearest expression in the works of the 19th-century economist Thomas Malthus, who feared that at prevailing population growth rates the planet would eventually be unable to feed itself.

Although the Malthusian view exercises a powerful influence on voters and politicians alike, it is by no means uncontested. Another line of reasoning, which flows from the work of the 20th-century economist and Nobel Prize winner Robert Solow, is that environmental and other problems can always be resolved through the exercise of human ingenuity. This view appeals to our natural optimism and underlies much advocacy for deregulation and the promotion of growth.

It's not hard to see why these two philosophies make uneasy bedfellows. Yet if we are to achieve real progress in solving the world's environmental problems, we will have to apply both of them.

THOMAS MALTHUS (1766-1834)
Anglican clergyman, political economist

One of the most influential thinkers of all time, Malthus was concerned with the relationship between human population and scarcity. Because he sought to constrain the former and reduce the latter, he was active in public policy in early 19th-century Britain, supporting high tariffs on grain and opposing the Poor Laws, which he felt increased population pressures. He had a profound influence on such luminaries as Charles Darwin, John Maynard Keynes, and Mao Zedong.

> "Population, when unchecked, increases in a geometrical ratio. Subsistence increases only in an arithmetical ratio."
>
> —*Thomas Malthus*

The World According to Malthus

In the original Malthusian argument, if the world's population grows faster than the planet's ability to produce food and other necessities, the cost of those necessities will rise while wages fall because more people will be available to work. At a certain point we will no longer be able to afford children and as a result will stop having them, leading to a sudden population collapse.

When he laid out this apocalyptic theory 200 years ago, Malthus was the center of intellectual attention. His dire view provoked strong arguments in support and in opposition. Among other things, it helped shape the Corn Laws, British tariffs designed to limit the availability of cheap foreign imports. Malthus was known to be one of Charles Darwin's many sources of inspiration.

But Malthus wrote at a time before agricultural mechanization, when 90% of Americans, for example, worked on farms. The linear growth in agricultural production that was central to his thesis turned dramatically geometric as the Americas, New Zealand, and Australia opened up to farming and then mechanized. Staggering productivity growth in manufacturing as well as agriculture followed. Malthus seemed to have entirely missed the mark, while Alfred Marshall, the dominant British economist of his time, explained to the world that productivity growth was now a centrally important feature of economic performance, spurring generations of economists to study it.

Malthus's ideas reentered the mainstream for a brief period 40 years ago, when Paul Erlich (*The Population Bomb*, 1968), the Club of Rome (*The Limits to Growth*, 1972), and William D. Nordhaus and James Tobin (*Is Growth Obsolete?*, 1972) all warned in vivid and uncompromising terms that conventional economic growth was on the verge of ruining the world. Once again events suggested that the warnings were

FOR ARTICLE REPRINTS CALL 800-988-0886 OR 617-783-7500, OR VISIT **HBR.ORG**

Idea in Brief

Businesses are at the center of sustainability debates—as both causes of and deliverers from environmental degradation. Clearly they have a major role to play in saving the planet. But how are they to contribute?

The answer comes in two lines of reasoning. One is derived from the works of Thomas Malthus and argues that rescuing the environment is about restraint and responsibility. The other flows from the work of the economist and Nobel Prize winner Robert Solow and proposes that environmental and other problems can always be solved by human ingenuity.

These two philosophies make uneasy bedfellows. But if we are to achieve real progress, we must apply both. That requires understanding when to favor one over the other and how to make each succeed.

---

misplaced: Energy and commodity prices fell, deregulation delivered the benefits of more-intense competition, and the technology revolution boosted opportunities and productivity. Today, however, as apprehension about environmental degradation mounts, Malthus's notion that we are headed inexorably toward our own destruction is back at the center of the public discourse, heating up the debate about the role of corporations in finding solutions to urgent global problems.

Modern Malthusianism generalizes the argument beyond food: The better we get at making things, the cheaper it is to consume and the faster we reproduce and use up the planet's resources. The fear is that economic growth comes at the expense of the world's natural resources, including oil, fish, clean air, clean water, carbon-absorbing forests, and so on. Our economic activity not only eats up nonrenewable resources but degrades the ecosystem while fueling faster and faster population growth. In other words, we are steadily approaching a metaphorical wall that lurks out there in the distance. Each year we get closer and closer; eventually we will smack into the wall, with devastating consequences that include natural disaster, plague, famine, and death. The only possible recourse is to slow our progress.

This is the dominant narrative of our time. In a sustainability-oriented world, a good citizen is one who reduces, reuses, and recycles. A good corporation should reduce, slow down, and conserve. To stay on the right side of the Malthusian narrative, it should stop burning through existing natural capital stocks and creating negative externalities such as pollution, CO$_2$, and waste. It should self-impose limits to growth in order to win a bigger fight—the fight for the planet. We look to government to encourage or even coerce this restraint.

**ROBERT SOLOW
(1924–)**
Professor emeritus at MIT and Nobel Prize winner in economics

Solow has examined the various factors in economic growth, recognizing the importance of technological change as well as increases in labor or capital. His remarkable skill in statistics is matched by his insightful theories and lifelong commitment to well-grounded public policy. He is an expert on growth and employment policies and capital theory, and has published significant work in the area of resource and conservation economics.

The World According to Solow

In counterpoint to Malthus, Robert Solow, one of the most influential heirs to Marshall's intellectual estate, has focused on changing levels of productivity. He believes that capital that takes advantage of new technology is more productive than old capital, and that technological and process innovation is the most powerful driver of productivity. According to Solow, humanity needn't conquer new worlds and acquire their resources to get richer: We need to innovate within our existing context.

A classically Solovian innovation came during World War II. When Japan conquered Malaysia and gained control of the world's only source of natural rubber, the Allies faced the prospect of grounding fighter planes for lack of tires. In all likelihood, that would have meant losing the war to the Axis powers. The Allies had no choice but to innovate—and the quick result was mass production of viable synthetic rubber.

Many have developed Solow's line of reasoning further. The economist Paul Romer is credited with leading the new growth theory, which holds that growth has no natural limits because the capacity for technological innovation is unlimited. Investments in human capital increase rates of return, in his view. Romer stressed in particular the value of the

"If it is easy to substitute other factors for natural resources, then there is in principle no 'problem.' The world can, in effect, get along without natural resources, so exhaustion is just an event, not a catastrophe."

—*Robert Solow*

April 2012 Harvard Business Review **5**

"spillover"—a positive externality whereby advances of knowledge in a particular industry stimulate technological advances in other fields. When Bell Labs created transistors for the phone system, it had no idea how much the spillovers into myriad other industries would benefit the world. When Martin Cooper invented the cell phone, at Motorola in 1973, no one had any idea how much the device would

> Dueling theories breed inaction. For a consumer, a company, or even a government, the easiest course is to wait and hope for clarification on which is the right strategy.

change daily life around the globe. That same year, when the wildlife photographer Dan Gibson created (and patented) the parabolic microphone to capture bird sounds, he didn't imagine that it would soon be seen on every football game sideline.

Technological innovation and knowledge spill-overs have resulted in dramatic advances in standards of living and thus far have offered escape routes from a Malthusian denouement. Believers in innovation often point to the green revolution that took hold in the late 1960s and raised the world's agricultural production beyond even the most optimistic prior estimates. Solovians suggest that technology and innovation can either stretch scarce resources further—pushing out that Malthusian wall ad infinitum—or allow us to simply scale the wall.

The Battle Rages

The theories stand in stark contrast to each other. Malthusians see Solovians as delusional and utopian because they seem to deny that the wall exists, much less that it is getting dangerously close. Malthusians believe that limits to growth are imposed by nature and cannot be overcome by man. Innovation is terrific, they argue, but not the panacea that Solovians think it is. Malthusians worry that by arguing that technological innovation will provide a solution, Solovians risk lulling the public into failing to reduce, reuse, and recycle as much as is required.

Solovians see Malthusians as dreary and depressive—modern Luddites. They fear that Malthusians will resist the possibilities contained in innovation and thereby hobble attempts to improve the quality of our lives. They perceive that the benefits of technological development have transformed society without creating upward pressures on population: Better health care and pharmaceuticals have lowered birth rates as countries develop, because parents feel that their children's survival is more secure. Solovians fear that if we focus on restraint, we may delay our collision with the Malthusian wall but we will never innovate our way over it—and thus the Malthusian prescription ensures the fate we are desperate to avoid.

Dueling theories breed inaction. It is hard for either a corporation or a government to choose a direction when it is presented with two such fundamentally different choices. For the individual consumer, company, or even government, the easiest—and often apparently most prudent—course is to wait and hope for clarification on which is the right strategy. Companies reduce the immediate risk to their investors with this approach, which may explain the behavior of U.S. automakers with respect to fuel efficiency over most of the past four decades. Unable to decide between making smaller, more fuel-efficient cars and investing in electrical and hydrogen-powered engines, they settled on continuing to build pickup trucks and SUVs—which almost certainly contributed to the industry's near collapse in 2008.

Of course, the world is not black-and-white, and the extremes of both philosophies are just plain wrong. If the hard-core Malthusians were right, progress would have stopped long ago and humanity would already be in decline if not extinct. If the hard-core Solovians were right, we wouldn't be reaching dangerously high levels of carbon in our atmosphere and Australians would enjoy the protection of a robust ozone layer above their heads.

But both worldviews are also partly right. Each provides compelling explanations and predictions. Unfortunately, attempts to combine the two have so far resulted in confusion and dysfunction. The Kyoto Protocol provides a cautionary tale. Its framers, using an implicitly Malthusian conceptual structure, hoped that measuring and pricing carbon emissions would encourage incremental reductions. But they also hoped that gradually increasing the cost and decreasing the amount of emissions allowed would generate Solovian innovation in alternative energy

FOR ARTICLE REPRINTS CALL 800-988-0886 OR 617-783-7500, OR VISIT **HBR.ORG**

systems and products along with carbon trading. Kyoto has produced little of either.

Instead we have created expensive new industries devoted to auditing emissions, assessing the ability of tropical forests to absorb carbon, and burying liquid CO_2 in abandoned mines. Our economies are still locked into burning fossil fuels, and the concentration of CO_2 in the atmosphere continues to rise. The world's leading environmental economist, William Nordhaus, has termed Kyoto's mechanisms "inefficient and ineffective" and urged their replacement with a global carbon tax that would force consumers and companies, not governments, to innovate.

So what went wrong?

The problem, we believe, is that reconciling the two theories is treated as an exercise in compromise: I will give a nod to restraint if you give one to growth, and we'll hope to get a bit of each. Many policy makers implicitly recognize that we need approaches derived from both theories to deal with the environmental crisis. But few have actually gone beyond that assumption when making policy or strategy.

Go beyond it we must. For if both theories are valid—if they provide a compelling description of the world and have predictive power—then other factors must exist that determine when each best applies. As consumers, companies, or governments, we have some power to influence those factors, and thus a choice about whether a Malthusian or a Solovian dynamic will play out. But first we need more-precise information about what warrants which strategy.

How to Make Innovation the Answer

The most obvious requirement for radical, technologically disruptive innovation is access to risk capital for relatively unspecified investment. Alta Devices, a classic Silicon Valley start-up, believed that gallium arsenide could increase the efficiency of photovoltaic cells by about 30% over the upper limit of silicon technology. To find out whether and how this could be done at a commercially feasible price, it needed to invest $72 million in speculative R&D. Investment of this kind on this scale is typically provided by venture capitalists or the corporate venturing arms of large corporations. But before parting with large amounts of capital for such a project, investors have to believe that solving the problem will generate high and sustained revenues in the future. The most productive context for Solovian innova-

EXAMPLES OF MALTHUSIAN RESTRAINT

The CAFE regulations enacted by Congress in 1975 were intended to double the average fuel economy of cars and light trucks and included stiff penalties for manufacturers that failed to meet the standard.

Widespread use of multipane windows beginning in the early 1970s reduced the energy required for home heating and cooling.

Refillable beer bottles play a role in 70% of beer sales in Canada. Return rates are nearly 100%, and most of these bottles are reused 15 to 20 times before being recycled.

The all-aluminum can introduced in 1963 by Reynolds Metals led to a huge increase in recycling because of the ease and profitability of recycling it.

Leadership in Energy and Environmental Design (LEED) standards promote reducing, reusing, and recycling.

tion features a stable, high price for either the problematic resource or its substitute.

Failure to recognize these preconditions explains what went wrong with the U.S. government's policy on ethanol. After the oil crisis of the 1970s, Congress passed a tax credit for the production of ethanol, which remains in place to this day. After a new spike in oil prices, President George W. Bush reinforced its effect by signing the Energy Policy Act of 2005, which mandates the blending of renewable fuels into gasoline and precipitated a major investment in ethanol production capacity. The idea, of course, was and is to reduce reliance on a nonrenewable fuel (gasoline) by replacing it with a renewable one (ethanol) and to reduce dependency on Middle Eastern oil. In addition, the government slapped a tariff on ethanol imported from Brazilian producers in order to promote domestic production. Naturally, U.S. ethanol production capacity increased.

Setting aside the pros and cons of ethanol as a fuel, the policy was doomed from the start because the government could not deliver stable, high gasoline prices. They have, in fact, been extremely volatile—tracking the international oil price—and often very low, and the profitability of and level of investment in ethanol production have been equally variable as a result, putting Solovian innovation out of reach. The expansion of production capacity with existing technologies has driven up domestic corn prices and thus increased food prices. As the failure of the policy becomes evident, the government has signaled that it may reverse itself, but that would mean writing off the investments already made in ethanol production—and suggesting to investors that the federal government will not be a reliable partner when it comes to other green technologies.

Consider, in contrast, the German government's solar energy policy. Germany's Renewable Energy Act was adopted in 2000 with the aim of encouraging investment in solar energy. The problem was that a serious, large-scale investment in delivering solar power required that producers get high prices for the power they generated.

Consequently, the government required grid operators to purchase solar at five times the cost of conventional power—a price that would decline only slowly over time, in a carefully planned way—creating an environment that simulated a very high price for fossil fuel used to generate power. This policy meant that investors could justify the high capital cost of investing in solar power technology.

As a result, Germany had installed nearly twice the expected solar capacity by 2010. This fast-growing capability was leveraged by German companies, which started to sell turnkey photovoltaic production facilities to Chinese companies. The Chinese, in turn, scaled up production and dramatically reduced the price of solar arrays.

From 1998 to 2011, the period during which Germany managed its prices, the cost per installed watt for solar energy dropped from about $11 to about $3. It is expected to halve or better by 2020. The price stability offered by the government allowed investors to rely on reasonable returns on investment in solar technology and to fund the innovation in solar panel technology and production scale that has pushed the costs of solar below the all-in costs of fossil fuel alternatives. The sector has achieved a scale and technological maturity such that it no longer needs the price protection.

What the German experience teaches us is that because the price of oil provides a reference point for every other kind of energy, the best thing the world could do to spur broader Solovian innovation in the energy sector would be to declare and enforce a floor oil price—either directly, or indirectly through price supports on oil-substitution technologies, like Germany's feed-in tariff for solar power. The biggest challenge for innovation in energy is that substantial

> The most powerful way to generate commitment is through social pressure. It was a desire to appear environmentally responsible, rather than the cost of fuel, that drove the Hummer, once a potent status symbol, out of existence.

vacillation in the price of oil, which discourages large-scale investment in substitutes. The carbon offset pricing featured in cap-and-trade programs, which does nothing to dampen profitability swings for alternative technologies, is therefore not the answer. Far preferable would be a variable gap-filling carbon tax to preserve a floor price for a barrel of oil.

Corporations are clearly well placed to influence that kind of decision. Many already collaborate to encourage enforcement of high prices on non-

renewable resources to spur their own innovation. The European Automobile Manufacturers' Association has advocated that "CO_2 should be the key criterion for taxation to provide incentives to buy lower CO_2 emitting cars." At a minimum, corporations can help by not fighting governmental attempts to create such a context. U.S. automakers resisted the 1975 Corporate Average Fuel Economy (CAFE) standards for years, trying to circumvent them by producing vehicles that could be classified as light trucks rather than focusing on Solovian innovation.

How Restraint Works

As the foregoing implies, promoting Solovian innovation usually entails government-level policy and corporate decisions. Although consumers can and do play a role, most of the responsibility rests with those who command large budgets. Malthusian restraint, by contrast, is a much more inclusive strategy and relies on lots of small actions rather than a limited number of big ones. The key factor determining its success is a broad commitment to reduce, reuse, and recycle, which holds for both individuals and corporations. That commitment is generated essentially in three ways: regulation, economic incentives, and social or moral pressure.

Regulation is arguably the simplest, if bluntest, tool in the box. For example, in Germany consumers are obliged to recycle electronics and batteries, and retailers and producers are required to take them back. When people are already receptive to the idea of restraint and the perceived costs are not too high, regulation can work well.

It is important to note, though, that regulation has its limits and should be applied in increments. It can begin with getting people to separate their glass and paper waste, for example. Once they are used to doing that, they can be asked to subdivide their glass waste into colors. But achieving restraint through regulation requires a lot of local sensitivity. It would take a long while to persuade most New York City residents to sort five types of waste—something that is required in Austria, a country with a long tradition of Malthusian restraint in this regard.

Mixing regulation with economic incentives can give history a shove. Toronto and a number of other cities across North America have mandated garbage collection that is priced by the size of the bin, giving households an economic incentive to reduce the amount of garbage they produce. Economic incentives are not, of course, infallible; human beings are adept at exploiting them, often with perverse consequences. Pricing garbage by volume without restricting the use of garbage disposals, for instance, has generated new forms of waste that are more expensive to process. A strategy of restraint that's overreliant on money, therefore, is unlikely to succeed.

An enabling infrastructure is absolutely essential to effective regulation and incentives. A commitment to recycling, for example, requires a widespread, viable recycling infrastructure. A reduction in usage requires a measurement infrastructure: Households will have limited interest in reducing their water use if it isn't measured and reflected in their bills. Government at the local and national levels often provides that infrastructure, but it can be supplied by corporations and other organizations as well.

The most powerful but most difficult way to generate commitment is through social pressure. It was a desire to appear environmentally responsible, rather than the cost of fuel, that drove the Hummer, once a potent status symbol, out of existence. Similarly, the Prius is probably more successful than the hybrid Camry because the former brand is unfailingly a hybrid, whereas the latter has a conventional sibling, making its driver less obviously a hybrid owner. Social pressure influences corporate decisions as well as consumer decisions. Intense social pressure on Walmart drove it to create a leading green purchasing initiative. Coca-Cola felt sufficient pressure regarding its use of clean water to establish ambitious water-stewardship goals: a commitment to watershed protection projects and to increasing supplies of clean drinking water.

It is impossible to dictate social pressure, but we can do much to amplify and direct it. In the case of environmental responsibility, NGOs set standards and offer certification and recognition for improvements in energy efficiency or waste recycling. For instance, McDonald's can demonstrate its commitment to conserving global fish stocks because the Marine Stewardship Council certifies that the fish in its Filet-O-Fish sandwiches comes from sustainable fisheries. Walmart contributes to rain-forest preservation by getting its lumber certified by the Forest Stewardship Council. Of course, social media have hugely multiplied opportunities to apply social pressure.

Working together, citizens, companies, and governments can make great strides. For a larger-scale example of conservation, consider the city of San

EXAMPLES OF SOLOVIAN INNOVATION

Chlorination, developed by the U.S. Army in 1910, enables the human use of otherwise unsafe water.

Geothermal or ground-source heat pumps, developed in the 1940s, provide a completely renewable energy source.

In 2005 Donald Mavinic, of the University of British Columbia, and colleagues created a technology to convert phosphorus in wastewater to a high-quality, slow-release fertilizer called Crystal Green.

Low-cost, low-technology solar cookers dramatically reduce pollution, deforestation, and desertification in poor countries and save rural women from spending many hours searching for firewood.

Videoconferencing promises a marked reduction in business travel.

Francisco, which surpassed its goal of 75% waste reduction two years earlier than planned, and on that basis has targeted zero waste by 2020.

Talk of reducing, reusing, and recycling can give the impression that the changes involved aren't radical, but that's a mistake. The luxury clothier Loro Piana provides a case in point. The company was a major buyer of ultra-high-end wool from vicuñas, llamalike wild animals that live in the Andes. For centuries Inca villagers slaughtered vicuñas and sold their wool. As demand for vicuña wool grew, the animal's numbers declined. When Loro Piana learned that fewer than 6,000 vicuñas were left in Peru, it submitted a proposal to the Peruvian government to work with mountain communities on developing a vicuña reserve and a process of shearing rather than slaughtering the animals. The change was Malthusian in that it involved reusing a resource, yet it radically altered both a business model and a way of life.

For Malthusian conservation to work, consumers, companies, and governments must share a sense of urgency about the resource. Prices can be a two-edged sword: High energy prices, for example, do encourage restraint by users within the range of their elasticity of demand. But high prices for rhino horns have encouraged poachers to drive the species to the brink of extinction because, as with oil and coal producers, their costs have not risen as quickly as their potential revenues. The promise of sustained high prices for vicuña wool encouraged the farmers involved to accept short-term pain (the expense of domesticating the animals and shearing them infrequently to aid their survival in a harsh climate) in exchange for a lasting increase in their standard of living (far more animals to shear).

Often, action of this sort requires a powerful sense of moral purpose. South Africa has made great strides toward solving what looked like an intractable litter problem, largely owing to the personal intervention of the country's revered former president Nelson Mandela, who launched a campaign to encourage environmental stewardship. The most productive Malthusian conservation comes, in the end, from a combination of the three tools—regulation, economic incentives, and social or moral pressure.

Making the Choice

After analyzing the successes of each of the two strategies, we've developed a few clear guidelines for determining when one strategy should dominate.

Responsible energy consumption need not imply long-term restraint in economic growth. Government should create pricing conditions that reward innovation.

Solovian innovation is patently a longer-term strategy, because new technologies take time to mature. Thus, if the resource in question is depleting rapidly with little or no potential for an immediate substitute, this is not the strategy to pursue. When we realized that hydrochlorofluorocarbons were destroying the ozone layer, we had to ban their use. When we recognized that the market for caviar would make sturgeon extinct in the Caspian and Black Seas, we included all sturgeon products in the Convention on International Trade in Endangered Species, bringing them under some of the tightest regulation available—and subsequently triggering the development of sustainable substitutes. In situations like these, consumers, corporations, and governments all need to move in the same Malthusian direction.

But if the crisis point is still some time away, an opportunity for Solovian innovation arises. For example, responsible energy consumption need not imply long-term restraint in economic growth. Rather, government should intervene to create pric-

ing conditions that reward companies for innovation. That is what the German government did with solar energy. If governments pour their resources into regulation and subsidies in an effort to change behavior rather than to stimulate new technologies, society may be worse off. Similarly, if corporations are motivated to make existing technologies more efficient only in small increments, they will miss out on the quantum leap in productivity that disruptive innovation can bring.

But prioritizing a Solovian strategy doesn't have to mean abandoning Malthusian restraint. This is not an either-or choice, and corporations and governments should continue developing ways to measure resource consumption and reward conservation. Malthusian restraint can buy time for Solovian innovation.

What we need is better framing to spur more-productive action on our environmental crisis. As if in a Hollywood western, the Malthusian framing has business playing the villain, government the sheriff, and citizens the pawns in their struggle. In the Solovian framing, business rides into town on a white horse and saves the day (with technology), while government (the sheriff) simply gets out of the way and citizens sit drinking in the saloon. Setting these perspectives in opposition means that we either argue, obfuscate, and delay or default to choosing one over the other. Blending them means we can inspire and empower all, which is what is required for this fight. Governments can regulate according to the desired outcome. Citizens can commit to a behavioral change or adopt a new technology. Business can do what it does best—innovate and create—to help save our planet. ▽

HBR Reprint R1204B

"So I go, 'Sir, with all due respect, perhaps you do have some unresolved control issues, because, um, you're making me wear a bell.'"

Roger Martin is the dean of the University of Toronto's Rotman School of Management, the director of the Michael Lee-Chin Family Institute for Corporate Citizenship, and the author of *Fixing the Game: Bubbles, Crashes, and What Capitalism Can Learn from the NFL* (Harvard Business Review Press, 2011). **Alison Kemper** is a PhD candidate at the Rotman School, a faculty member at York University in Toronto, and the Lee-Chin Institute's senior researcher.

CARTOON: PAT BURNS

Article   Prepared by: Richard Eathorne, *Northern Michigan University*

Saving the Planet: A Tale of Two Strategies

Roger Martin and Alison Kemper

Learning Outcomes

After reading this article, you will be able to:

- Compare and contrast the two competing philosophies for saving the planet.
- Outline the contribution that the business community can make to address the sustainability issue.
- Explain how a combination of "constraint" and "innovation" can help solve environmental challenges.

Critical Thinking

1. Compare and contrast the ideas presented in "the world according to Malthus" and "the world according to Solow."
2. How can "innovation" contribute to achieve the goals of sustainability?
3. Would these two philosophies provide equally valid approaches to "saving the planet" regardless of a country's level of "development"? Discuss.

Create Central

www.mhhe.com/createcentral

Internet References

Alliance for Global Sustainability (AGS)
www.global-sustainability.org

Collaborative Consumption Hub
collaborativeconsumption.com

Global Trends Project
www.globaltrendsproject.org

Sustainable Development.Org
www.sustainabledevelopment.org